AN INTRODUCTION TO THE LIE THEORY OF ONE-PARAMETER GROUPS

WITH APPLICATIONS TO THE SOLUTION OF DIFFERENTIAL EQUATIONS

BY

ABRAHAM COHEN, PH.D.

COLLEGIATE PROFESSOR IN MATHEMATICS, JOHN HOPKINS UNIVERSITY

Reprint of Edition 1911

G. E. STECHERT & CO.
NEW YORK
1931

Reprints of Rare Mathematical Books and Logarithm Tables.

PREFACE

THE object of this book is to present in an elementary manner, in English, an introduction to Lie's theory of one-parameter groups, with special reference to its application to the solution of differential equations invariant under such groups.

The treatment is sufficiently elementary to be appreciated, under proper supervision, by undergraduates in their senior year as well as by graduates during their first year of study.

While a knowledge of the elementary theory of differential equations is not absolutely essential for understanding the subject matter of this book, frequent references being made to places where necessary information can be obtained, it would seem preferable to approach for the first time the problem of classifying and solving differential equations by direct, even if miscellaneous, methods to doing so by the elegant general methods of Lie ; and this book is intended primarily for those who have some acquaintance with the elementary theory. To such persons it should prove of great interest and undoubted practical value. An attempt has been made throughout the work to emphasize the rôle played by the Lie theory in unifying the elementary theory of differential equations, by bringing under a relatively small number of heads the various known classes of differential equations invariant under continuous groups, and the methods for their solution. Special attention may be called to the lists of invariant differential equations and applications in §§ 19, 28, 30; while the two tables in the appendix include most of the ordinary differential equations likely to be met.

Only as many examples involving the solution of differential equations as seem necessary to illustrate the text have been intro-

iii

duced. The large number usually given in the elementary text-
books seems ample for practice.

The short chapter on contact transformations, while not essential
to the work, has been added for purposes of reference and to give
the student sufficiently clear ideas, so as to provide a working
knowledge, in case he has occasion to apply them. For the same
reasons, the rather sketchy note on r-parameter groups has been
added, where an attempt is made to bring out, as concisely as
seems consistent with clearness, the relations between r-parameter
groups and their infinitesimal transformations. An exposition of
the general theory would be beyond the scope of this work.

To a large extent Lie's proofs and general mode of presentation
have been retained, both because of their elementary, direct char-
acter, and because the subject is so essentially Lie's own. An
attempt has been made, however, at a more systematic arrange-
ment of the subject matter and at identifying more closely the
classes of differential equations invariant under known groups with
those considered in the elementary theory.

The author takes pleasure in expressing his appreciation of the
valuable suggestions made by Dr. J. R. Conner, who kindly con-
sented to read the proofs.

ABRAHAM COHEN.

JOHNS HOPKINS UNIVERSITY,
    BALTIMORE, MD., August, 1911.

CONTENTS

CHAPTER I

LIE'S THEORY OF ONE-PARAMETER GROUPS

CHAPTER II

DIFFERENTIAL EQUATIONS OF THE FIRST ORDER

CHAPTER III

MISCELLANEOUS THEOREMS AND GEOMETRICAL APPLICATIONS

CHAPTER IV

DIFFERENTIAL EQUATIONS OF THE SECOND AND HIGHER ORDERS

CHAPTER V

LINEAR PARTIAL DIFFERENTIAL EQUATIONS OF THE FIRST ORDER

CHAPTER VI

ORDINARY DIFFERENTIAL EQUATIONS OF THE SECOND ORDER

CHAPTER VII

CONTACT TRANSFORMATIONS

APPENDIX

LIE'S THEORY OF
DIFFERENTIAL EQUATIONS

CHAPTER I

LIE'S THEORY OF ONE–PARAMETER GROUPS

1. Group of Transformations. — The set of transformations

(1) $$x_1 = \phi(x, y, a), \quad y_1 = \psi(x, y, a),^*$$

each one being determined by some value of the parameter a, constitutes a *group* if the transformation resulting from the successive performance of any two of them is one of the transformations of the aggregate. In other words, assigning a definite but arbitrarily selected value to the parameter a, and then any second value b (where b may or may not be equal to a), this second transformation being

(1$_b$) $$x_2 = \phi(x_1, y_1, b), \quad y_2 = \psi(x_1, y_1, b),$$

the transformations of type (1) form a group if the results of eliminating x_1 and y_1 from (1) and (1$_b$), *i.e.*

$$x_2 = \phi[\phi(x, y, a), \psi(x, y, a), b], \quad y_2 = \psi[\phi(x, y, a), \psi(x, y, a), b]$$

---

* Here ϕ and ψ are supposed to be generally analytic, real functions of the three quantities x, y, a; and, unless especially stated, it will be understood that x and y are real, and that a takes such values only as render x_1 and y_1 real. Besides, ϕ and ψ are independent functions with respect to x and y, alone; *i.e.*

$$\begin{vmatrix} \dfrac{\partial \phi}{\partial x} & \dfrac{\partial \phi}{\partial y} \\[2ex] \dfrac{\partial \psi}{\partial x} & \dfrac{\partial \psi}{\partial y} \end{vmatrix} \not\equiv 0;$$

so that equations (1) can be solved for x and y.

reduce identically to

$$x_2 = \phi(x, y, c), \ y_2 = \psi(x, y, c),$$

where c is a function of a and b only. If (1) be represented by T_a and (1_b) by T_b, the group property may be expressed symbolically

$$T_a T_b = T_c.$$

We shall speak of $T_a T_b$ as the *product* of T_a and T_b; and shall understand that it represents the transformation resulting from the successive performance of T_a and T_b, in the order named. With this in mind, the *group property* of a set of transformations may be expressed in the words, *the product of any two transformations of the group is equal to some transformation of the aggregate.*

As an example, consider the *translations* *

I $x_1 = x, \ y_1 = y + a.$

After having fixed upon some value a of the parameter, a second transformation of the set, corresponding to the value b, is

$$x_2 = x_1, \ y_2 = y_1 + b.$$

The result of the successive performance of the two is

$$x_2 = x, \ y_2 = y + a + b,$$

which is again a translation of the set, with $a + b$ as the value of the parameter.

Hence, all translations of the type I form a group.

As another example, consider the *rotations* †

II $x_1 = x \cos a - y \sin a, \ y_1 = x \sin a + y \cos a.$

---

* It will frequently be found convenient to consider this subject from a geometrical point of view. A transformation of the form (1) may be looked upon as transforming the point (x, y) into the point (x_1, y_1). The effect of a transformation I is, obviously, to carry any point the distance a in the direction of the axis of y. So that the effect on all the points of the plane is that of a translation of the whole plane over a distance a in the direction of the axis of y.

† Obviously the effect of a transformation of this type on the various points of the plane is that of a rotation of the whole plane, through the angle a, about the origin.

The result of first performing the transformation corresponding to some definite value of a, and then a second one,

$$x_2 = x_1 \cos b - y_1 \sin b, \quad y_2 = x_1 \sin b + y_1 \cos b,$$

is $\quad x_2 = x \cos (a + b) - y \sin (a + b), \quad y_2 = x \sin (a + b) + y \cos (a + b),$

which is again a rotation of the set, with $a + b$ as the value of the parameter.

Hence, all rotations of the type II form a group.

The *affine** transformations,

III $\qquad\qquad\qquad\qquad x_1 = x, \ y_1 = ay,$

form a group, since the result of two transformations in which the values of the parameter are a and b, respectively, is

$$x_2 = x, \quad y_2 = aby,$$

where ab is the value of the parameter.

In the same way it is readily seen that the *perspective* or *similitudinous* † transformations,

IV $\qquad\qquad\qquad\qquad x_1 = ax, \ y_1 = ay,$

form a group.

In the groups considered in the Lie theory it is presupposed that the transformations can be arranged in pairs, the members of which are mutually *inverse* ‡ ; that is, if (1) be solved for x and y, their values in terms of x_1 and y_1 assume the forms

$(\overline{1})$ $\qquad\qquad\qquad x = \phi(x_1, y_1, \bar{a}), \ y = \psi(x_1, y_1, \bar{a}),$

where $\bar{a}$ is some function of a.

Thus in the examples above we have the inverse transformations :

I. $\qquad x = x_1, \qquad\qquad\qquad y = y_1 - a ; \qquad$ here $\quad \bar{a} = -a.$

II. $\qquad x = x_1 \cos a + y_1 \sin a, \ y = -x_1 \sin a + y_1 \cos a ; \ \bar{a} = -a.$

III. $\qquad x = x_1, \qquad\qquad\qquad y = \frac{1}{a} y_1 ; \qquad\qquad \bar{a} = \frac{1}{a}.$

IV. $\qquad x = \frac{1}{a} x_1, \qquad\qquad y = \frac{1}{a} y_1 ; \qquad\qquad \bar{a} = \frac{1}{a}.$

---

* Following Lie, this name is used here in a restricted sense to apply to transformations of the types III and III′, § 19. The term goes back to Moebius (1790–1868), and usually includes all entire linear transformations $x_1 = a_1 x + b_1 y + c_1, y_1 = a_2 x + b_2 y + c_2.$

† So called because the effect of any one of them is to stretch the vector going from the origin to the point (x, y) in the ratio $\frac{a}{1}$, leaving its direction unaltered. Any figure in the plane is, therefore, transformed into one similar to it by a transformation IV.

‡ Such groups will be referred to as *Lie groups* when this property is to be emphasized.

Since the successive performance of two mutually inverse transformations results in the *identical** transformation, the latter must always be a transformation in every group considered in this theory† ; hence, there must always exist a value, a_0, of the parameter which reduces the corresponding transformation to an identity

$$(1_0) \qquad \begin{cases} x_1 = \phi(x, y, a_0) = x, \\ y_1 = \psi(x, y, a_0) = y. \end{cases}$$

It is readily seen that in the case of I, II, III, IV the values of a_0 are 0, 0, 1, 1 respectively.

Since ϕ and ψ are continuous functions of the parameter a, if we start with the value a_0, and allow a to vary continuously, the effect of the corresponding transformations on x and y will be to transform them continuously ; that is, for a sufficiently small change in a the changes in x and y are as small as one pleases.   Looked at geometrically, the effect will be to transform the point (x, y) to the various points on some curve, which is known as a *path-curve* of the group.

Thus in the case of I, the point (x, y) is transformed into the various points on the line through it, parallel to the axis of y; in the case of II, the path-curves are obviously circles having the origin for center ; in III the path-curves are again lines parallel to the axis of y, while in IV the path-curves are straight lines through the origin.

It is evident that when x and y are considered as constants while x_1 and y_1 are taken as variables, the equations (1) are the parametric equations of the path-curve through the fixed point (x, y).   Hence, *the path-curve corresponding to any point (x, y) may be obtained by eliminating a from the two equations of* (1).

---

* *Identical* transformation is the name given to a transformation that leaves unaltered all the elements upon which it operates.

† Groups exist in which the parameter enters in such a way that there is no identical transformation.   (See Lie, *Transformationsgruppen*, Vol. I, § 44.)   Such groups will not be included among those considered here.

Remark 1. — It is readily seen that, in general, the path-curve corresponding to any point corresponds equally well to every other point on it.

There is a possible exception to this statement.   A point may be left un-altered by every transformation of the group; as, for example, the origin in the case of II.   Such a point would naturally not have a path-curve.   In the case of III, every point on the axis of x is left unaltered; hence, a line parallel to the axis of y is the path-curve of every point on it, except the point where it cuts the axis of x.   In IV a line through the origin is the path-curve of every point on it, except the origin, which is left unaltered.

Remark 2. — The parameter may appear in various forms in the transformations that determine a given group.

Thus $x_1 = x, y_1 = y + a^2$ also determines the group of translations I.   In this case a must take imaginary values, as well as real ones, in order to give all the transformations of I.   As a matter of fact $\bar{a} = ia$.   On the other hand, a negative value for a determines the same transformation as the corresponding positive value.

The group of rotations II can also obviously be written

$$x_1 = x\sqrt{1 - a^2} - ya, \ \ y_1 = xa + y\sqrt{1 - a^2}.$$

It is always possible (and in an indefinite number of ways) to choose as a new parameter such a function of the parameter appearing in any group that the value giving the identical transformation is any desired number.   For example, this number will be θ if a is replaced by $a_0 e^{a-\theta}$.   In particular it will be zero if a is replaced by $a_0 e^a$.

Thus if III and IV, where $a_0 = 1$, are written

$$x_1 = x, y_1 = e^a y \text{ and } x_1 = e^a x, y_1 = e^a y,$$

respectively, $a = 0$ will determine the identical transformation.   In this form, complex values of a are necessary to determine transformations which cor-respond to negative values of the parameter in the original forms of the trans-formations of these groups.

Show that the following transformations constitute a group.   Find the respective values of the parameter that give both the inverse and the identical transformations.   Also find the path-curves : —

$$\text{Ex. 1. } x_1 = ax, y_1 = \frac{1}{a}y. \quad \text{Ex. 2. } x_1 = a^2x, y_1 = ay.$$

$$\text{Ex. 3. } x_1 = a^2x, y_1 = a^3y.$$

Ex. 4. $x_1 = +\sqrt{x^2 + 2\,a}, y_1 = +\sqrt{y^2 - a}.$

Ex. 5. $x_1 = x \cosh a + y \sinh a, y_1 = x \sinh a + y \cosh a.$

Ex. 6. $x_1 = \dfrac{x}{1 - ax}, y_1 = \dfrac{y}{1 - ax}.$

Ex. 7. $x_1 = ax + (a - 1)y, y_1 = y.$

Ex. 8. $x_1 = e^a(x \cos a - y \sin a), y_1 = e^a(x \sin a + y \cos a).$

2. Infinitesimal Transformation. — Since ϕ and ψ are continuous functions, the transformation

$$x_1 = \phi(x, y, a_0 + \delta a), \quad y_1 = \psi(x, y, a_0 + \delta a),$$

where a_0 is the value of the parameter determining the identical transformation and δa is an infinitesimal, changes x and y by infinitesimal amounts.   Developing by Taylor's Theorem

$$x_1 = \phi(x, y, a_0) + \left(\frac{\partial \phi}{\partial a}\right)_{a_0} \delta a + \cdots,$$

$$y_1 = \psi(x, y, a_0) + \left(\frac{\partial \psi}{\partial a}\right)_{a_0} \delta a + \cdots.$$

Noting that $\phi(x, y, a_0) = x$, $\psi(x, y, a_0) = y$, the changes in x and y due to the transformation are

$$x_1 - x \equiv \delta x = \left(\frac{\partial \phi}{\partial a}\right)_{a_0} \delta a + \cdots,$$

$$y_1 - y \equiv \delta y = \left(\frac{\partial \psi}{\partial a}\right)_{a_0} \delta a + \cdots,$$

where terms in higher powers of δa are indicated by dots. Since $a_{\mathfrak{e}}$ is a fixed value of the parameter, the only variables remaining in $\left(\dfrac{\partial \phi}{\partial a}\right)_{a_0}$ and $\left(\dfrac{\partial \psi}{\partial a}\right)_{a_0}$ are x and y. Writing

$$\left(\frac{\partial \phi}{\partial a}\right)_{a_0} \equiv \xi(x,\ y), \quad \left(\frac{\partial \psi}{\partial a}\right)_{a_0} \equiv \eta(x, y),$$

the transformation takes the form

$$\delta x = \xi(x, y)\delta a + \cdots, \ \delta y = \eta(x, y)\delta a + \cdots.$$

Higher powers of the infinitesimal δa may be neglected, provided at least one of ξ and η does not vanish identically (*i.e.* for all values of x and y), and neither of them is infinite. In this case the transformation producing an infinitesimal change in the variables is

(2) $$\delta x = \xi(x, y)\delta a, \quad \delta y = \eta(x, y)\delta a.$$

This is known as an *infinitesimal* transformation.

Remark 1. — Since $k\delta a$, where k is any finite constant different from zero, is an infinitesimal when δa is, the latter may be replaced by the former in (2). Hence, the infinitesimal transformation (2) is the same as $$\delta x = k\xi(x, \eta)\delta a, \quad \delta y = k\eta(x, y)\delta a.$$

On the other hand, if $f(x, y)$ is not a constant,

$$\delta x = f(x, y) \cdot \xi(x, y)\delta a, \quad \delta y = f(x, y) \cdot \eta(x, y)\delta a$$

is *distinct* from (2).

Remark 2. — In case $\left(\dfrac{\partial \phi}{\partial a}\right)_{a_0}$ and $\left(\dfrac{\partial \psi}{\partial a}\right)_{a_0}$ are both identically zero, or if one of them is infinite, the method of this section for finding an infinitesimal transformation of the group must be modified. In Note I of the Appendix *the existence of an infinitesimal transformation of the group is established in every case,* and a method for finding it is also given. Moreover, in the same note it is proved that *a one-parameter group contains only one distinct infinitesimal transformation.*

In general, the method of this section for finding ξ and η will be found applicable ; when not, that of Note I may be employed.

In the case of I the infinitesimal transformation is

$$x_1 = x, \quad y_1 = y + \delta a,$$

or
$$\delta x = 0, \quad \delta y = \delta a ;$$

i.e.
$$\xi = 0, \quad \eta = 1. \qquad \left[\frac{\partial \phi}{\partial a} = 0, \frac{\partial \psi}{\partial a} = 1.\right]$$

For II, the infinitesimal transformation is

$$x_1 = x \cos(\delta a) - y \sin(\delta a), \qquad y_1 = x \sin(\delta a) + y \cos(\delta a).$$

Since $\cos(\delta a) = 1 - \dfrac{(\delta a)^2}{2!} + \cdots$, and $\sin(\delta a) = \delta a - \dfrac{(\delta a)^3}{3!} + \cdots$, and infinitesimals of higher order than the first may be neglected, $\cos(\delta a)$ may be replaced by 1, and $\sin(\delta a)$ by δa. Hence,

$$\delta x = -y\delta a, \quad \delta y = x\delta a ;$$

i.e.
$$\xi = -y, \quad \eta = x. \quad \left[\left(\frac{\partial \phi}{\partial a}\right)_0 = -y, \left(\frac{\partial \psi}{\partial a}\right)_0 = x\right]$$

Similarly, it is readily seen that for

III
$$\xi = 0, \quad \eta = y,$$
IV
$$\xi = x, \quad \eta = y.$$

Ex.   Find the infinitesimal transformations of the groups in the exercises of § 1.

3. Symbol of Infinitesimal Transformation. — In the infinitesimal transformation

$$(2) \qquad \delta x = \xi(x, y)\delta a, \qquad \delta y = \eta(x, y)\delta a,$$

δ is the symbol for differentiation with respect to the parameter a ; but in a restricted sense, since it is used to designate the value which the differential of the new variable x_1 or y_1 assumes when $a = a_0$.[*] Thus

$$\delta x = \xi \, \delta a = \left(\frac{\partial x_1}{\partial a}\right)_{a_0} \delta a, \quad \delta y = \eta \, \delta a = \left(\frac{\partial y_1}{\partial a}\right)_{a_0} \delta a.$$

---

[*] The exceptional cases noted in Remark 2, § 2 are due to the way in which the parameter enters and are not peculiar to any group. (See § 4.) Hence, no modification of the statement made in the text need be insisted upon, provided it is understood that the parameter is chosen in proper form.

If $f(x, y)$ is a generally analytic function of x and y, the effect of the infinitesimal transformation on it is to replace it by $f(x + \xi \, \delta a, \ y + \eta \, \delta a)$, which on expanding by Taylor's Theorem becomes

$$f(x + \xi \, \delta a, \ y + \eta \, \delta a) = f(x, y) + \left(\xi \frac{\partial f}{\partial x} + \eta \frac{\partial f}{\partial y} \right) \delta a + \cdots.$$

Hence,
$$\delta f = \left(\xi \frac{\partial f}{\partial x} + \eta \frac{\partial f}{\partial y} \right) \delta a + \cdots.$$

Lie introduced the very convenient symbol Uf for the coefficient of δa in this expansion; so that

$$\delta f = Uf \, \delta a + \cdots,$$

where

(3)
$$Uf \equiv \xi \frac{\partial f}{\partial x} + \eta \frac{\partial f}{\partial y}.$$

It is readily seen that
$$Uf = \left(\frac{\partial f_1}{\partial a} \right)_{a_0}$$

where
$$f_1 \equiv f(x_1, y_1).$$

In particular
$$Ux = \xi, \quad Uy = \eta.$$

Since Uf can be written when the infinitesimal transformation (2) is known, and conversely, (2) is known when Uf is given, Uf is said to *represent* (2). For convenience of language we shall usually speak of " the infinitesimal transformation Uf" instead of " the transformation represented by Uf." But it must be borne in mind that Uf is *not* a transformation; it is only the representative of one.

The infinitesimal transformations in the cases of I, II, III, IV are

$$Uf \equiv \frac{\partial f}{\partial y}, \ \ Uf \equiv - y \frac{\partial f}{\partial x} + x \frac{\partial f}{\partial y}, \ \ Uf \equiv y \frac{\partial f}{\partial y}, \ \ Uf \equiv x \frac{\partial f}{\partial x} + y \frac{\partial f}{\partial y}$$

respectively.

Remark. — The differential operator $U \equiv \xi \frac{\partial}{\partial x} + \eta \frac{\partial}{\partial y}$ has striking properties, many of which will be brought out in the course of this work. It is, to a large extent, because of these properties that Lie's introduction of the idea of the infinitesimal transformation has proven so prolific of results.

4. Group Generated by an Infinitesimal Transformation. — In § 2 was given a method for finding the infinitesimal transformation of a one-parameter group when the finite transformations are given. Conversely, the finite transformations can be obtained when the infinitesimal transformation is known.

Attention was called in Remark 2, § 1, to the fact that the parameter may be made to enter in such a way that the identical transformation is given by any desired value of the parameter. It is frequently convenient to have the parameter in such a form that its vanishing gives the identical transformation. In future, when this is specifically understood, t will be used for the parameter. In the general case, when this form is not insisted upon, a will be retained.

The infinitesimal transformation $Uf \equiv \xi \dfrac{\partial f}{\partial x} + \eta \dfrac{\partial f}{\partial y}$, or

$$(2') \qquad \delta x = \xi(x, y)\delta t, \quad \delta y = \eta(x, y)\delta t,$$

carries the point (x, y) to the neighboring position $(x + \xi\delta t, y + \eta\delta t)$. The repetition of this transformation an indefinite number of times has the effect of carrying the point along a path* which is precisely that integral curve of the system of differential equations

$$(4) \qquad \frac{dx_1}{dt} = \xi(x_1, y_1), \quad \frac{dy_1}{dt} = \eta(x_1, y_1),$$

which passes through the point (x, y). At any stage of the above process x and y have been transformed into x_1 and y_1, and the

---

* This is obviously the path-curve (§ 1) of the group, corresponding to the point (x, y).

formulae of transformation are given by those solutions of (4) or of their equivalents

$$(5) \qquad \frac{dx_1}{\xi(x_1, y_1)} = \frac{dy_1}{\eta(x_1, y_1)} = \frac{dt}{1},$$

for which x_1 reduces to x and y_1 to y for $t = 0$.

The first two members of (5) being free of t form a differential equation whose solution may be written

$$u(x_1, y_1) = const. = u(x, y),$$

since $x_1 = x$, $y_1 = y$ when $t = 0$. *This is the equation of the path-curve corresponding to the point (x, y).*

Solving $u(x_1, y_1) = c$ for one of the variables,* to fix the idea, say $x_1 = \omega(y_1, c)$, and replacing x_1 in η by ω, the resulting differential equation

$$\frac{dy_1}{\eta[\omega(y_1, c), y_1]} = dt$$

can be solved by a quadrature. Replacing c by its value in terms of x_1 and y_1 this solution takes the form

$$v(x_1, y_1) - t = const. = v(x, y).$$

Hence it follows that

$$(6) \qquad \begin{cases} u(x_1, y_1) = u(x, y), \\ v(x_1, y_1) = v(x, y) + t, \end{cases}$$

determine x_1 and y_1 as those solutions of (4) or (5) which reduce to x and y respectively for $t = 0$.

Looking upon (6) as a transformation, the following may be noted :

1° The result of the successive performance of two transformations

$$\left. \begin{matrix} u(x_1, y_1) = u(x, y) \\ v(x_1, y_1) = v(x, y) + t \end{matrix} \right\} \text{ and } \begin{cases} u(x_2, y_2) = u(x_1, y_1), \\ v(x_2, y_2) = v(x_1, y_1) + t', \end{cases}$$

---

* At times it will be more practical to use some of the other methods given in the author's Elementary Treatise on Differential Equations (in future referred to as El. Dif. Eq.) § 65 for finding a second solution of (5).

is the same as that of the single transformation

$$u(x_2, y_2) = u(x, y),$$
$$v(x_2, y_2) = v(x, y) + t + t'.$$

2° The value $-t$ determines the transformation **inverse** to that obtained by using t.

3° $t = 0$ gives the identical transformation.

Hence the aggregate of all the transformations (6) for all values of t constitute a group of the kind considered in the Lie theory (§1). This group (either in the form (6) or when solved for x_1 and y_1) is known as the group *generated* by the infinitesimal transformation $(2')$.*

Moreover, the parameter enters in such a way that $\left(\dfrac{\partial x_1}{\partial t}\right)_0 = \xi(x, y)$, $\left(\dfrac{\partial y_1}{\partial t}\right)_0 = \eta(x, y)$. Since there was no restriction placed on the ξ and η in $(2')$, other than that they are generally analytic, which is always presupposed, we have shown that it *is always possible to put the finite transformations of a one-parameter group in such form that the exceptional cases noted in Remark 2, § 2 will not arise.*

In I, equations (5) are $\qquad \dfrac{dx_1}{0} = \dfrac{dy_1}{1} = \dfrac{dt}{1}.$

$$\therefore u(x_1, y_1) \equiv x_1 = x.$$
$$v(x_1, y_1) \equiv y_1 = y + t.$$

In II, $\qquad\qquad\qquad \dfrac{dx_1}{-y_1} = \dfrac{dy_1}{x_1} = \dfrac{dt}{1}.$

$$\therefore u(x_1, y_1) \equiv x_1^2 + y_1^2 = x^2 + y^2.$$

Using method 3°(a) of § 65, *El. Dif. Eq.*

$$\frac{x_1 dy_1 - y_1 dx_1}{x_1^2 + y_1^2} = dt.$$

$$\therefore v(x, y) \equiv \tan^{-1}\frac{y_1}{x_1} = \tan^{-1}\frac{y}{x} + t.$$

---

* Since the finite transformations of a group can be calculated when its infinitesimal transformation is known, the latter may be looked upon as the representative of the group. We shall often speak of " the group Uf," understanding by this " the group whose infinitesimal transformation is represented by Uf."

To solve these two equations for x_1 and y_1, so as to obtain the transformation in the usual form, one may proceed as follows :

Taking the tangent of each side of the second relation,

$$\frac{y_1}{x_1} = \frac{y + x\tau}{x - y\tau}, \text{ where } \tau \equiv \tan t.$$

Adding 1 to the square of each side and taking account of the first relation,

$$\frac{1}{x_1^2} = \frac{1 + \tau^2}{(x - y\tau)^2}.$$

Whence

$$x_1 = \frac{x - y\tau}{\sqrt{1 + \tau^2}} = x \cos t - y \sin t,$$

since

$$\frac{1}{\sqrt{1 + \tau^2}} = \cos t \text{ and } \frac{\tau}{\sqrt{1 + \tau^2}} = \sin t;$$

and

$$y_1 = \frac{x\tau + y}{\sqrt{1 + \tau^2}} = x \sin t + y \cos t.$$

In III, it is readily seen that

$$u(x_1, y_1) \equiv x_1 = x,$$
$$v(x_1, y_1) \equiv \log y_1 = \log y + t, \text{ or } y_1 = e^t y.$$

Note. — It is evident that the solutions of (5) need not always be found in the form (6). Other forms may be easier to solve for x_1 and y_1. Thus in IV

$$\log x_1 = \log x + t \text{ and } \log y_1 = \log y + t$$

are a pair of obvious solutions of the differential equations (5), and lead at once to

$$x_1 = e^t x, \ y_1 = e^t y.$$

Find the groups whose infinitesimal transformations are the following :

Ex. **1.** $\ x \dfrac{\partial f}{\partial x} - y \dfrac{\partial f}{\partial y}.$

Ex. **2.** $\ 2 x \dfrac{\partial f}{\partial x} + y \dfrac{\partial f}{\partial y}.$

Ex. **3.** $\ 2 x \dfrac{\partial f}{\partial x} + 3 y \dfrac{\partial f}{\partial y}.$

Ex. **4.** $\ \dfrac{1}{x} \dfrac{\partial f}{\partial x} - \dfrac{1}{2 y} \dfrac{\partial f}{\partial y}.$

Ex. **5.** $\ y \dfrac{\partial f}{\partial x} + x \dfrac{\partial f}{\partial y}.$

Ex. **6.** $\ x^2 \dfrac{\partial f}{\partial x} + xy \dfrac{\partial f}{\partial y}.$

Ex. **7.** $\ (x + y) \dfrac{\partial f}{\partial x}.$

Ex. **8.** $\ (x - y) \dfrac{\partial f}{\partial x} + (x + y) \dfrac{\partial f}{\partial y}.$

5. Another Method of Finding the Group from its Infinitesimal Transformation. — Starting with an infinitesimal transformation

$$Uf \equiv \xi \frac{\partial f}{\partial x} + \eta \frac{\partial f}{\partial y},$$

it was seen in § 4 that the finite transformations of the group

$$(1') \qquad x_1 = \phi(x, y, t), \; y_1 = \psi(x, y, t)$$

generated by it can be found in such form that

$$\xi = \left(\frac{\partial \phi}{\partial t}\right)_0, \quad \eta = \left(\frac{\partial \psi}{\partial t}\right)_0.$$

The finite transformations can be obtained (expanded in powers of t) without integration by means of the following considerations :

The effect of any transformation $(1')$ being to replace x and y by x_1 and y_1, it will change any function $f(x, y)$ into $f(x_1, y_1)$. Assuming $f(x, y)$ to be generally analytic, since $f(x_1, y_1)$ depends upon t it can be developed by Maclaurin's Theorem.

$$f_1 = f + \left(\frac{\partial f_1}{\partial t}\right)_0 t + \left(\frac{\partial^2 f_1}{\partial t^2}\right)_0 \frac{t^2}{2!} + \cdots,$$

where $\qquad f \equiv f(x, y), f_1 \equiv f(x_1, y_1)$.   Writing likewise

$$\xi_1 \equiv \frac{\partial x_1}{\partial t}, \; \eta_1 \equiv \frac{\partial v_1}{\partial t}, U_1 f_1 \equiv \xi_1 \frac{\partial f_1}{\partial t} + \eta_1 \frac{\partial f_1}{\partial t},$$

so that $\qquad (\xi_1)_0 = \xi, \; (\eta_1)_0 = \eta, \; (U_1 f_1)_0 = Uf$, it follows that

$$\frac{\partial f_1}{\partial t} = U_1 f_1, \text{ whence } \left(\frac{\partial f_1}{\partial t}\right)_0 = Uf.$$

Moreover $\quad \dfrac{\partial^2 f_1}{\partial t^2} = \dfrac{\partial}{\partial t} U_1 f_1 = U_1 U_1 f_1 \equiv U_1^2 f_1.$

Hence $\quad \left(\dfrac{\partial^2 f_1}{\partial t^2}\right)_0 = UUf \equiv U^2 f.$

Similarly $\left(\dfrac{\partial^3 f_1}{\partial t^3}\right)_0 = UUUf \equiv U^3 f$; and so on.   Hence the effect of any finite transformation $(1')$ on f is given by

$$(7) \qquad f_1 = f + Uf\, t + U^2 f \frac{t^2}{2!} + \cdots {}^{*}$$

In particular the finite transformations of the group are given by the formula (7) when f is simply x and y, thus

$$(8) \qquad \begin{cases} x_1 = e^{tU} x = x + Ux\, t + U^2 x \dfrac{t^2}{2!} + \cdots, \\[2mm] y_1 = e^{tU} y = y + Uy\, t + U^2 y \dfrac{t^2}{2!} + \cdots, \end{cases}$$

where, it will be recalled (§ 3), $Ux = \xi$, $Uy = \eta$.

It is readily seen that for the group in the form (8) as in the form

(6) § 4 $\qquad T_t I_{t'} = T_{t+t'}, \quad \bar{t} = -t, \quad t_0 = 0.$

In I $\qquad Uf \equiv \dfrac{\partial f}{\partial y}.$

$\qquad\qquad Ux = 0, \ U^2 x = 0, \cdots; \ Uy = 1, \ U^2 y = 0, \ U^3 y = 0, \cdots.$

Hence $\qquad x_1 = x, \ y_1 = y + t.$

In II $\qquad Uf \equiv -y \dfrac{\partial f}{\partial x} + x \dfrac{\partial f}{\partial y}$

$\qquad\qquad Ux = -y, \ U^2 x = U(-y) = -x, \ U^3 x = U(-x) = y,$ and so on.

Hence $\qquad x_1 = x \left(1 - \dfrac{t^2}{2!} + \dfrac{t^4}{4!} - \cdots \right) - y \left(t - \dfrac{t^3}{3!} + \dfrac{t^5}{5!} - \cdots \right)$

$\qquad\qquad = x \cos t - y \sin t.$

Similarly $\quad y_1 = x \left(t - \dfrac{t^3}{3!} + \dfrac{t^5}{5!} - \cdots \right) + y \left(1 - \dfrac{t^2}{2!} + \dfrac{t^4}{4!} - \cdots \right)$

$\qquad\qquad = x \sin t + y \cos t.$

In III $\qquad Uf \equiv y \dfrac{\partial f}{\partial y}.$

$\qquad\qquad Ux = 0, \ U^2 x = 0, \cdots; \ Uy = y, \ U^2 y = y, \ U^3 y = y, \cdots.$

Hence $\qquad x_1 = x, \ y_1 = y \left(1 + t + \dfrac{t^2}{2!} + \dfrac{t^3}{3!} + \cdots \right)$

$\qquad\qquad = y e^t$

* Symbolically this may be written $f_1 = e^{tU} f.$

In exactly the same way the finite transformations of IV are found to be

$$x_1 = xe^t, \, y_1 = ye^t.$$

Ex. Solve the problems of § 4 by the method of this section.

6. Invariants. — A function of the variables is said to be an *invariant* of a group (or invariant under the group) if it is left unaltered by every transformation of the group.

Thus, it is immediately obvious that any function of x alone is invariant under the groups I and III, while any function of $x^2 + y^2$ is such under II.

We saw (§ 5) that

$$(7) \qquad f(x_1, y_1) - f(x, y) = Uft + U^2 f \frac{t^2}{2\,!} + \cdots.$$

In order that $f(x_1, y_1) = f(x, y)$ for all values of x and y, and the corresponding values of x_1 and y_1 into which they are transformed by each of the transformations of the group, *i.e.* for every value of t, it is necessary and sufficient that each coefficient in the right-hand member of (7) be zero for all values of x and y. In particular, it is necessary that

$$(9) \qquad\qquad Uf \equiv \xi \frac{\partial f}{\partial x} + \eta \frac{\partial f}{\partial y} = 0.$$

Moreover, since $U^2 f = UUf$, $U^3 f = UU^2 f$, $\cdots$, it follows at once that (9) is also the sufficient condition that $f(x_1, y_1) = f(x, y)$ for all values of x, y, and t. Hence, the

THEOREM. — *The necessary and sufficient condition that $f(x, y)$ be invariant under the group Uf is $Uf = 0$.*

Remark. — This theorem may also be expressed as follows : *The necessary and sufficient condition that $f(x, y)$ be invariant under a one-parameter group is that it be left unaltered by the infinitesimal transformation of the group.* On succeeding pages will be found conditions for invariance of curves, families of curves, differential equations of various types, and so on. In each case it will be found (although specific mention of the fact will not be made) that the condition for invariance under the group always reduces to that of invariance under the infinitesimal transformation of the group.

To determine invariant functions, it is necessary to solve the partial differential equation

$$Uf \equiv \xi \frac{\partial f}{\partial x} + \eta \frac{\partial f}{\partial y} = 0.$$

The corresponding system of ordinary differential equations is

(10)
$$\frac{dx}{\xi} = \frac{dy}{\eta} = \frac{df}{0}.$$

$f = const.$ is one solution of the system.

If, besides, $u(x, y) = const.$ is the solution of the equation involving the first two members, the general solution of (9) is, by Lagrange's method,*

$$f = F(u).$$

In I and III
$$\frac{dx}{0} = \frac{dy}{\eta} = \frac{df}{0}.$$

$$\therefore \ u \equiv x; \text{ and } f = F(x).$$

In II
$$u \equiv x^2 + y^2; \text{ and } f = F(x^2 + y^2).$$

In IV
$$u \equiv \frac{y}{x}; \text{ and } f = F\left(\frac{y}{x}\right).$$

Ex. Find the invariants of the groups in the problems of § 4.

7. Path-curves. Invariant Points and Curves. — As was seen in § 4, the differential equation of the path-curves of a group is readily obtained from the infinitesimal transformation of the group. Thus, using x and y as the variables, it is

$$\frac{dy}{dx} = \frac{\eta}{\xi},$$

or

(11)
$$\frac{dx}{\xi} = \frac{dy}{\eta}.$$

---

* See *El. Dif. Eq.* § 79.

The general solution of this equation,

$$u(x, y) = const.,$$

is the equation of the family of path-curves. As $u(x, y)$ is an invariant of the group (§ 6), it follows that *the equation of a path-curve is obtained by equating an invariant to a constant.* *Moreover,* it is clear that *this property is characteristic of an invariant;* that is, if equating a function to any constant whatever gives the equation of a path-curve, that function must be an invariant.

But this is not the only form in which the equation of a path-curve may appear.* A path-curve is an *invariant curve* of the group, hence its equation must be invariant. If $f(x, y) = 0$ is to be an *invariant equation,* $f(x_1, y_1)$ must vanish for all values of x_1 and y_1 into which the various values of x and y which satisfy $f(x, y) = 0$ are transformed by the transformations of the group. Now, we have seen

$$(7) \qquad f(x_1, y_1) = f(x, y) + Uf\, t + U^2 f \frac{t^2}{2\,!} + \cdots.$$

If the right-hand member is to vanish whenever $f(x, y)$ does, for every value of t, it is necessary and sufficient that each coefficient should do so. In particular, it is necessary that

$$(12) \qquad Uf = 0, \text{ whenever } f(x, y) = 0,$$

that is, Uf must contain $f(x, y)$ as a factor.†

But if
$$Uf = \omega(x, y) f(x, y),$$

then
$$U^2 f \equiv UUf = U\omega f + \omega Uf = (U\omega + \omega^2)f;$$

i.e. $U^2 f$ also contains $f(x, y)$ as a factor.

---

* Thus, while $\frac{y}{x} = c$ is readily seen to be the equation of the family of path-curves of the group $Uf \equiv x\frac{\partial f}{\partial x} + y\frac{\partial f}{\partial y}$, $y - cx = 0$ is another form for it. $U(y - cx) \equiv - cx + y$ does not vanish for all values of x and y; but it does vanish for those values satisfying the equation of the path-curves ; see (12) below.

† It is presupposed that $f(x, y)$ contains no repeated factors.

In the same way it can be shown that every coefficient in (7) contains $f(x, y)$ as a factor, whenever Uf does ; for if

$$U^n f = \theta(x, y) f(x, y), \quad U^{n+1} f \equiv U U^n f = (U\theta + \theta\omega) f.$$

Hence *the vanishing of Uf whenever $f(x, y)$ does is both the necessary and sufficient condition that $f(x, y) = 0$ be an invariant equation.*

In case $Uf = 0$ for all values for x and y, the above condition is fulfilled. But this we recognize as the condition (9) that $f(x, y)$ be an invariant. Hence, not only is $f(x, y) = 0$ a path-curve, but $f(x, y) = $ *any constant* is one in this case.

Remark. — It should be noted that

$$Uf \equiv \xi \frac{\partial f}{\partial x} + \eta \frac{\partial f}{\partial y}$$

may vanish because $\xi = 0$ and $\eta = 0$ * for certain values of the variables. In general these two equations determine a finite number of values of the variables. Remembering the significance of ξ and η, these values of the variables are left unaltered by all the transformations of the group ; so that the points having these values for coördinates are *invariant points.* If it happens that ξ and η contain a common factor, $\omega(x, y)$, it is obvious that $\omega(x, y) = 0$ is an invariant curve, in that every point of it is invariant. Following Lie, and desiring to preserve the significance of the name, we shall not include this class of invariant curves among the path-curves.

Summing up the results of this and the preceding section we have the

THEOREM. — *The necessary and sufficient condition that $f(x, y) = 0$ be invariant under the group Uf is that $Uf = 0$ for all values of x and y for which $f(x, y) = 0$, it being presupposed that $f(x, y)$ has no repeated factors.*

---

* Still another possibility is that $\dfrac{\partial f}{\partial x} = 0$ and $\dfrac{\partial f}{\partial y} = 0$ whenever $f = 0$. But this is excluded by the restriction that $f(x, y)$ have no repeated factors.

Points whose coördinates satisfy the two equations $\xi(x, y) = 0$, $\eta(x, y) = 0$ are invariant under the group. If $\xi(x, y) = 0$ and $\eta(x, y) = 0$ whenever $f(x, y) = 0$, this curve is composed of invariant points. Curves of this type are not included among the path-curves of the group.

In all other cases $f(x, y) = 0$ is a path-curve.

If $Uf = 0$ for all values of x and y, $f(x, y)$ is an invariant, and $f(x, y) =$ any constant (including zero) is a path-curve.

In I, $\xi \equiv 0, \ \eta \equiv 1$.

$\therefore u \equiv x = const.$ is the equation of the path-curves.

There are no invariant points.

In II, $\xi \equiv -y, \ \eta \equiv x$.

$\therefore u \equiv x^2 + y^2 = const.$ is the equation of the path-curves.

There are no other invariant curves. The point $x = 0, y = 0$ is invariant.

In III, $\xi \equiv 0, \ \eta \equiv y$.

$\therefore u \equiv x = const.$ is the equation of the path-curves.

$y = 0$ is an invariant curve, each point of which is invariant.

Ex.   Examine for invariant curves and points the groups appearing in the problems of § 4.

8. Invariant Family of Curves. — A family of curves is said to be *invariant* under a group, if every transformation of the group transforms each curve into some curve of the family. We shall consider at this time families containing a single infinity of curves only, that is, those whose equations involve a single parameter or arbitrary constant. Writing the equation of the family in the form

$$f(x, y) = c,$$

it will be invariant, if

$$f(x_1, y_1) = f[\phi(x, y, t), \psi(x, y, t)] \equiv \omega(x, y, t) = c'$$

is the equation of the same family of curves for every value of t, c and c' being arbitrary constants.

A single infinity of curves determined by an equation involving an arbitrary constant is equally determined by a unique differential equation of the first order, of which the equation involving the arbitrary constant is the general solution.   If $f(x, y) = c$ and $\omega(x, y, t) = c'$ are to be the same family of curves, these equations must be solutions of the same differential equation of the first order.   Hence the left-hand member of the one must be a function of that of the other,* *i.e.*

$$\omega = F(f).$$

Making use of the relation (7) § 5, viz.

$$f(x_1, y_1) = f(x, y) + Uf\, t + U^2 f \frac{t^2}{2\,!} + \cdots,$$

we see that $f(x_1, y_1)$ will be a function of $f(x, y)$ for all values of t if and only if each coefficient in the expansion on the right is a function of $f(x, y)$.   In particular we must have

(13) $Uf = F(f).$

If (13) is true,

$$U^2 f \equiv UUf = UF(f) = \frac{dF(f)}{df}\, Uf = \frac{dF(f)}{df}\, F(f),$$

which is again a function of f.

In the same way each coefficient on the right is seen to be a function of f; for if $U^n f = \Phi(f)$, $U^{n+1} f \equiv UU^n f = U\Phi(f) = \frac{d\Phi(f)}{df}\, F(f)$. Hence (13) *is both the necessary and sufficient condition that the family of curves* $f(x, y) = c$
be invariant.

---

* The differential equations arising from these equations are

$$\frac{\partial f}{\partial x}\, dx + \frac{\partial f}{\partial y}\, dy = 0 \quad \text{and} \quad \frac{\partial \omega}{\partial x}\, dx + \frac{\partial \omega}{\partial y}\, dy = 0.$$

In order that these be one and the same equation it is necessary and sufficient that

$$\begin{vmatrix} \dfrac{\partial f}{\partial x} & \dfrac{\partial f}{\partial y} \\[2mm] \dfrac{\partial \omega}{\partial x} & \dfrac{\partial \omega}{\partial y} \end{vmatrix} = 0.$$

But this is the condition that ω be a function of f. See *El. Dif. Eq.*, Note 1 of the Appendix.

Remark. — A special case should be noted.　If $Uf = 0$ for all values of x and y, $f(x, y) = c$ is a family of path-curves, each one of which is invariant, hence the family is.　This particular family is characterized by the fact that its differential equation is

$$\eta \, dx - \xi \, dy = 0.$$

The problem of finding all the families of curves invariant under a given group Uf will be considered later in another form (§ 18). The general type of such families* may be found by noting that $f(x, y)$ must satisfy (13), where $F(f)$ is some function of f, not determined.　As a matter of fact, $F(f)$ may be taken as any convenient function of f, as may be seen from the following consideration :

The family of curves $f(x, y) = c$ may equally well be written $\Phi[f(x, y)] = const.$, where $\Phi(f)$ is any holomorphic function of f. Applying (13)

$$U\Phi(f) \equiv \frac{d\Phi}{df} Uf = \frac{d\Phi}{df} F(f).$$

This will be any desired function of f, say $\Omega(f)$, if

$$\frac{d\Phi}{df} F(f) = \Omega(f) ; \ i.e. \ \Phi(f) = \int \frac{\Omega(f)}{F(f)} \, df.$$

Since the family of path-curves is excluded, $F(f) \not\equiv 0$.　Hence the function Φ can be obtained by a quadrature, such that when the equation of the invariant family of curves is written $\Phi[f(x, y)] = const.$ the right-hand member of (13) will assume the desired form $\Omega(f)$.

In the case of I, equation (13) is $Uf \equiv \dfrac{\partial f}{\partial y} = F(f)$.

From the corresponding system of ordinary differential equations

$$\frac{dx}{0} = \frac{dy}{1} = \frac{df}{F(f)}$$

---

* In this discussion the family of path-curves is excluded, since a method for finding these curves has already been given (§ 7).

the general solution is seen to be of the form

$$y - \phi(f) = \psi(x),$$

where ψ is an arbitrary function, and $\phi = \int \dfrac{df}{F(f)}$ Solving for f, this takes the

form $\qquad\qquad\qquad\qquad f = \Phi(y - \psi(x)).$

The most general family of curves invariant under the group $Uf \equiv \dfrac{\partial f}{\partial y}$ is then

$$\Phi(y - \psi(x)) = const., \text{ or simply } y - \psi(x) = c.$$

Geometrically this is obvious at once. For such an equation represents a family of curves all of which may be obtained by moving any one of them continually, in either direction, parallel to the axis of y.

In II, $-y \dfrac{\partial f}{\partial x} + x \dfrac{\partial f}{\partial y} = F(f)$ leads to $\dfrac{dx}{-y} = \dfrac{dy}{x} = \dfrac{df}{F(f)}$, whence the general

solution is of the form $\tan^{-1}\dfrac{y}{x} - \phi(f) = \psi(x^2 + y^2)$,

or $\qquad\qquad\qquad f = \Phi\left(\tan^{-1}\dfrac{y}{x} - \psi(x^2 + y^2)\right).$

The equation $\dfrac{y}{x} = c$, representing the family of straight lines through the origin is a simple example under this head, as is immediately obvious geometrically.

As an exercise, the student may show that

$$y\psi(x) = c$$

is a general type for III, while $\qquad x\psi\left(\dfrac{y}{x}\right) = c$

is such for IV.   Simple examples are

$x^2 + \dfrac{y^2}{c} = 1$, a family of central conics of fixed transverse axis for III,

$\alpha x^2 + \beta y^2 = c$, a family of similar central conics for IV,

as is readily obvious geometrically, and as may be verified easily analytically.

9. Change of Variables. — The form of the transformations of a group depends upon the choice of variables that are operated upon by them.

Thus it is obvious that while the group of rotations II affecting the rectangular coördinates is $\qquad x_1 = x \cos a - y \sin a, \ \ y_1 = x \sin a + y \cos a,$

when operating upon polar coördinates, it is

$$\rho_1 = \rho, \quad \theta_1 = \theta + a,$$

which, in form, is identical with the group of translations **I.**

To find the effect of the change of variables *

(14) $$x = F(x, y), \quad y = \Phi(x, y),$$

which, of course, carries with it

(14') $$x_1 = F(x_1, y_1), \quad y_1 = \Phi(x_1, y_1),$$

on the form of the finite transformations of the group

(1) $$x_1 = \phi(x, y, a), \quad y_1 = \psi(x, y, a),$$

x, y, x_1, y_1 must be eliminated from the six relations, (14), (14'), (1) and the resulting two relations solved for x_1 and y_1. This elimination is usually effected by solving (14) and (14') for x, y, x_1, y_1, and substituting these in (1).

---

* The introduction of new variables in a transformation involves the following processes :

Designating by S the transformation of variables (14), or (14'), and by S^{-1} its inverse

$$x = F(x, y), \, y = \Phi(x, y)$$

obtained by solving (14) for x and y, the new coördinates (x, y) of any point are expressed by means of S^{-1} in terms of the old coördinates (x, y). These in turn are transformed by (1) or T_a (§ 1) into (x_1, y_1) of the new point. Finally S transforms the latter into (x_1, y_1), the new coördinates of this point. Designating by T_a the transformation in the new variables corresponding to T_a in the old, the above may be expressed symbolically

$$T_a = S^{-1} T_a S.$$

The transformation T_a is known as the *transform of T_a by S.*

That the aggregate of the transforms of all the transformations of the group (1) form a group follows, of course, from the fact that the transformations imply certain operations which are independent (except as to form, but not as to effect) of the kind of variables operated upon by them. It is very easy to verify this, however, as follows :

$$T_a T_b = S^{-1} T_a S S^{-1} T_b S = S^{-1} T_a T_b S = S^{-1} T_c S = T_c$$

since $S S^{-1}$ is the identical transformation, and $T_a T_b = T_c$ (§ 1).

In the case of the above example the formulae for the change of variables will be chosen in the inverse form

$$x = \rho \cos \theta, \quad y = \rho \sin \theta.$$

Eliminating x, y, x_1, y_1,

$$\rho_1 \cos \theta_1 = \rho \cos \theta \cos a - \rho \sin \theta \sin a = \rho \cos (\theta + a),$$

$$\rho_1 \sin \theta_1 = \rho \cos \theta \sin a + \rho \sin \theta \cos a = \rho \sin (\theta + a).$$

Whence, solving for ρ_1 and θ_1,

$$\rho_1 = \rho, \quad \theta_1 = \theta + a.$$

(The other possible solution, $\rho_1 = -\rho$, $\theta_1 = \theta + \pi + a$, while exactly the same geometrically is not to be used here, since the above transformation must reduce to the identical one for $a = 0$. In the above transformation of variables, it is understood that $\rho = +\sqrt{x^2 + y^2}$).

In general, the actual work required to carry out this process is long, to say the least; on the other hand, the problem of finding the new form of the infinitesimal transformation is a very simple one. For, remembering that

$$\xi (x, y) = \frac{\partial x}{\partial a} = \left(\frac{\partial x_1}{\partial a} \right)_{a_0},$$

$$\boldsymbol{\xi} (x, y) = \left(\frac{\partial x_1}{\partial a} \right)_{a_0} = \frac{\partial x}{\partial x} \left(\frac{\partial x_1}{\partial a} \right)_{a_0} + \frac{\partial x}{\partial y} \left(\frac{\partial y_1}{\partial a} \right)_{a_0} = \xi \frac{\partial x}{\partial x} + \eta \frac{\partial x}{\partial y}.$$

$$\therefore \boldsymbol{\xi} (x, y) = Ux.$$

Similarly $\qquad\qquad \eta (x, y) = Uy.$

Hence

(15) $\qquad\qquad Uf(x, y) \equiv Ux \frac{\partial f}{\partial x} + Uy \frac{\partial f}{\partial y},$

where Ux and Uy are to be expressed in terms of x and y by means of (14).

In the above example, choose (14) in the form

$$\rho = +\sqrt{x^2 + y^2}, \quad \theta = \tan^{-1}\frac{y}{x}.$$

Since

$$Uf \equiv -y\frac{\partial f}{\partial x} + x\frac{\partial f}{\partial y},$$

$$\xi = U\sqrt{x^2 + y^2} = 0, \quad \eta = U\tan^{-1}\frac{y}{x} = 1.$$

$$\therefore Uf \equiv \frac{\partial f}{\partial \theta}.$$

10. Canonical Form and Variables. — It is always possible theoretically, and often practically, to find the change of variables that reduces the group to a desired form. Thus, in order to have the group take the form

$$Uf \equiv \xi \frac{\partial f}{\partial x} + \eta \frac{\partial f}{\partial y}$$

any convenient pair of independent solutions of

$$(16) \quad \begin{cases} Ux \equiv \xi(x, y)\dfrac{\partial x}{\partial x} + \eta(x, y)\dfrac{\partial x}{\partial y} = \xi(x, y), \\[2mm] Uy \equiv \xi(x, y)\dfrac{\partial y}{\partial x} + \eta(x, y)\dfrac{\partial y}{\partial y} = \eta(x, y), \end{cases}$$

may be taken as the new variables x and y. In particular, to reduce the group to one of translations in the direction of the axis of y, when it takes the form $Uf \equiv \dfrac{\partial f}{\partial y}$, the equations to be integrated are

$$(16') \quad \begin{cases} \xi\dfrac{\partial x}{\partial x} + \eta\dfrac{\partial x}{\partial y} = 0, \\[2mm] \xi\dfrac{\partial y}{\partial x} + \eta\dfrac{\partial y}{\partial y} = 1. \end{cases}$$

The first of these is (9), § 6 ; so that for x may be taken any convenient invariant of the group, $u(x, y)$.

To solve the second equation, Lagrange's method leads to the system of ordinary differential equations

$$\frac{dx}{\xi} = \frac{dy}{\eta} = \frac{dy}{1},$$

which are equations (5), § 4. Making use of the fact that $u(x, y) = $ *const.* is the solution of $\frac{dx}{\xi} = \frac{dy}{\eta}$, y may be obtained by a quadrature.*

Following Lie we shall say that the group is in the *canonical form* when it has the form $Uf \equiv \frac{\partial f}{\partial y}$, and the variables which reduce it to this form will be called *canonical variables*. The above result may then be stated :

Every group can be reduced to the canonical form $Uf \equiv \frac{\partial f}{\partial y}$. *In order to find the canonical variables, it is only necessary to solve the differential equation of the first order*

$$\frac{dx}{\xi} = \frac{dy}{\eta},$$

and to follow this with a quadrature. In case an invariant of the group (or what is the same thing, the equation of its path-curves) *is known, a quadrature alone is necessary.*

Remark. — If the equations (16) cannot be solved readily, it may be practicable to find the canonical variables for both the original and the desired forms of the group. A proper combination of these will then give the required transformation of variables.

In II, $\xi \equiv -y$, $\eta \equiv x$. Here, as was seen (§ 4), $u \equiv x^2 + y^2$, $v \equiv \tan^{-1}\frac{y}{x}$. These are a possible set of canonical variables. But it is customary to choose $\sqrt{u}$ instead of u for x, thus giving the usual polar coördinates. In III, $\xi \equiv 0$,

---

* Inspection of equations (6), § 4 shows that the transformation $x = u(x, y)$, $y = v(x, y)$ reduces the group to the form

I $$x_1 = x, \quad y_1 = y + t.$$

$\eta \equiv y$. Here, as was also seen (§ 4), $u \equiv x$, $v \equiv \log y$. In IV, $\dfrac{dx}{x} = \dfrac{dy}{y}$ gives $u \equiv \dfrac{y}{x}$, which may be taken as x. By composition the system of equations $\dfrac{dx}{x} = \dfrac{dy}{y} = \dfrac{dy}{\mathrm{I}}$ gives $\dfrac{dx + dy}{x + y} = \dfrac{dy}{\mathrm{I}}$; whence $y = \log (x + y)$.

Another set of canonical variables for this group is of some interest. By composition, after having multiplied numerator and denominator of the first member by x and of the second member by y, we have $\dfrac{x\,dx + y\,dy}{x^2 + y^2} = \dfrac{dy}{\mathrm{I}}$; whence $y = \log \sqrt{x^2 + y^2}$. Choosing this form for y and $\tan^{-1} u \equiv \tan^{-1}\dfrac{y}{x}$ for x, the canonical variables are very similar to the usual polar coördinates, in that the old variables, in terms of them, are

$$ x = e^y \cos x, \quad y = e^y \sin x. $$

From their nature, it is obvious that in passing to the usual polar coördinates the transformations IV assume the form of the affine transformations III, as may also be verified readily analytically.

Ex. Find the canonical variables of the groups in the problems of § 4.

11. Groups Involving More than Two Variables. — The previous theory of one-parameter groups involving two variables can be generalized in two directions : the number of variables can be enlarged, and the number of parameters can be increased. In this section* will be considered one-parameter groups involving more than two variables ; and as the argument is almost the same for n variables as for three, the latter number will usually be employed. As a matter of fact, the previous arguments for two variables hold, with only slight modification, for a larger number ; hence, as a rule, only the facts will be given here, it being left as a reviewing exercise for the student to fill in the supplementary arguments.

* A brief extension of the above theory to groups involving more than one-parameter will be given in Note VI of the Appendix.

Starting with the transformations

$$[1] \qquad \begin{cases} x_1 = \phi(x, y, z, a), \\ y_1 = \psi(x, y, z, a), \\ z_1 = \chi(x, y, z, a), \end{cases}$$

where ϕ, ψ, χ are supposed to be generally analytic, independent, real functions of x, y, z, a, they will constitute a Lie group provided the set has the following properties :

1° The result of carrying out in succession two transformations of the aggregate, determined by any two values a and b of the parameter, is the same as performing a single transformation of the set determined by some value c of the parameter, where c is a function of a and b.

2° Solving [1] for x, y, z in terms of x_1, y_1, z_1, the resulting formulae take exactly the same forms as [1], some function of a taking the place of a. In other words, the transformations of the group occur in pairs of mutually inverse ones.

As a consequence the group contains the identical transformation.

A group of this type contains one and only one infinitesimal transformation (§ 2, and Remark, Note I of the Appendix), which may be written *

$$[3] \qquad Uf \equiv \xi(x, y, z)\frac{\partial f}{\partial x} + \eta(x, y, z)\frac{\partial f}{\partial y} + \zeta(x, y, z)\frac{\partial f}{\partial z},$$

where, in general,

$$\xi \equiv \frac{\partial x}{\partial a} = \left(\frac{\partial \phi}{\partial a}\right)_{a_0},$$

$$\eta \equiv \frac{\partial y}{\partial a} = \left(\frac{\partial \psi}{\partial a}\right)_{a_0},$$

$$\xi \equiv \frac{\partial z}{\partial a} = \left(\frac{\partial \chi}{\partial a}\right)_{a_0}.$$

---

* For n variables we have likewise

$$[3'] \qquad Uf \equiv \xi_1\frac{\partial f}{\partial x_1} + \xi_2\frac{\partial f}{\partial x_2} + \cdots + \xi_n\frac{\partial f}{\partial x_n}.$$

The finite transformations of the group may be obtained from the infinitesimal transformation either in the form of a power series in the parameter (§ 5)

[8]
$$\begin{cases} x_1 = x + Uxt + U^2x\,\dfrac{t^2}{2\,!} + \cdots, \\[2mm] y_1 = y + Uyt + U^2y\,\dfrac{t^2}{2\,!} + \cdots, \\[2mm] z_1 = z + Uzt + U^2z\,\dfrac{t^2}{2\,!} + \cdots, \end{cases}$$

or as solutions of the differential equations (§ 4)

[5]
$$\frac{dx_1}{\xi(x_1, y_1, z_1)} = \frac{dy_1}{\eta(x_1, y_1, z_1)} = \frac{dz_1}{\zeta(x_1, y_1, z_1)} = \frac{dt}{1}.$$

If $u_1(x_1, y_1, z_1) = const.$ and $u_2(x_1, y_1, z_1) = const.$ are the solutions of the first two equations (not involving t), and $v(x_1, y_1, z_1) - t = const.$ is a third solution of the system independent of the other two, then

[6]
$$\begin{cases} u_1(x_1, y_1, z_1) = u_1(x, y, z), \\ u_2(x_1, y_1, z_1) = u_2(x, y, z), \\ v(x_1, y_1, z_1) = v(x, y, z) + t \end{cases}$$

determine the finite transformations of the group.

In both these cases the parameter t enters in such a way that $t = 0$ gives the identical transformation, and $\bar{t} = -t$ determines the inverse transformation.*

---

* In the case of n variables, the development form of the finite transformations is exactly the same. To obtain the second form, the system of differential equations is

[5']
$$\frac{dx_1{}'}{\xi_1{}'} = \frac{dx_2{}'}{\xi_2{}'} = \cdots = \frac{dx_n{}'}{\xi_n{}'} = \frac{dt}{1},$$

and their solutions are of the form

[6']
$$\begin{cases} u_1(x_1{}', x_2{}', \cdots, x_n{}') = u_1(x_1, x_2, \cdots, x_n), \\ \quad \cdot \qquad \cdot \qquad \cdot \qquad\qquad \cdot \\ u_{n-1}(x_1{}', x_2{}', \cdots, x_n{}') = u_{n-1}(x_1, x_2, \cdots, x_n), \\ v(x_1{}', x_2{}', \cdots, x_n{}') = v(x_1, x_2, \cdots, x_n) + t. \end{cases}$$

Primed letters are used here to designate the transformed variables, since the subscript, previously employed, is no longer available.

The effect of a finite transformation of the group on any function $f(x, y, z)$, is (§ 5)

$$[7] \qquad f(x_1, y_1, z_1) = f(x, y, z) + Uf\, t + U^2 f \frac{t^2}{2\,!} + \cdots.$$

A function $f(x, y, z)$ is invariant under the group Uf if

$$[9] \qquad Uf \equiv \xi \frac{\partial f}{\partial x} + \eta \frac{\partial f}{\partial y} + \zeta \frac{\partial f}{\partial z} = 0$$

for all values of x, y, z (§ 6).

This equation, involving three independent variables, has two independent solutions. Hence a one-parameter group in three variables has two independent invariants. Since $u_1(x, y, z)$ and $u_2(x, y, z)$ are such a set, every invariant of the group is a function of u_1 and u_2.*

Those points whose coördinates satisfy the three equations

$$\xi(x, y, z) = 0, \quad \eta(x, y, z) = 0, \quad \zeta(x, y, z) = 0$$

are invariant under the group (§ 7). In general, that is, in case the three functions are independent, there is only a finite number of such points. But if only two of the functions are independent (which will show itself by having their Jacobian vanish, without all of its first minors doing so) the two independent equations will be the equations of a curve, every point of which is invariant. If all the two-rowed determinants in the Jacobian vanish, there is only one independent equation, and it is the equation of a surface, every point of which is invariant under the group.

The path-curves are obtained

1° either by eliminating a from the finite transformations of the group (§ 1),

2° or by solving the system of ordinary equations (§ 7)

$$[11] \qquad \frac{dx}{\xi} = \frac{dy}{\eta} = \frac{dz}{\zeta}.$$

---

* In the case of n variables, every invariant of the group is a function of the $n-1$ independent ones $u_1, u_2, \cdots, u_{n-1}$.

From the latter we see that if u_1 and u_2 are two independent invariants of the group, $u_1 = const.$ and $u_2 = const.$ are the equations of the path-curves.

Each of the surfaces $u_1 = const.$ and $u_2 = const.$ is invariant, being made up of an infinity of path-curves obtained in either case by keeping one of the constants in the equations of the path-curves fixed and allowing the other to run through its full range of values.*

The equation $f(x, y, z) = 0$, or the surface represented by it is invariant (§ 7) if

[12] $Uf = 0$ whenever $f = 0$, †

provided f contains no repeated factors. (If Uf vanishes because $\xi = 0$, $\eta = 0$, $\zeta = 0$ whenever $f = 0$, every point of the surface is invariant.)

The curve $f_1(x, y, z) = 0$, $f_2(x, y, z) = 0$ is invariant if

[12'] $Uf_1 = 0$ and $Uf_2 = 0$ whenever $f_1 = 0$ and $f_2 = 0$,

provided f_1 and f_2 contain no repeated factors and are independent functions, not containing a common factor. This last condition assures us that not all of the two-rowed determinants in the matrix

$$\begin{Vmatrix} \dfrac{\partial f_1}{\partial x} & \dfrac{\partial f_1}{\partial y} & \dfrac{\partial f_1}{\partial z} \\ \dfrac{\partial f_2}{\partial x} & \dfrac{\partial f_2}{\partial y} & \dfrac{\partial f_2}{\partial z} \end{Vmatrix}$$

vanish for all values of x, y, z.

* In the case of n variables, 1° holds without change ; in 2° the differential equations of the path-curves are

[11'] $$\frac{dx_1}{\xi_1} = \frac{dx_2}{\xi_2} = \cdots = \frac{dx_n}{\xi_n},$$

and their finite equations are $u_1 = const.$, $u_2 = const.$, $\cdots$, $u_{n-1} = const.$, where $u_1 u_2, \cdots$, u_{n-1}, are any $n-1$ independent invariants. Each of the $(n-1)$-way spreads in n dimensions $u_1 = const.$, $u_2 = const.$, $\cdots$, $u_{n-1} = const.$ is invariant, as well as the various spreads of lower dimensions obtained by taking these invariant relations two, three, $\cdots$, $n-1$ together, the last case giving the path-curves.

† This condition holds when the equation involves any number of variables.

The argument employed in establishing this theorem for a curve in three dimensions is different from that available in the case of a surface $f(x, y, z) = 0$ (in the latter case the one employed for a curve in two dimensions (§ 7) applies).

The necessity of the condition is seen as before; for, using formula [7]

$$f_1(x_1, y_1, z_1) = f_1(x, y, z) + Uf_1\, t + U^2 f_1 \frac{t^2}{2!} + \cdots,$$

$$f_2(x_1, y_1, z_1) = f_2(x, y, z) + Uf_2\, t + U^2 f_2 \frac{t^2}{2!} + \cdots.$$

If $f_1(x_1, y_1, z_1)$ and $f_2(x_1, y_1, z_1)$ are to vanish whenever $f_1(x, y, z)$ and $f_2(x, y, z)$ do, for all values of t, it is necessary that $U_1 f = 0$ and $U_2 f = 0$ whenever $f_1 = 0$ and $f_2 = 0$.

The sufficiency of the condition follows at once from the fact that since

$$Uf_1 \equiv \xi \frac{\partial f_1}{\partial x} + \eta \frac{\partial f_1}{\partial y} + \zeta \frac{\partial f_1}{\partial z} = 0,$$

$$Uf_2 \equiv \xi \frac{\partial f_2}{\partial x} + \eta \frac{\partial f_2}{\partial y} + \zeta \frac{\partial f_2}{\partial z} = 0$$

all along the curve $f_1 = 0$, $f_2 = 0$, ξ, η, ζ* are proportional to the direction cosines of the tangent of this curve at each point (x, y, z); that is, this curve is the path-curve through the point (x, y, z).

Remark. — If $Uf_1 = 0$ whenever $f_1 = 0$, and $Uf_2 = 0$ whenever $f_2 = 0$, the surfaces $f_1 = 0$ and $f_2 = 0$ are separately invariant; and their intersection is also invariant. In the case under consideration above, however, [12'] is the condition for invariance of the curve without regard to the nature of these surfaces.

The change of variables

[14] $$x = F(x, y, z), \quad y = \Phi(x, y, z), \quad z = \Psi(x, y, z)$$

---

* If $\xi = 0$, $\eta = 0$, $\zeta = 0$ whenever $f_1 = 0$, $f_2 = 0$, every point on this curve is invariant, and hence, the curve itself is; so that the sufficiency is also established in this case. But such a curve is not included among the path-curves of the group (Remark, § 7).

causes the infinitesimal transformation to take the form (§ 9)

$$[15] \qquad Uf \equiv Ux \frac{\partial f}{\partial x} + Uy \frac{\partial f}{\partial y} + Uz \frac{\partial f}{\partial z}.$$

So that the new variables satisfy the differential equations (§ 10)

$$Ux \equiv \xi \frac{\partial x}{\partial x} + \eta \frac{\partial x}{\partial y} + \zeta \frac{\partial x}{\partial z} = \xi(x, y, z),$$

$$Uy \equiv \xi \frac{\partial y}{\partial x} + \eta \frac{\partial y}{\partial y} + \zeta \frac{\partial y}{\partial z} = \eta(x, y, z),$$

$$Uz \equiv \xi \frac{\partial z}{\partial x} + \eta \frac{\partial z}{\partial y} + \zeta \frac{\partial z}{\partial z} = \zeta(x, y, z).$$

In particular, when $\xi = 0$, $\eta = 0$, $\zeta = 1$, the group is said to be in the *canonical form.** If the equations of the path-curves are known, the canonical variables can be found by means of a single quadrature.

To illustrate all that has gone before consider the group of screw motions

$$x_1 = x \cos t - y \sin t,$$
$$y_1 = x \sin t + y \cos t,$$
$$z_1 = z + mt,$$

where m is any constant.

The student will have no difficulty in proving that these transformations have the group property, and that in this case (§ 1)

$$T_{t_1} T_{t_2} = T_{t_1+t_2};$$

also $\qquad \bar{t} = -t$, and $t_0 = 0$.

The infinitesimal transformation is readily seen to be

$$Uf \equiv -y \frac{\partial f}{\partial x} + x \frac{\partial f}{\partial y} + m \frac{\partial f}{\partial z}.$$

* More generally, the group will be said to be in the *canonical form* when any one of ξ, η, ζ equals a constant, and the other two are zero.

Conversely, starting with the infinitesimal transformation the finite transformations are found to be, using [8],

$$x_1 = x\left(1 - \frac{t^2}{2!} + \frac{t^4}{4!} - \cdots\right) - y\left(t - \frac{t^3}{3!} + \frac{t^5}{5!} - \cdots\right) = x\cos t - y\sin t,$$

$$y_1 = x\left(t - \frac{t^3}{3!} + \frac{t^5}{5!} - \cdots\right) + y\left(1 - \frac{t^2}{2!} + \frac{t^4}{4!} - \cdots\right) = x\sin t + y\cos t,$$

$$z_1 = z + mt \qquad\qquad\qquad\qquad\qquad\qquad = z + mt;$$

or, using the other method,

$$\frac{dx_1}{-y_1} = \frac{dy_1}{x_1} = \frac{dz_1}{m} = \frac{dt}{1}.$$

$$\therefore\; u_1 \equiv x_1{}^2 + y_1{}^2 = x^2 + y^2,$$

$$u_2 \equiv \tan^{-1}\frac{y_1}{x_1} - \frac{z_1}{m} = \tan^{-1}\frac{y}{x} - \frac{z}{m},$$

$$v \equiv \frac{z_1}{m} \qquad\qquad = \frac{z}{m} + t.$$

For practical purposes it will be simpler to replace z, in the second equation by its value in the third one.   Then

$$x_1{}^2 + y_1{}^2 = x^2 + y^2,$$

$$\tan^{-1}\frac{y_1}{x_1} = \tan^{-1}\frac{y}{x} + t,$$

$$z_1 = z + mt.$$

The third equation is already in proper form.

The first two equations are free of z, and, as was found in § 4, reduce to

$$x_1 = x\cos t - y\sin t,$$

$$y_1 = x\sin t + y\cos t.$$

Two independent invariants are $u_1 \equiv x^2 + y^2$, $u_2 \equiv \tan^{-1}\frac{y}{x} - \frac{z}{m}$.   Hence the path-curves are

$$x^2 + y^2 = r^2,\; \tan^{-1}\frac{y}{x} - \frac{z}{m} = c;$$

or, introducing the parameter θ,

$$x = r\cos\theta,\; y = r\sin\theta,\; z = m(\theta - c),$$

which is a family of helices, involving the arbitrary constants r and c.

If $m \neq 0$ there are no invariant points.

Two of the canonical variables, x and y, must satisfy the differential equation

$$-y\frac{\partial f}{\partial x} + x\frac{\partial f}{\partial y} + m\frac{\partial f}{\partial z} = 0,$$

while the third, z, must satisfy

$$-y\frac{\partial f}{\partial x} + x\frac{\partial f}{\partial y} + m\frac{\partial f}{\partial z} = 1.$$

Knowing the invariants of the group, u_1 and u_2, we may put

$$x = \sqrt{x^2 + y^2}, \quad y = \tan^{-1}\frac{y}{x} - \frac{z}{m}.$$

By inspection, z may take the simple form

$$z = \frac{z}{m}.$$

Solving for the old variables, the formulae of transformation of variables are seen to be

$$x = x\cos(y + z), \quad y = y\sin(y + z), \quad z = mz.$$

It is obvious that the change to cylindrical coördinates

$$x = \rho\cos\theta, \quad y = \rho\sin\theta, \quad z = z$$

reduces the group to the form

$$\rho_1 = \rho, \quad \theta_1 = \theta + t, \quad z_1 = z + mt,$$

which is a group of translations, but not in the canonical form.

Discuss as was done in the text the following groups :

Ex. **1.** $x_1 = x, \quad y_1 = y, \quad z_1 = az.$

Ex. **2.** $x_1 = ax, \quad y_1 = ay, \quad z_1 = z.$

Ex. **3.** $x_1 = ax, \quad y_1 = ay, \quad z_1 = az.$

Ex. **4.** $x_1 = ax, \quad y_1 = ay, \quad z_1 = z + \frac{1}{2}(a^2 - 1)xy.$

Ex. **5.** $x_1 = e^a(x\cos a - y\sin a), \quad y_1 = e^a(x\sin a + y\cos a), \quad z_1 = e^a z.$

CHAPTER II

DIFFERENTIAL EQUATIONS OF THE FIRST ORDER

12. Integrating Factor. — We have seen (§ 8) that if $\phi(x, y) = const.$ is a family of curves invariant under the group

$$Uf \equiv \xi \frac{\partial f}{\partial x} + \eta \frac{\partial f}{\partial y},$$

(13) $$U\phi = F(\phi).$$

Moreover, it was also shown in § 8 that if the curves of the family are not path-curves of the group, the equation of the family can be chosen in such form that the right-hand member of (13) shall become any desired function of ϕ. In particular, there is no loss in assuming the equation so chosen that this right-hand member is 1 ; for if a given choice $\phi = const.$ leads to $F(\phi)$, the selection $\Phi(\phi) = const.$, where $\Phi(\phi) = \int \frac{d\phi}{F(\phi)}$, will give $U\Phi(\phi) = 1.$

Suppose now that

(17) $$M\, dx + N\, dy = 0$$

is a differential equation whose family of integral curves

(18) $$\phi(x, y) = const.$$

is invariant under the group Uf, the integral curves not being path-curves of the latter. Let ϕ be so chosen that

(19) $$U\phi \equiv \xi \frac{\partial \phi}{\partial x} + \eta \frac{\partial \phi}{\partial y} = 1.$$

37

Since (18) is the solution of (17),

$$d\phi \equiv \frac{\partial \phi}{\partial x}\, dx + \frac{\partial \phi}{\partial y}\, dy = 0$$

must be the same equation as (17) ; hence

or,
$$\frac{\dfrac{\partial \phi}{\partial x}}{M} = \frac{\dfrac{\partial \phi}{\partial y}}{N},$$

(20)
$$N\frac{\partial \phi}{\partial x} - M\frac{\partial \phi}{\partial y} = 0.$$

From equations (19) and (20) the values of $\dfrac{\partial \phi}{\partial x}$ and $\dfrac{\partial \phi}{\partial y}$ are found to be

$$\frac{\partial \phi}{\partial x} = \frac{M}{\xi M + \eta N}, \qquad \frac{\partial \phi}{\partial y} = \frac{N}{\xi M + \eta N}.$$

$$\therefore\ d\phi = \frac{M\,dx + N\,dy}{\xi M + \eta N}.$$

Hence the

THEOREM.* — *If the family of integral curves of the differential equation* $Mdx + Ndy = 0$ *is left unaltered by the group* $Uf \equiv \xi\dfrac{\partial f}{\partial x} + \eta\dfrac{\partial f}{\partial y}$, $\dfrac{1}{\xi M + \eta N}$ *is an integrating factor of the differential equation.*

Remark 1. — This theorem ceases to hold in case the curves (18) are path-curves of the group Uf. In this case (19) becomes, $\xi\dfrac{\partial \phi}{\partial x} + \eta\dfrac{\partial \phi}{\partial y} = 0$; whence, taking account of (20), $\xi M + \eta N = 0$. As a matter of fact, it is obvious that in this case the curves (18), being the integral curves of (17), are the path-curves for every group of the type

$$Uf \equiv \rho(x, y) \cdot N\frac{\partial f}{\partial x} - \rho(x, y) \cdot M\frac{\partial f}{\partial y},$$

---

* This theorem of Lie was first published by him in the Verhandlungen der Gesell-schaft der Wissenschaften zu Christiania, November, 1874.

where $\rho(x, y)$ is any holomorphic function of x and y.   Such groups are said to be *trivial* for purposes of assisting in solving the differential equation (17).

Remark 2.— At times it is obvious from the nature of the problem that the family of integral curves is invariant under a certain group. This will be found to be the case in the following examples :

Ex. 1.   Find the curves whose tangent at each point makes an isosceles triangle with the axis of x and the radius vector to the point of contact.

This family of curves is clearly invariant under the similitudinous group $Uf \equiv x\dfrac{\partial f}{\partial x} + y\dfrac{\partial f}{\partial y}$.   Its differential equation is

$$\frac{\dfrac{dy}{dx} - \dfrac{y}{x}}{1 + \dfrac{y}{x}\dfrac{dy}{dx}} = -\frac{dy}{dx}, \text{ or } y\left(\frac{dy}{dx}\right)^2 + 2x\frac{dy}{dx} - y = 0.$$

Reducing to the form (17), which is characterized by being of the first degree in dx and dy,
$$(x \pm \sqrt{x^2 + y^2})dx + y\,dy = 0.$$

The integrating factor

$$\frac{1}{\xi M + \eta N} \equiv \frac{1}{x^2 + y^2 \pm x\sqrt{x^2 + y^2}} = \frac{1}{\pm\sqrt{x^2 + y^2}(x \pm \sqrt{x^2 + y^2})}$$

gives
$$\frac{dx}{\pm\sqrt{x^2 + y^2}} + \frac{y\,dy}{\pm\sqrt{x^2 + y^2}(x \pm \sqrt{x^2 + y^2})} = 0.$$

Integrating, $\log(x \pm \sqrt{x^2 + y^2}) = const.$ or $x \pm \sqrt{x^2 + y^2} = c.$

This reduces at once to $y^2 = c^2 - 2cx$, a family of parabolas having the origin as common focus and the axis of x as common axis.

Ex. 2.   Find the curves such that the radius vector to each point makes an isosceles triangle with the tangent at the point and the axis of x.

Ex. 3. Find the curves such that the length of the radius vector to each point equals the tangent of the angle between the radius vector and the tangent to the curve at that point.

Ex. 4. Find the curves such that the radius vector to each point makes a constant angle with the tangent to the curve at that point.

Ex. 5. Find the curves such that the perpendicular distance from the origin to the tangent to a curve at any point is equal to the abscissa of that point.

13. Differential Equation Invariant under Extended Group. — While at times it is possible to tell from the nature of the problem whether the integral curves of a differential equation form an invariant family under a certain group, it is desirable in order to extend the usefulness of the theorem of the previous section, to be able to tell when this is the case from the form of the differential equation itself.

A *point transformation*

$$x_1 = \phi(x, y), \quad y_1 = \psi(x, y)*$$

carries with it the transformation

$$\frac{dy_1}{dx_1} = \frac{\dfrac{\partial \psi}{\partial x} dx + \dfrac{\partial \psi}{\partial y} dy}{\dfrac{\partial \phi}{\partial x} dx + \dfrac{\partial \phi}{\partial y} dy},$$

or

$$y_1' = \frac{\dfrac{\partial \psi}{\partial x} + \dfrac{\partial \psi}{\partial y} y'}{\dfrac{\partial \phi}{\partial x} + \dfrac{\partial \phi}{\partial y} y'} \equiv \chi(x, y, y'),$$

---

* This is called a point transformation because it transforms the point (x, y) into (x_1, y_1). It thus transforms the various points of a curve $F(x, y) = 0$ into the corresponding points of some other curve $F_1(x_1, y_1) = 0$, and may therefore be said to transform the curve $F(x, y) = 0$ into $F_1(x_1, y_1) = 0$.

where $y' \equiv \dfrac{dy}{dx}$ and $y_1' \equiv \dfrac{dy_1}{dx_1}$. Since χ is a function of x, y, y' only, it follows that the point transformation implies the transformation

$$x_1 = \phi(x, y), \; y_1 = \psi(x, y), \; y_1' = \dfrac{\dfrac{\partial \psi}{\partial x} + \dfrac{\partial \psi}{\partial y} y'}{\dfrac{\partial \phi}{\partial x} + \dfrac{\partial \phi}{\partial y} y'} \equiv \chi(x, y, y')$$

affecting the three variables x, y, y'. The latter transformation is known as an *extended point transformation.**

Starting with the one-parameter group of point transformations

(1) $$x_1 = \phi(x, y, a), \; y_1 = \psi(x, y, a)$$

it is easily seen that the corresponding extended transformations

(21) $$x_1 = \phi(x, y, a), \; y_1 = \psi(x, y, a), \; y_1' = \dfrac{dy_1}{dx_1} \equiv \chi(x, y, y,' a)$$

also constitute a one-parameter group in the three variables x, y, y'. For, since the equations of a point transformation are precisely the first two of the corresponding extended transformation, and since the third equation of the latter is determined uniquely by the first two, the fact that the transformations (1) have the group property (§ 1) predicates the existence of the group property in the case of (21).

Thus if a and b are any two selected values of the parameter, the result of performing successively the two point transformations

$$x_1 = \phi(x, y, a), \quad y_1 = \psi(x, y, a)$$
and
$$x_2 = \phi(x_1, y_1, b), \quad y_2 = \psi(x_1, y_1, b)$$
is
$$x_2 = \phi(x, y, c), \quad y_2 = \psi(x, y, c)$$

* An extended point transformation is a special kind of a contact transformation (§ 49) ; for it transforms (x, y, y') into (x_1, y_1, y_1'), where, if (x, y) is some point on some curve $F(x, y) = 0$, y' is the slope of the tangent to the curve at that point and y_1' is the slope of curve $F_1(x_1, y_1) = 0$ (into which the other is transformed by the point transformation) at the corresponding point (x_1, y_1). Since the value of y_1' depends upon x, y, y' only, any curve tangent to $F(x, y) = 0$ at (x, y) will be transformed into a curve tangent to $F_1 (x_1, y_1) = 0$ at the point (x_1, y_1).

where c is a function of a and b. This follows from the group property of (1). In the case of the corresponding extended transformations

$$x_1 = \phi(x, y, a), \quad y_1 = \psi(x, y, a), \quad y_1' = \frac{d\psi(x, y, a)}{d\phi(x, y, a)} \equiv \chi(x, y, y,' a),$$

and

$$x_2 = \phi(x_1, y_1, b), y_2 = \psi(x_1, y_1, b), y_2' = \frac{d\psi(x_1, y_1, b)}{d\phi(x_1, y_1, b)} \equiv \chi(x_1, y_1, y_1', b),$$

the result of replacing x_1 and y_1 in the first two equations of the second transformation by the values given in the first transformation is therefore

$$x_2 = \phi(x, y, c), y_2 = \psi(x, y, c).$$

Hence in the last equation of the second transformation,

$$y_2' = \frac{dy_2}{dx_2} = \frac{d\psi(x, y, c)}{d\phi(x, y, c)} \equiv \chi(x, y, y', c).$$

In exactly the same way, the fact that a value of the parameter exists giving the identical transformation for the group (1), and also the fact that the transformations of (1) can be separated into pairs of mutually inverse transformations, assure these same properties for the transformations of (21). The latter therefore constitute a Lie one-parameter group. This group is known as the *once-extended group* corresponding to (1).

With Lie, we shall write as the symbol of the infinitesimal transformation of the once-extended group

$$(22) \qquad U'f \equiv \xi(x, y)\frac{\partial f}{\partial x} + \eta(x, y)\frac{\partial f}{\partial y} + \eta'(x, y, y')\frac{\partial f}{\partial y'},$$

where, as before, $\xi \equiv \dfrac{\delta x}{\delta a}$, $\eta \equiv \dfrac{\delta y}{\delta a}$, while $\eta' \equiv \dfrac{\delta y'}{\delta a} = \dfrac{\delta}{\delta a}\left(\dfrac{dy}{dx}\right)$.

It was seen in § 4 that, with a proper selection of the parameter,

$$\xi = \left(\frac{\partial x_1}{\partial a}\right)_{a_0}, \quad \eta = \left(\frac{\partial y_1}{\partial a}\right)_{a_0}, \quad \text{and, for any function } f, \frac{\delta f}{\delta a} = \left(\frac{\partial f_1}{\partial a}\right)_{a_0}.$$

In a sense then δ is a differential operator, so that δ and d are commutative operators ; thus, for example,

$$\frac{\delta}{\delta a}(dx) = \left(\frac{\partial}{\partial a}dx_1\right)_{a_0} = \left(d\frac{\partial x_1}{\partial a}\right)_{a_0} = d\xi = d\left(\frac{\delta x}{\delta a}\right).$$

Hence $\eta' = \dfrac{\delta}{\delta a}\left(\dfrac{dy}{dx}\right) = \dfrac{\dfrac{\delta}{\delta a}(dy)}{dx} - \dfrac{dy\,\dfrac{\delta}{\delta a}(dx)}{(dx)^2} = \dfrac{d\left(\dfrac{\delta y}{\delta a}\right)}{dx} - \dfrac{dy}{dx}\dfrac{d\left(\dfrac{\delta x}{\delta a}\right)}{dx}.$

$$(23) \qquad\qquad \therefore \eta' = \frac{d\eta}{dx} - y'\frac{d\xi}{dx}.$$

Remark. — Attention should be called to the fact that, while y' is equal to $\dfrac{dy}{dx}$, η' is usually different from $\dfrac{d\eta}{dx}$. Expanding the right-hand member of (23), we have

$$(24) \qquad\qquad \eta' = \frac{\partial\eta}{\partial x} + \left(\frac{\partial\eta}{\partial y} - \frac{\partial\xi}{\partial x}\right)y' - \frac{\partial\xi}{\partial y}y'^2,$$

where it is to be noted that η' is a quadratic polynomial in y' when

$$\frac{\partial\xi}{\partial y} \not\equiv 0.$$

Given a differential equation of the first order

$$(25) \qquad\qquad f(x, y, y') = 0,$$

the effect of any transformation (1) on the variables x and y is to transform the differential equation (considered as an equation in the three variables x, y, y') by the corresponding extended transformation (21). The family of integral curves of (25) is invariant under the group if each integral curve is transformed into some curve of the family by every transformation (1). Hence every transformation (21) must leave the differential equation unaltered.   The condition for this is ([12], § 11)

$$(26) \qquad U'f \equiv \xi \frac{\partial f}{\partial x} + \eta \frac{\partial f}{\partial y} + \eta' \frac{\partial f}{\partial y'} = 0 \text{ whenever } f(x, y, y') = 0.$$

Hence the

THEOREM. — *The family of integral curves of the differential equation $f(x, y, y') = 0$, and, therefore, the differential equation itself, is invariant under the group Uf if $U'f = 0$ whenever $f = 0$.*

In the case of II, $\xi \equiv -y$, $\eta \equiv x$. Hence, from (23) $\eta' \equiv 1 + y'^2$. The extended group of rotations is then

$$U'f \equiv -y \frac{\partial f}{\partial x} + x \frac{\partial f}{\partial y} + (1 + y'^2) \frac{\partial f}{\partial y'}.$$

The differential equation of the family of lines $\frac{y}{x} = c$ (which is invariant under II) is $xy' - y = 0$.   Here

$$U'(xy' - y) = -yy' - x + (1 + y'^2)x = y'(xy' - y).$$

This vanishes whenever $xy' - y$ does.

14. Alternant. — Let U_1 and U_2 be any two homogeneous linear partial differential operators *

$$U_1 \equiv \xi_1(x, y) \frac{\partial}{\partial x} + \eta_1(x, y) \frac{\partial}{\partial y},$$

$$U_2 \equiv \xi_2(x, y) \frac{\partial}{\partial x} + \eta_2(x, y) \frac{\partial}{\partial y}.$$

Then

$$U_1 U_2 f = U_1 \xi_2 \frac{\partial f}{\partial x} + U_1 \eta_2 \frac{\partial f}{\partial y} + \xi_1 \xi_2 \frac{\partial^2 f}{\partial x^2} + (\xi_1 \eta_2 + \eta_1 \xi_2) \frac{\partial^2 f}{\partial x \partial y} + \eta_1 \eta_2 \frac{\partial^2 f}{\partial y^2},$$

$$U_2 U_1 f = U_2 \xi_1 \frac{\partial f}{\partial x} + U_2 \eta_1 \frac{\partial f}{\partial y} + \xi_2 \xi_1 \frac{\partial^2 f}{\partial x^2} + (\xi_2 \eta_1 + \eta_2 \xi_1) \frac{\partial^2 f}{\partial x \partial y} + \eta_2 \eta_1 \frac{\partial^2 f}{\partial y^2}.$$

$$(27) \quad \therefore \ U_1 U_2 f - U_2 U_1 f = (U_1 \xi_2 - U_2 \xi_1) \frac{\partial f}{\partial x} + (U_1 \eta_2 - U_2 \eta_1) \frac{\partial f}{\partial y}.$$

* For the sake of simplicity we shall suppose that two variables are involved.   But this entire section holds without any modification for n variables.

Writing $$U_1 U_2 f - U_2 U_1 f \equiv (U_1 U_2) f,^*$$

the *operator* $(U_1 U_2)$, which is known as the *alternant*† of U_1 and U_2, *is* seen to be *one of the same type as* U_1 and U_2.

The following properties of alternants are immediate :

$$(U_1 U_2) = -(U_2 U_1),$$

$$(U_1 U_1) = 0,$$

$$(U_1, \; U_2 \pm U_3) = (U_1 U_2) \pm (U_1 U_3),$$

$$(\phi(x, y) U_1, \; U_2) = \phi(x, y)(U_1 U_2) - U_2 \phi U_1.$$

15. Another Criterion for Invariance of a Differential Equation under a Group. — A second form for expressing the condition that a group leave a differential equation unaltered plays a very important rôle in the further development of the theory.   It was seen (§ 12), that if

(18) $$\phi(x, y) = const.$$

is the solution of

(17) $$M \, dx + N \, dy = 0,$$

ϕ is a solution of the partial differential equation (20)

(28) $$A\phi \equiv N \frac{\partial \phi}{\partial x} - M \frac{\partial \phi}{\partial y} = 0.$$

Moreover, if the family of curves (18) is invariant under the group Uf (without being path-curves of the latter), ϕ may be so chosen that

(19) $$U\phi \equiv \xi \frac{\partial \phi}{\partial x} + \eta \frac{\partial \phi}{\partial y} = 1.$$

Consider now the alternant of U and A (§ 14)

(27) $$(UA)f \equiv UAf - AUf = (UN - A\xi)\frac{\partial f}{\partial x} - (UM + A\eta)\frac{\partial f}{\partial y}.$$

---

* Lie writes $(U_1 U_2)$ or $(U_1 f, \, U_2 f)$ instead of $(U_1 U_2) f$.
† Also sometimes called the *commutator* of U_1 and U_2.

Because of (28) and (19) $(UA)\phi \equiv U(0) - A(1) = 0.$

$$(29) \qquad \therefore (UN - A\xi)\frac{\partial \phi}{\partial x} - (UM + A\eta)\frac{\partial \phi}{\partial y} = 0.$$

Since ϕ is a function of at least one of the variables x and y, $\frac{\partial \phi}{\partial x}$ and $\frac{\partial \phi}{\partial y}$ are not both identically zero. Hence the coefficients of (29) must be proportional to those of (28); *i.e.*

$$(30) \qquad \frac{UN - A\xi}{N} = \frac{UM + A\eta}{M} = \lambda(x, y),*$$

or $\qquad UN - A\xi = \lambda N, \quad UM + A\eta = \lambda M.$

Putting these in (27)

$$(31) \qquad (UA)f = \lambda(x, y)Af.$$

Hence (31) is a necessary condition that the integral curves of (17) be invariant under Uf.

Conversely, if (31) holds

$$(UA)\phi \equiv UA\phi - AU\phi = \lambda A\phi = 0,$$

because of (28). Hence $\qquad AU\phi = 0.$

Since every solution of (28) is a function of ϕ

$$U\phi = F(\phi).$$

This is the condition [§ 8, (13)] that the family (18) be invariant under the group Uf. Hence the

THEOREM. — *The necessary and sufficient condition that the differential equation $M\,dx + N\,dy = 0$ be invariant under the group Uf is*

$$(31) \qquad (UA)f = \lambda(x, y)\,Af$$

where $\qquad Af \equiv N\frac{\partial f}{\partial x} - M\frac{\partial f}{\partial y}.$

---

* The common ratio $\lambda(x, y)$ is, at most, a function of the variables. It may be a constant or zero.

The condition (31) was found independently of what has gone before. It may be obtained at once by means of (26). It is suggested as an exercise, that the student do this. Here $f(x, y, y') \equiv M + Ny'$. The expanded form of η', given by (24), must be employed.

This theorem leads to another one, of some interest, which is, as a matter of fact, the converse of the theorem of § 12.

If $\xi(x, y)$ and $\eta(x, y)$ are any two functions such that

$$\mu \equiv \frac{1}{\xi M + \eta N}$$

is an integrating factor of

(17) $$M\,dx + N\,dy = 0,$$

$$\frac{\partial}{\partial x}\left(\frac{N}{\xi M + \eta N}\right) - \frac{\partial}{\partial y}\left(\frac{M}{\xi M + \eta N}\right) = 0,^*$$

or $\xi M \dfrac{\partial N}{\partial x} - \xi N \dfrac{\partial M}{\partial x} - MN \dfrac{\partial \xi}{\partial x} - N^2 \dfrac{\partial \eta}{\partial x} - \eta N \dfrac{\partial M}{\partial y} + \eta M \dfrac{\partial N}{\partial y} + M^2 \dfrac{\partial \xi}{\partial y}$

$$+ MN \frac{\partial \eta}{\partial y} = 0.$$

Dividing by MN and rearranging the terms,

$$\frac{\xi \dfrac{\partial N}{\partial x} + \eta \dfrac{\partial N}{\partial y} - N \dfrac{\partial \xi}{\partial x} + M \dfrac{\partial \xi}{\partial y}}{N} = \frac{\xi \dfrac{\partial M}{\partial x} + \eta \dfrac{\partial M}{\partial y} + N \dfrac{\partial \eta}{\partial x} - M \dfrac{\partial \eta}{\partial y}}{M}$$

or

(30) $$\frac{UN - A\xi}{N} = \frac{UM + A\eta}{M};$$

from which follows (31) as before. Hence, *if $\mu(x, y)$ is an integrating factor of the differential equation $M\,dx + N\,dy = 0$, and $\xi(x, y)$ and $\eta(x, y)$ are any holomorphic functions of the variables satisfying the relation*

(32) $$\frac{1}{\xi M + \eta N} = \mu,$$

* See *El. Dif. Eq.* § 7.

the differential equation is invariant under the group

$$Uf \equiv \xi \frac{\partial f}{\partial x} + \eta \frac{\partial f}{\partial y}.$$

Since ξ and η are subject to the single condition (32), one of them may be chosen at pleasure, and then the other is determined uniquely. Hence, *starting with an integrating factor of a differential equation of the first order, an infinite number of groups can be found which leave the differential equation unaltered.*

It will be seen in § 17 that the general expression for such groups involves two arbitrary functions. As a matter of fact, this can also be seen from the form of (32). For if μ is an integrating factor giving $\mu(Mdx + Ndy) \equiv du$, then for $F(u)$ any function of u, $\mu F(u)$ is also an integrating factor. (See *El. Dif. Eq.* § 5.) Using this as the right-hand member of (32), and selecting $\xi(x, y)$ arbitrarily, $\eta = \dfrac{1}{N\mu F(u)} - \dfrac{M\xi(x, y)}{N}$. The general type of group leaving (17) unaltered may, therefore, be put in the form

$$Uf \equiv \xi(x, y) \frac{\partial f}{\partial x} + \left(\frac{1}{N\mu F(u)} - \frac{M\xi(x, y)}{N} \right) \frac{\partial f}{\partial y},$$

where ξ and F are arbitrary functions.

16. Two Integrating Factors. — Since the knowledge of a group which leaves a differential equation unaltered gives an integrating factor, thus reducing the problem of solving the differential equation to a mere quadrature, it should be expected that the knowledge of a second group which leads to a distinct integrating factor still further simplifies the problem of solving the equation. This is actually the case.

Suppose μ_1 and μ_2 to be two integrating factors of (17). Then

$$\frac{\partial(\mu_1 M)}{\partial y} - \frac{\partial(\mu_1 N)}{\partial x} = 0, \quad \frac{\partial(\mu_2 M)}{\partial y} - \frac{\partial(\mu_2 N)}{\partial x} = 0,$$

or

$$\frac{\partial M}{\partial y} - \frac{\partial N}{\partial x} = \frac{1}{\mu_1} \left(N \frac{\partial \mu_1}{\partial x} - M \frac{\partial \mu_1}{\partial y} \right) = \frac{1}{\mu_2} \left(N \frac{\partial \mu_2}{\partial x} - M \frac{\partial \mu_2}{\partial y} \right).$$

Remembering that $\dfrac{1}{\mu}\dfrac{\partial \mu}{\partial x} = \dfrac{\partial(\log \mu)}{\partial x}$, $\dfrac{1}{\mu}\dfrac{\partial \mu}{\partial y} = \dfrac{\partial(\log \mu)}{\partial y}$, and

$\log \mu_1 - \log \mu_2 = \log \dfrac{\mu_1}{\mu_2}$, the last equation becomes

$$N\dfrac{\partial}{\partial x}\left(\log \dfrac{\mu_1}{\mu_2}\right) - M\dfrac{\partial}{\partial y}\left(\log \dfrac{\mu_1}{\mu_2}\right) = 0 \ ;$$

i.e., $\log \dfrac{\mu_1}{\mu_2}$ is an integral of

(28) $$Af \equiv N\dfrac{\partial f}{\partial x} - M\dfrac{\partial f}{\partial y} = 0.$$

Hence $\dfrac{\mu_1}{\mu_2}$ is also an integral of (28), and

$$\dfrac{\mu_1}{\mu_2} = const.$$

is a solution of (17). So that *the knowledge of two integrating factors gives the solution of the differential equation without any analytic work whatever.*

Remark. — It is interesting to note that in the proof usually given for the theorem that when one integrating factor μ is known, an infinite number of others can be found [viz. if $\mu(Mdx + Ndy) \equiv du$, then $\mu F(u)$ is an integrating factor where $F(u)$ is any function of u],[*] all possible integrating factors are found.

17. General Expression for Group under which a Differential Equation is Invariant. — We have just seen that if $U_1 f$ and $U_2 f$ are any two groups which leave the equation (17) unaltered,

$$\dfrac{\mu_1}{\mu_2} \equiv \dfrac{\xi_2 M + \eta_2 N}{\xi_1 M + \eta_1 N} = const.$$

[*] See *El. Dif. Eq.* § 5.

is a solution of (17) ; hence,

$$(33) \qquad \frac{\xi_2 M + \eta_2 N}{\xi_1 M + \eta_1 N} = F(\phi),$$

where $\phi(x, y) = const.$ is any selected form of solution of (17). Rearranging the terms in (33),

$$(34) \qquad \frac{\xi_2 - F(\phi) \cdot \xi_1}{N} = - \frac{\eta_2 - F(\phi) \cdot \eta_1}{M} = \rho(x, y),$$

where $\rho(x, y)$ is the common value of the two fractions. Whence

$$\xi_2 = F(\phi)\xi_1 + \rho N, \quad \eta_2 = F(\phi)\eta_1 - \rho M.$$

$$(35) \qquad \therefore \ U_2 f = F(\phi) U_1 f + \rho A f.$$

Conversely, if $U_1 f$ leaves the differential equation unaltered, $U_2 f$ given by (35) will also do so, no matter how $F(\phi)$ and $\rho(x, y)$ may be chosen (it being understood throughout that all functions involved are to be generally analytic). For, by hypothesis, using (31)

$$(U_1 A) f = \lambda A f ;$$

then
$$\begin{aligned}(U_2 A) f &= (F(\phi) U_1, A) f + (\rho A, A) f \\ &= F(\phi)(U_1 A) f - A F(\phi) U_1 f + \rho(A A) f - A \rho A f \\ &= [F(\phi)\lambda - A\rho] A f \\ &= \nu(x, y) A f.\end{aligned}$$

Hence *every group which leaves the differential equation unaltered is given by* (35), *$U_1 f$ being one group of this sort.*

If $F(\phi)$ is a constant, the resulting group gives the same integrating factor as $U_1 f$.

If $F(\phi)$ is identically zero, the resulting group is trivial (§ 12).

18. Differential Equations Invariant under a Given Group. — In order to make use of the theorem of § 12, a group leaving the differential equation unaltered must be known. While such groups always exist, and are sometimes suggested by the nature of the problem giving rise to the differential equation, the number of equations for which they are known is comparatively small. The converse problem of finding the general type of the differential equations invariant under a given group is much more direct. And while its complete solution requires the knowledge of the path-curves of the group and usually one or several quadratures, it is practicable to supply these in a large number of cases of interest.

It is clear that the differential equation obtained by equating an invariant of the extended group (§ 13) to an arbitrary constant is invariant. The general type of invariant of the extended group is obtained by taking an arbitrary function of two independent solutions of ([9], § 11)

$$(36) \qquad U'f \equiv \xi \frac{\partial f}{\partial x} + \eta \frac{\partial f}{\partial y} + \eta' \frac{\partial f}{\partial y'} = 0.$$

Passing to the corresponding system of ordinary differential equations

$$(37) \qquad \frac{dx}{\xi(x, y)} = \frac{dy}{\eta(x, y)} = \frac{dy'}{\eta'(x, y, y')},$$

the first equation is recognized as (11), § 7. Its solution is

$$u(x, y) = c.$$

A second solution, independent of this one, must involve y'. Writing this in the form

$$u'(x, y, y') = const.*,$$

the general solution of (36) will be of the form $f(u, u')$. Equating this to an arbitrary constant gives the general type of invariant differential equation. There is no loss of generality in equating $f(u, u')$

---

* Since $u'(x, y, y')$ is an invariant of the extended group $U'f$ and involves y', it is known as a *first differential invariant* of the group Uf.

to zero, the arbitrary constant being incorporated in the arbitrary function f. So that the general type of invariant equation is

$$(38) \qquad f(u, u') = 0, \text{ or } u' = F(u).$$

Several methods for finding u' suggest themselves:

(*a*) Solving $u(x, y) = c$ for y, and replacing it by its value in terms of x and c wherever it occurs in the first and last members of (37), the Riccati equation

$$(39) \qquad \frac{dy'}{dx} = \frac{1}{\xi}\frac{\partial\eta}{\partial x} + \frac{1}{\xi}\left(\frac{\partial\eta}{\partial y} - \frac{\partial\xi}{\partial x}\right)y' - \frac{1}{\xi}\frac{\partial\xi}{\partial y}y'^2$$

results. In Note II of the Appendix it is shown that this equation can be solved by quadratures.

(*b*) The introduction of canonical variables (which can be found by a quadrature when u is known, § 10) reduces the invariant differential equation to the simple form

$$\frac{dy}{dx} = \frac{\dfrac{\partial y}{\partial x} + \dfrac{\partial y}{\partial y}y'}{\dfrac{\partial x}{\partial x} + \dfrac{\partial x}{\partial y}y'} = F(x),$$

as will be shown, I, § 19. Since the one canonical variable x is the invariant u or a function of it (§ 10), $F(x)$ is a function of u. Because of the general type

of invariant differential equation (38), $\dfrac{\dfrac{\partial y}{\partial x} + \dfrac{\partial y}{\partial y}y'}{\dfrac{\partial x}{\partial x} + \dfrac{\partial x}{\partial y}y'}$ may be taken as u'.

(*c*) Frequently some special method (see *El. Dif. Eq.* § 65) may be found which is more direct.

19. Illustrations and Applications.

I. $Uf \equiv \dfrac{\partial f}{\partial y}$. $\xi \equiv 0, \eta \equiv 1$. $\therefore \eta' \equiv 0$. Equations (37) are

$$\frac{dx}{0} = \frac{dy}{1} = \frac{dy'}{0}.$$

$\therefore u \equiv x, u' \equiv y'$. Hence *the general type of differential equation invariant under* $Uf \equiv \dfrac{\partial f}{\partial y}$ *is* $f(x, y') = 0$, *or* $y' = F(x)$.

This equation is characterized by the absence of y.   The variables are separated when the equation is solved for y'.

I'. $Uf \equiv \dfrac{\partial f}{\partial x}$.   It is readily seen * that *the general type of differential equation invariant under this group* (of translations in the direction of the axis of x) *is* $y' = F(y)$.

This equation is characterized by the absence of x.   The variables are separable, thus $\dfrac{dy}{F(y)} = dx$.

II. $Uf \equiv -y\dfrac{\partial f}{\partial x} + x\dfrac{\partial f}{\partial y}$. $\xi \equiv -x, \ \eta \equiv x.$ $\therefore \eta' \equiv 1 + y'^2.$

Equations (37) are $\dfrac{dx}{-y} = \dfrac{dy}{x} = \dfrac{dy'}{1+y'^2}.$

$\therefore u \equiv x^2 + y^2$.   To find u', multiply numerator and denominator of the first member by $-y$, and those of the second member by x; then by composition (*El. Dif. Eq.* § 65, 3°),

$$\frac{x\,dy - y\,dx}{x^2 + y^2} = \frac{dy'}{1+y'^2}.$$

$\therefore u' \equiv \tan^{-1}\dfrac{y}{x} - \tan^{-1}y'$.   It is simpler to take the tangent of this function as the second invariant; *i.e.* $u' \equiv \dfrac{y - xy'}{x + yy'}$.   Hence *the general type of differential equation invariant under* $Uf \equiv -y\dfrac{\partial f}{\partial x} + x\dfrac{\partial f}{\partial y}$ *is* $f\left(x^2 + y^2, \dfrac{y-xy'}{x+yy'}\right) = 0$, *or* $\dfrac{y-xy'}{x+yy'} = F(x^2 + y^2)$.

---

* It is suggested as an exercise that the student actually carry out the work here and in the cases below, where results alone are given.

Of course, the differential equation invariant under a group whose number is primed may be obtained from that invariant under the corresponding unprimed one by interchanging x and y and y' and $\dfrac{1}{y'}$.   But as an attempt is being made here to make a collection of differential equations invariant under known groups, the forms by which these differential equations are most readily recognized are given.

Note. — This form of the invariant differential equation is obvious from geometrical considerations, since u is the square of the radius vector to any point on an integral curve, and u' is the tangent of the angle between the radius vector and the tangent to the curve. Since any function of u and u', containing y', can be used as a first differential invariant, $\sqrt{\dfrac{u}{1 + u'^2}}$ or $\dfrac{x + yy'}{\sqrt{1 + y'^2}}$ is available. So also is $u'\sqrt{\dfrac{u}{1 + u'^2}}$ or $\dfrac{y - xy'}{\sqrt{1 + y'^2}}$. These are respectively the distance of the normal and that of the tangent from the origin, each of which is left unaltered by the group of rotations about the origin. Hence *the general type of differential equation invariant under this group may also be written*

$$x + yy' = \sqrt{1 + y'^2}\,F(x^2 + y^2), \text{ or } y - xy' = \sqrt{1 + y'^2}\,F(x^2 + y^2).$$

III. $Uf \equiv y\dfrac{\partial f}{\partial y}.$ $\xi \equiv 0,\ \eta \equiv y.$ $\therefore \eta' \equiv y'.$ Equations (37) are

$$\frac{dx}{0} = \frac{dy}{y} = \frac{dy'}{y'}.$$

$\therefore u \equiv x,\ u' \equiv \dfrac{y'}{y}.$ Hence *the general type of differential equation invariant under* $Uf \equiv y\dfrac{\partial f}{\partial y}$ *is* $f\left(x, \dfrac{y'}{y}\right),$ *or* $\dfrac{y'}{y} = F(x).$

This equation is characterized by being homogeneous in y and y'. The variables are separated when the equation is solved for $\dfrac{y'}{y}$.

III'. $Uf \equiv x\dfrac{\partial f}{\partial x}.$ It is readily seen that *the general type of differential equation invariant under this group* (of affine transformations) *is* $xy' = F(y).$

The variables are separable, thus $\dfrac{dy}{F(y)} = \dfrac{dx}{x}.$

IV. $Uf \equiv x\dfrac{\partial f}{\partial x} + y\dfrac{\partial f}{\partial y}.$ Here $\eta' \equiv 0,$ and $u \equiv \dfrac{y}{x},\ u' \equiv y'.$ Hence *the general type of differential equation invariant under*

$$Uf \equiv x\frac{\partial f}{\partial x} + y\frac{\partial f}{\partial y} \text{ is } f\left(\frac{y}{x}, y'\right) = 0, \text{ or } y' = F\left(\frac{y}{x}\right).$$

This equation is characterized by being homogeneous in x and y.

Note. — An equation $M\,dx + N\,dy = 0$ is of this type when M and N are homogeneous functions of x and y, and of the same degree. In this case the integrating factor of § 12 is $\dfrac{1}{xM + yN}$. (Compare *El. Dif. Eq.* § 17.)

V. $Uf \equiv x\dfrac{\partial f}{\partial x} - y\dfrac{\partial f}{\partial y}$.   Here $\eta' \equiv -2y'$, and $u \equiv xy$, $u' \equiv x^2 y'$.

Hence *the general type of differential equation invariant under*

$$Uf \equiv x\frac{\partial f}{\partial x} - y\frac{\partial f}{\partial y} \text{ is } f(xy, x^2y') = 0, \text{ or } xy' = yF(xy).$$

This equation is characterized by being homogeneous in x, y, y', when these elements are given the weights 1, -1, -2 respectively. (Compare VI below.)

Note. — An equation $M\,dx + N\,dy = 0$ is of this type when $M \equiv yf_1(xy)$, $N \equiv xf_2(xy)$. In this case the integrating factor of § 12 is $\dfrac{1}{xM - yN}$. (Compare *El. Dif. Eq.* § 17.)

VI. $Uf \equiv x\dfrac{\partial f}{\partial x} + ny\dfrac{\partial f}{\partial y}.*$ $\xi \equiv x$, $\eta \equiv ny$. $\therefore \eta' \equiv (n-1)y'$, and $u \equiv \dfrac{y}{x^n}$, $u' \equiv \dfrac{y'}{x^{n-1}}$.   Hence *the general type of differential equation*

---

* n may be any number. In particular $n = 1$ gives IV, while $n = -1$ gives V, and $n = 0$ gives III'.

If the group be written in the more symmetrical form $Uf \equiv ax\dfrac{\partial f}{\partial x} + by\dfrac{\partial f}{\partial y}$, the invariant differential equation takes the form $xy' = yF\left(\dfrac{y^a}{x^b}\right)$. $a = b$ gives IV, $a = -b$ gives V, $a = 0$ gives III, $b = 0$ gives III'.

invariant under $Uf \equiv x\dfrac{\partial f}{\partial x} + ny\,\dfrac{\partial f}{\partial y}$ *is* $f\left(\dfrac{y}{x^n},\ \dfrac{y'}{x^{n-1}}\right) = 0,$

$$\text{or } y' = x^{n-1}F\left(\frac{y}{x^n}\right),\ \text{or } xy' = yF\left(\frac{y}{x^n}\right).$$

This equation is characterized by being homogeneous in x, y, y' when these elements are given the weights $1, n, n-1$ respectively.

Thus the differential equation

$$xy^2y'^2 - y^3y' + x = 0$$

comes under this head; for giving x, y, y' the weights $1, n, n-1$ respectively, the separate terms have the weights $1 + 2n + 2n - 2$ or $4n - 1$, $3n + n - 1$ or $4n - 1$, 1 respectively. These are equal to 1 if $n = \frac{1}{2}$. Hence the differential equation is invariant under the group

$$Uf \equiv 2x\,\frac{\partial f}{\partial x} + y\,\frac{\partial f}{\partial y}.$$

VII. $Uf \equiv \phi(x)\dfrac{\partial f}{\partial y}.$ $\xi \equiv 0,\ \eta \equiv \phi(x).$ $\therefore \eta' \equiv \phi'(x),$ and $u \equiv x,$ $u' \equiv \phi(x)y' - \phi'(x)y.$ Hence *the general type of differential equation invariant under*

$$Uf \equiv \phi(x)\frac{\partial f}{\partial x} \text{ is } f[x,\ \phi(x)y' - \phi'(x)y] = 0,\ \text{or } y' - \frac{\phi'(x)}{\phi(x)}y = F(x).$$

This equation is characterized by being linear in y and y'.

Note. — Using the usual notation for the linear equation

$$y' + P(x)y = Q(x),$$

the group which leaves it unaltered is $Uf \equiv e^{-\int P\,dx}\dfrac{\partial f}{\partial y}.$ The integrating factor of § 12 is $e^{\int P\,dx}.$ (Compare *El. Dif. Eq.* § 13.)

VII′. $Uf \equiv \psi(y)\dfrac{\partial f}{\partial x}.$ It is readily seen that *the general type of differential equation invariant under this group is*

$$f\left(y, \frac{1}{y'} - \frac{\psi'(y)}{\psi(y)} x\right) = 0, \ or \ \frac{dx}{dy} - \frac{\psi'(y)}{\psi(y)} x = F(y).$$

This equation is linear in x and $\frac{dx}{dy}$.

VIII. $Uf \equiv \psi(y) \frac{\partial f}{\partial y}$.   *The general type of differential equation invariant under this group* (which includes III as a special case) *is*
$$\frac{y'}{\psi(y)} = F(x).$$

In this equation the variables are separated.

VIII'. $Uf \equiv \phi(x) \frac{\partial f}{\partial x}$.   *The general type of differential equation invariant under this group* (which includes III' as a special case) *is*
$y'\phi(x) = F(y)$.

The variables are separable.

IX. $Uf \equiv \phi(x)\psi(y) \frac{\partial f}{\partial y}$. $\xi \equiv 0, \ \eta \equiv \phi(x)\psi(y)$.

$\therefore \eta' = \phi'(x)\psi(y) + \phi(x)\psi'(y)y'$.   Equations (37) are

$$\frac{dx}{0} = \frac{dy}{\phi(x)\psi(y)} = \frac{dy'}{\phi'(x)\psi(y) + \phi(x)\psi'(y)y'}.$$

$\therefore u \equiv x$. u' may be obtained by solving the linear equation

$$\frac{dy'}{dy} - \frac{\psi'(y)}{\psi(y)} y' = \frac{\phi'(x)}{\phi(x)},$$

in which x is treated as a constant.   An integrating factor is $\frac{1}{\psi(y)}$.

$$\therefore u' \equiv \frac{y'}{\psi(y)} - \frac{\phi'(x)}{\phi(x)} \int \frac{dy}{\psi(y)}.$$

Hence *the general type of differential equation invariant under*

$$Uf \equiv \phi(x)\psi(y)\frac{\partial f}{\partial y} \text{ is } \frac{y'}{\psi(y)} - \frac{\phi'(x)}{\phi(x)}\int\frac{dy}{\psi(y)} = F(x).$$

The transformation $v = \int\dfrac{dy}{\psi(y)}$ reduces this to the linear equation

$$\frac{dv}{dx} - \frac{\phi'(x)}{\phi(x)}\,v = F(x).$$

Note. — In particular, if $\psi(y)$ is y^s, $Uf \equiv \phi(x)y^s\dfrac{\partial f}{\partial y}$ leaves unaltered the equation $y' + \dfrac{\phi'(x)}{(s-1)\phi(x)}y = y^s F(x)$. Hence *the Bernoulli equation* $\dfrac{dy}{dx} + Py = Qy^s$ *is invariant under the group* $Uf \equiv y^s e^{\int(s-1)Pdx}\dfrac{\partial f}{\partial y}$. The integrating factor of § 12 for this equation is $\dfrac{e^{\int(1-s)Pdx}}{y^s}$. (Compare *El. Dif. Eq.* § 14.)

IX'. $Uf \equiv \phi(x)\psi(y)\dfrac{\partial f}{\partial x}$. *The general type of differential equation invariant under this group is* $\dfrac{1}{\phi(x)}\dfrac{dx}{dy} - \dfrac{\psi'(y)}{\psi(y)}\int\dfrac{dx}{\phi(x)} = F(y).$

Considering y as the independent variable in this equation, the latter is reduced to the linear form by the transformation $t = \int\dfrac{dx}{\phi(x)}$.

X. $Uf \equiv \phi(x)\left(x\dfrac{\partial f}{\partial x} + ny\dfrac{\partial f}{\partial y}\right)$. $\xi \equiv x\phi(x), \eta \equiv ny\phi(x)$. $\therefore u \equiv \dfrac{y}{x^n}$.
u' is easily found by method (*b*) of § 18. The canonical variables are

$$x = \frac{y}{x^n},\ y = \int\frac{dx}{x\phi(x)}.\quad \therefore u' \equiv \frac{dx}{dy} = \frac{xy' - ny}{x^n}\,\phi(x).$$

Hence *the general type of differential equation invariant under*

$$Uf \equiv \phi(x)\left(x\frac{\partial f}{\partial x} + ny\frac{\partial f}{\partial y}\right) \text{ is } f\left(\frac{y}{x^n}, \frac{xy' - ny}{x^n}\,\phi(x)\right),$$

or $xy' - ny = \dfrac{x^n}{\phi(x)}F\left(\dfrac{y}{x^n}\right)$, or $xy' - ny = \dfrac{y}{\phi(x)}F\left(\dfrac{y}{x^n}\right)$.

Note. — Several particular cases are of special interest : —

1° If $\phi(x) = x^r$, the general type of differential equation invariant under

$$Uf \equiv x^r \left(x \frac{\partial f}{\partial x} + ny \frac{\partial f}{\partial y} \right) \text{ is } xy' - ny = x^{n-r} F\left(\frac{y}{x^n}\right).$$

Hence $xy' - ny = x^k F\left(\dfrac{y}{x^n}\right)$ *is invariant under*

$$Uf \equiv x^{n-k} \left(x \frac{\partial f}{\partial x} + ny \frac{\partial f}{\partial y} \right).$$

The Riccati equation

$$x \frac{dy}{dx} - ay + by^2 = cx^n,$$

comes under this head when $n = 2a$; for in this case

$$xy' - ay = x^{2a} \left[c - b\left(\frac{y}{x^a}\right)^2 \right].$$

(Compare Boole, *Differential Equations*, p. 92 ; Forsyth, *Differential Equations*, § 109.)

2° If $\phi(x) = x^r$, $n = 1$, the invariant differential equation reduces to $xy' - y = x^{1-r} F\left(\dfrac{y}{x}\right)$. The right-hand member is simply a homogeneous function of x and y of degree $1 - r$. Hence *a differential equation of the form* $y - xy' = x^k F\left(\dfrac{y}{x}\right)$, *where the right-hand member is a homogeneous function of x and y of degree k, is invariant under the group*

$$Uf \equiv x^{1-k} \left(x \frac{\partial f}{\partial x} + y \frac{\partial f}{\partial y} \right).$$

The integrating factor of § 12 is $\dfrac{1}{x^2 F\left(\frac{y}{x}\right)}$. (Compare *El. Dif. Eq.* § 16.)

$3°$ If $\phi(x) = x^r$, $n = -1$, the invariant differential equation reduces to $xy' + y = x^{-1-r}F(xy)$, or $xy' + y = y^{1+r}F(xy)$. Hence *a differential equation of the form* $xy' + y = y^k F(xy)$ *is invariant under the group*

$$Uf \equiv x^{k-1}\left(x\frac{\partial f}{\partial x} - y\frac{\partial f}{\partial y}\right).$$

The integrating factor of § 12 is $\dfrac{1}{x^k y^k F(xy)}$, a well-known fact.

X'. $Uf \equiv \psi(y)\left(x\dfrac{\partial f}{\partial x} + ny\dfrac{\partial f}{\partial y}\right).$ *The general type of differential equation invariant under this group is* $xy' - ny = \dfrac{xy'}{\psi(y)}F\left(\dfrac{y}{x^n}\right).$

$1°$ If $\psi(y) = y^s$, this differential equation reduces to

$$xy' - ny = \frac{xy'}{y^s}F\left(\frac{y}{x^n}\right).$$

$2°$ If $\psi(y) = y^s$, $n = 1$, the differential equation takes the form

$$xy' - y = \frac{xy'}{y^s}F\left(\frac{y}{x}\right), \quad \text{or} \quad xy' - y = y'x^{1-s}F\left(\frac{y}{x}\right).$$

Hence *a differential equation of the form*

$$y - xy' = y' \; [\text{a homogeneous function of } x \text{ and } y \text{ of degree } k]$$

is invariant under the group $Uf \equiv y^{1-k}\left(x\dfrac{\partial f}{\partial x} + y\dfrac{\partial f}{\partial y}\right).$

$3°$ If $n = -1$, $\psi(y) = y^s$, the differential equation reduces to $xy' + y = y'x^{s+1}F(xy)$. Hence *a differential equation of the form*

$$xy' + y = x^k y' F(xy)$$

is invariant under the group

$$Uf \equiv y^{k-1}\left(x\frac{\partial f}{\partial x} - y\frac{\partial f}{\partial y}\right).$$

The student should show that the following groups leave the corresponding differential equations unaltered :

$$\text{XI.}\quad Uf \equiv x^r y^s \left(x\,\frac{\partial f}{\partial x} + ny\,\frac{\partial f}{\partial y} \right), \qquad xy' - ny = \frac{ry - sxy'}{x^r y^s}\,F\!\left(\frac{y}{x^n}\right).$$

$$\text{XII.}\quad Uf \equiv a\,\frac{\partial f}{\partial x} + b\,\frac{\partial f}{\partial y}, \qquad y' = F(bx - ay).$$

$$\text{XIII.}\quad Uf \equiv y\,\frac{\partial f}{\partial x} + x\,\frac{\partial f}{\partial y}, \qquad \frac{1 - y'}{1 + y'} = \frac{x - y}{x + y}\,F(x^2 - y^2),$$

$$\text{using method } (c), \S\,18,$$

$$\frac{x - yy'}{1 + y'} = (x - y)\,F(x^2 - y^2),$$

$$\text{using method } (b), \S\,18.$$

$$\text{XIV.}\quad Uf \equiv \phi(x)\left(\frac{\partial f}{\partial x} \pm \frac{x}{y}\,\frac{\partial f}{\partial y} \right), \qquad x \mp yy' = \frac{1}{\phi(x)}\,F(x^2 \mp y^2).$$

$$\text{XIV'.}\quad Uf \equiv \psi(y)\left(\frac{y}{x}\,\frac{\partial f}{\partial x} \pm \frac{\partial f}{\partial y} \right), \qquad x \mp yy' = \frac{y'}{\psi(y)}\,F(x^2 \mp y^2).$$

$$\text{XV.}\quad Uf \equiv x^r\,\frac{\partial f}{\partial x} \pm y^s\,\frac{\partial f}{\partial y},\ r, s \neq 1, \qquad \frac{x^r y'}{y^s} = F\!\left(\frac{x^{1-r}}{r-1} \mp \frac{y^{1-s}}{s-1} \right).$$

$$\text{XVI.}\quad Uf \equiv \phi_1(x)\left(\frac{\partial f}{\partial x} - [\phi_2(x)y + \phi_3(x)]\,\frac{\partial f}{\partial y} \right)^*,$$

$$\phi_1(x)(\mu y' + \mu'y + \nu') = F(\mu y + \nu),$$

$$\textbf{where}\ \ \mu \equiv e^{\int \phi_2(x)dx},\ \nu \equiv \int \mu \phi_3(x)\,dx.$$

---

* This group is characterized by having ξ a function of x only, and η a linear function of y. It is mentioned by Professor Dickson, *Bulletin of the Am. Math. Soc.*, Vol. V. p. 453.

XVI'. $Uf \equiv \psi_1(y)\Big([x\psi_2(y)+\psi_3(y)] \dfrac{\partial f}{\partial x} - \dfrac{\partial f}{\partial y} \Big),$

$$\psi_1(y)[\rho + (x\rho' + \sigma')y'] = y' F(x\rho + \sigma),$$

where $\rho \equiv e^{\int \psi_2(y)dy}$, $\sigma \equiv \int \rho\psi_3(y)\,dy.$

Remark. — When a differential equation is recognized as coming under several of the above heads, and the corresponding integrating factors are distinct, the solution of the differential equation is obtained at once by equating the quotient of two distinct integrating factors to an arbitrary constant (§ 16).

Thus the differential equation

$$xy' - y = x^r$$

is linear. Hence, from VII, the group $Uf \equiv x \dfrac{\partial f}{\partial y}$ leaves it unaltered, and gives the obvious integrating factor $\dfrac{1}{x^2}$.

But it is also readily seen that each term of the equation is of the weight r when x, y, y' have the weights $1, r, r-1$ respectively; hence, from VI, the group $Uf \equiv x \dfrac{\partial f}{\partial x} + ry \dfrac{\partial f}{\partial y}$ leaves the equation unaltered, and gives the second integrating factor $\dfrac{1}{(r-1)xy - x^{r+1}}$. The solution of the equation is therefore

$$\frac{(r-1)xy - x^{r+1}}{x^2} = (r-1)\frac{y}{x} - x^{r-1} = const.$$

It may be noted that the equation also comes under X, 2°, and is therefore invariant under $Uf \equiv x^{2-r} \dfrac{\partial f}{\partial x} + x^{1-r}y \dfrac{\partial f}{\partial y}$. This leads to the previously found integrating factor $\dfrac{1}{x^2}$.

As another illustration of a class of equations obviously invariant under several distinct groups, the equation

$$xy^r y' - y^{r+1} = x^r \text{ or } xy' - y = \left(\frac{x}{y}\right)^r$$

may be mentioned.   Under the head of VI it is readily seen to be invariant under $Uf \equiv (r+1)x\dfrac{\partial f}{\partial x} + ry\dfrac{\partial f}{\partial y}$; as a Bernoulli equation, IX, it is invariant under $Uf \equiv \dfrac{x^{r+1}}{y^r}\dfrac{\partial f}{\partial y}$.   From these its solution is found at once to be

$$\frac{y^{r+1} + (r+1)x^r}{x^{r+1}} = const.$$

This equation also comes under X, 2°.

20. Second General Method for Solving a Differential Equation. Separation of Variables.* — The simple form of the differential equations invariant under the group of translations $Uf \equiv \dfrac{\partial f}{\partial y}$ (I, § 19) suggests as a practical method for solving a differential equation invariant under a known group the introduction of canonical variables (§ 10).   The reduction of the group to the canonical form reduces the differential equation to the form

$$y' \equiv \frac{dy}{dx} = F(x),$$

in which the variables are separated.   The solution is then obtained by the quadrature

$$y = \int F(x)dx + c.$$

Finally it is necessary to pass back from the canonical variables to the original ones.

---

* This method was discovered by Lie in 1869, thus antedating the method of § 12 by five years.   Historically it is of interest because it is the first known method of integration which makes use of the invariance of a differential equation under a group.

Since the differential equation invariant under $Uf \equiv \dfrac{\partial f}{\partial x}$ * (I', § 19) is of the form $\dfrac{dy}{F(y)} = dx$, the reduction of the group, under which a differential equation is invariant, to this form also enables one to separate the variables in the differential equation.

While either of the above transformations brings the differential equation into a very simple form, the actual introduction of canonical variables into the differential equation and the final passing back to the original variables may not prove as simple as in the case of other variables that could be used to equal advantage. Thus, for example, if, in the group $Uf \equiv \xi \dfrac{\partial f}{\partial x} + \eta \dfrac{\partial f}{\partial y}$ which leaves the differential equation unaltered, ξ is a function of x only, the introduction of the new variables (§ 9)

$$x = x, \quad y = u(x, y)$$

reduces the group to the form

$$Uf \equiv \xi(x)\dfrac{\partial f}{\partial x},$$

whence the differential equation must take the form (VIII', § 19)

(40) $$\xi(x)y' = F(y),$$

in which the variables are separable at once.

This set of variables works especially well in the case of two perfectly well-known classes of differential equations, and leads to the usual methods for solving them:

1° The homogeneous equation

$$Mdx + Ndy = 0,$$

* Owing to the complete symmetry of the two groups $Uf \equiv \dfrac{\partial f}{\partial x}$ and $Uf \equiv \dfrac{\partial f}{\partial y}$, we shall say that the group in either case is in the *canonical form*, and the variables that reduce a group to either form will be said to be the *canonical variables* of the group.

where M and N are homogeneous and of the same degree, is left unaltered by the group (IV, Note, § 19)

$$Uf \equiv x\frac{\partial f}{\partial x} + y\frac{\partial f}{\partial y}.$$

The new variables $x = x$, $y = \frac{y}{x}$ reduce the group to the form

$$Uf \equiv x\frac{\partial f}{\partial x},$$

whence the differential equation assumes the form (40), and the variables are separable. (Compare *El. Dif. Eq.* § 10.)

2° The equation

$$yf_1(xy)dx + xf_2(xy)dy = 0$$

is left unaltered by the group (V, Note, § 19)

$$Uf \equiv x\frac{\partial f}{\partial x} - y\frac{\partial f}{\partial y}.$$

Hence, the new variables $x = x$, $y = xy$ reduce the equation to the form (40) in which the variables are separable. (Compare *El. Dif. Eq.* § 12.)

In an analogous manner, if η is a function of y only, the introduction of the new variables

$$x = u(x, y), \quad y = y$$

reduces the group to the form

$$Uf \equiv \eta(y)\frac{\partial f}{\partial y},$$

whence the differential equation must take the form (VIII, § 19)

$$\frac{y'}{\eta(y)} = F(x),$$

in which the variables are separated.

More generally, if $\phi(x)$ and $\psi(y)$, any functions of the respective canonical variables, are taken as new variables, it is readily seen that the resulting differential equation will have its variables separated. In certain cases such forms can be chosen for these functions as to simplify the actual work required in introducing new variables.

Remark. — It is interesting to note that the knowledge of a group, under which a given differential equation of the first order is invari-ant, enables one to find both an integrating factor (§ 12) and a set of variables which are separable in the transformed equation. (Com-pare *El. Dif. Eq.* § 17.)

The integrating factor can be written down at once when the dif-ferential equation has been solved for $\dfrac{dy}{dx}$, or what is the same thing, when it has the form $M\,dx + N\,dy = 0$.

To find the new variables that are to be separable, the solution of another (frequently simple) differential equation of the first order (giving the path-curves of the group) and usually one or several quad-ratures are necessary.

In actual practice, neither method should be insisted upon to the exclusion of the other. In Table I of the Appendix will be found a list of the more commonly occurring and easily recognizable classes of equations of the first order, and methods for solving them.

21. Singular Solution.* — Let

$$(25) \qquad\qquad f(x, y, y') = 0$$

be an invariant differential equation under the non-trivial group

$$Uf \equiv \xi\,\frac{\partial f}{\partial x} + \eta\,\frac{\partial f}{\partial y}.$$

Its family of integral curves being left unaltered, as a whole, if this family has an envelope, the latter must be an invariant curve of the group ; moreover, it is a path-curve, since the group is supposed to be non-trivial, thus interchanging the integral curves among themselves. The equation of the envelope being a singular solution of the dif-ferential equation (*El. Dif. Eq.* § 30) the value of its slope y' at each

---

* This section is based on an article by J. M. Page, entitled " Note on Singular Solutions " in the *American Journal of Mathematics*, Vol. XVIII, p. 95.

point (x, y) must satisfy (25). Since the slope of a path-curve at the point (x, y) is $\dfrac{\eta(x, y)}{\xi(x, y)}$, the equation of the envelope must be contained in

$$(41) \qquad\qquad f\left(x, y, \frac{\eta}{\xi}\right) = 0.$$

Remark. — In the above process (41) was found as the equation of a path-curve which satisfies the differential equation. If a particular integral curve happens to be a path-curve of the group, its equation is also included in (41). But all extraneous loci, such as nodal, cuspidal, and tac-loci (*El. Dif. Eq.*, § 33) which may be path-curves but are not solutions of (25) will not be included in (41).

Ex. 1. $xy^2y'^2 - y^3y' + x = 0.$

This equation is invariant under $Uf \equiv 2x\dfrac{\partial f}{\partial x} + y\dfrac{\partial f}{\partial y}$ (VI, § 19). Its general solution is $c^2x^2 - cy^2 + 1 = 0$.

Replacing y', wherever it occurs in the differential equation, by $\dfrac{y}{2x}$ gives
$$x(4x^2 - y^4) = 0.$$

$x = 0$ is a particular solution for $c = \infty$.

$4x^2 - y^4 = 0$ is the singular solution.

Ex. 2. $(1 + x^2)y'^2 = 1.$

This equation is invariant under $Uf \equiv \dfrac{\partial f}{\partial y}$. (I, § 19.)

$y' = \dfrac{1}{0} = \infty$. In this case, writing the differential equation in the form
$$\frac{1}{y'^2} = 1 + x^2,$$

$\dfrac{1}{y'} = 0$ gives the singular solution $1 + x^2 = 0$.

Ex. 3. $x^4y'^2 - xy' - y = 0.$ (VI, § 19. $n = -2$.)

Ex. 4. $a^2yy'^2 - 2xy' + y = 0.$ (IV, § 19.)

Ex. **5.** $y'^3 - 4\,xyy' + 8\,y^2 = 0.$ (VI, § 19. $n = 3$.)

Ex. **6.** $y = 2\,xy' + y^2y'^3.$ (VI, § 19. $n = \tfrac{3}{4}$.)

Ex. **7.** $x^3y'^2 + x^2yy' + 1 = 0.$ (VI, § 19. $n = -\tfrac{1}{2}$.)

It is suggested as an interesting exercise that the student examine, in the light of the Lie theory as presented in this chapter, the various examples involving differential equations of the first order to be found, for example, in Chapters II, IV, V of the author's *Elementary Treatise on Differential Equations.*

CHAPTER III

MISCELLANEOUS THEOREMS AND GEOMETRICAL APPLICATIONS

22. New Form for Integrating Factor. — In § 12 it was seen that

$$\mu \equiv \frac{1}{\xi M + \eta N}$$

is an integrating factor for

$$M\,dx + N\,dy = 0$$

if the latter is invariant under

$$Uf \equiv \xi \frac{\partial f}{\partial x} + \eta \frac{\partial f}{\partial y}.$$

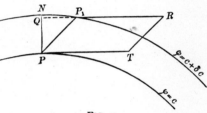

FIG. 1

Lie, by purely geometrical considerations, gave a new form * to this factor, which is not only interesting but also useful in certain classes of problems.   In Fig. 1, let

$$\phi(x, y) = c$$

be some one of the integral curves of the differential equation.   The infinitesimal transformation of the group transforms this into an infinitely near curve of the family

$$\phi(x, y) = c + \delta c$$

by transforming any point (x, y) of it into $(x + \xi\,\delta a, y + \eta\,\delta a)$.

$PP_1 \equiv$ the distance between these points is $\sqrt{\xi^2 + \eta^2}\,\delta a$.

---

* First published in the *Gesellschaft der Wissenschaften zu Christiania*, 1874.

The slope of the tangent at P is $-\dfrac{M}{N}$. If T is the point $(x - N,$ $y + M)$, the length of PT is $\sqrt{M^2 + N^2}$, and the area of the parallelogram $PTRP_1$ is $(\xi M + \eta N)\delta a$, or $\dfrac{\delta a}{\mu}$.

Let $\delta n \equiv PN$, the length of the normal to the first curve at P, intercepted by the second curve ; this is, to within infinitesimals of higher order than the first, equal to PQ, the altitude of the above parallelogram. Hence

$$\frac{\delta a}{\mu} = \sqrt{M^2 + N^2}\,\delta n,$$

or

(42)
$$\mu = \frac{1}{\sqrt{M^2 + N^2}}\frac{\delta a}{\delta n}.$$

This form of the integrating factor is serviceable in the case of an interesting class of differential equations :

If the integral curves of a differential equation are known to be a family of *parallel curves*,* for which $\dfrac{\delta n}{\delta a}$ is constant all along each one of the curves, it follows at once from (42) that

(42')
$$\mu \equiv \frac{1}{\sqrt{M^2 + N^2}}$$

is an integrating factor. The *involutes* of a curve, which are the orthogonal trajectories of the tangents to the curve, are known to form a family of parallel curves. Hence an integrating factor of the form (42') is known at once for their differential equation.

Ex. Find the involutes of the circle $x^2 + y^2 = 1$.

The differential equation of the tangents to the curve is $\left(\text{writing } p \text{ for } \dfrac{dy}{dx}\right)$

$$y = px + \sqrt{1 + p^2}.$$

* Two curves are said to be *parallel*, if the distance between them measured along the normal to one of them is constant all along the curve. (In this case, it is well known that the normal to either curve is normal to the other.)

Hence the differential equation of the family of involutes is

$$y = -\frac{x}{p} + \frac{\sqrt{1 + p^2}}{p},$$

or
$$(xy + \sqrt{x^2 + y^2 - 1})dx + (y^2 - 1)dy = 0.$$

The integrating factor given by (42) is

$$\frac{1}{x + y\sqrt{x^2 + y^2 - 1}}.$$

To integrate the exact equation

$$\frac{(xy + \sqrt{x^2 + y^2 - 1})dx + (y^2 - 1)dy}{x + y\sqrt{x^2 + y^2 - 1}},$$

one may proceed in the usual way (see *El. Dif. Eq.* § 8) to integrate

$$\int^x \frac{xy + \sqrt{x^2 + y^2 - 1}}{x + y\sqrt{x^2 + y^2 - 1}}\, dx,$$

where y is considered a constant.   Multiplying numerator and denominator by $x - y\sqrt{x^2 + y^2 - 1}$, this becomes

$$\int^x \frac{y + x\sqrt{x^2 + y^2 - 1}}{x^2 + y^2}\, dx.$$

$$\int^x \frac{y\, dx}{x^2 + y^2} = -\tan^{-1}\frac{y}{x}.$$

Letting $x^2 + y^2 = t$,

$$\int^x \frac{x\sqrt{x^2 + y^2 - 1}}{x^2 + y^2}\, dx = \tfrac{1}{2}\int \frac{\sqrt{t - 1}}{t}\, dt = \sqrt{t - 1} + \sin^{-1}\frac{1}{\sqrt{t}}$$

$$= \sqrt{x^2 + y^2 - 1} + \sin^{-1}\frac{1}{\sqrt{x^2 + y^2}}.$$

Hence, the equation of the family of involutes is

$$\sqrt{x^2 + y^2 - 1} + \sin^{-1}\frac{1}{\sqrt{x^2 + y^2}} - \tan^{-1}\frac{y}{x} = const.$$

Remark. — From the nature of the problem, it is evident that the family of involutes is invariant under the group of rotations $Uf \equiv -y \dfrac{\partial f}{\partial x} + x \dfrac{\partial f}{\partial y}.$ * Hence, the methods of §§ 12 and 20 are also applicable. It is readily seen that the integrating factor given by the method of § 12 is the same as that found in the text. The method of § 20 should be carried out as an exercise.

23. Two Differential Equations with Common Integrating Factor. If μ is an integrating factor for two distinct differential equations,

$$M_1\,dx + N_1\,dy = 0 \quad \text{and} \quad M_2\,dx + N_2\,dy = 0,$$

$$\frac{\partial(\mu M_1)}{\partial y} - \frac{\partial(\mu N_1)}{\partial x} = 0 \quad \text{and} \quad \frac{\partial(\mu M_2)}{\partial y} - \frac{\partial(\mu N_2)}{\partial x} = 0.$$

$$(43) \qquad \therefore \begin{cases} N_1 \dfrac{\partial \log \mu}{\partial x} - M_1 \dfrac{\partial \log \mu}{\partial y} = \dfrac{\partial M_1}{\partial y} - \dfrac{\partial N_1}{\partial x}, \\[2ex] N_2 \dfrac{\partial \log \mu}{\partial x} - M_2 \dfrac{\partial \log \mu}{\partial y} = \dfrac{\partial M_2}{\partial y} - \dfrac{\partial N_2}{\partial x}. \end{cases}$$

Here $N_1 M_2 - N_2 M_1 \neq 0$, since the differential equations are supposed to be distinct. Hence (43) can be solved for $\dfrac{\partial \log \mu}{\partial x}$ and $\dfrac{\partial \log \mu}{\partial y}$; $\log \mu$ can then be determined by a quadrature, and μ may be obtained at once from this. Hence the

THEOREM. — *If two differential equations of the first order are known to have a common integrating factor, the latter can be found by means of a quadrature.*

24. Isothermal Curves. — A family of curves which, together with the family of orthogonal trajectories, divides the plane into infinitesimal squares, is called a family of *isothermal curves.* In general,

---

* This is also obvious from the form of the differential equation, when cleared of fractions, viz.: $\qquad x + yp = \sqrt{1 + p^2}.$ (See II, Note, § 19.)

a family of curves and their
orthogonal trajectories divide
the plane into infinitesimal
rectangles. For, selecting
any pair of neighboring
curves, *I* and *II* (Fig. 2), of
the one family it is always
possible to find a pair, *A*
and *B*, of the second family
to form an infinitesimal
square * with them; besides,
selecting any third curve *III*
of the first family, a fourth
curve *IV* can be found such

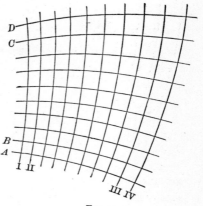

FIG. 2

that *A, B, III, IV* form a square also; again, selecting any third
curve *C* of the second family, a fourth curve *D* can be found such
that *C, D, I, II* form a
square. But with these se-
lections made, the curves
C, D, III, IV do not, in
general, form a square.

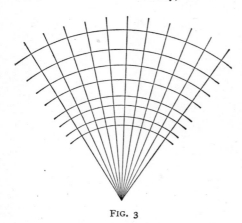

FIG. 3

Concentric circles are readily seen to be isothermal curves.
Their orthogonal trajectories
are the straight lines through
the common center (Fig. 3).
Any pair of circles of radii
r and $r + \Delta r$ respectively
($r > 0$) form an infinitesimal
square with any two of the

---

* This curvilinear quadrilateral is a square when infinitesimals of higher order than
the first are neglected, the length of arc of one of the sides being taken as an infinitesimal of the first order.

straight lines which intercept the length Δr on the inner circle. Moreover these same two lines form squares with any other pair of circles of radii kr and $k(r + \Delta r)$, respectively, k being any constant different from zero.

From the definition of isothermal curves, δn (of § 22) can be made the same, at any point, for this family of curves and for that of their orthogonal trajectories. Moreover, if the differential equation of the one family is

$$(17) \qquad\qquad M\,dx + N\,dy = 0,$$

that of the other is

$$(17') \qquad\qquad N\,dx - M\,dy = 0.$$

Hence the two equations have a common integrating factor, as is evident from the form (42). To determine this integrating factor, the method of § 23 applies. The equations (43) take the form

$$N\frac{\partial \log \mu}{\partial x} - M\frac{\partial \log \mu}{\partial y} = \frac{\partial M}{\partial y} - \frac{\partial N}{\partial x},$$

$$M\frac{\partial \log \mu}{\partial x} + N\frac{\partial \log \mu}{\partial y} = -\frac{\partial N}{\partial y} - \frac{\partial M}{\partial x};$$

whence

$$
(44)\quad
\begin{cases}
\dfrac{\partial \log \mu}{\partial x} = \dfrac{N\dfrac{\partial M}{\partial y} - M\dfrac{\partial N}{\partial y} - M\dfrac{\partial M}{\partial x} - N\dfrac{\partial N}{\partial x}}{M^2 + N^2} \\[4mm]
\qquad\quad = -\dfrac{\partial}{\partial y}\tan^{-1}\dfrac{N}{M} - \dfrac{1}{2}\dfrac{\partial}{\partial x}\log\,(M^2 + N^2), \\[4mm]
\dfrac{\partial \log \mu}{\partial y} = \dfrac{M\dfrac{\partial N}{\partial x} - N\dfrac{\partial M}{\partial x} - M\dfrac{\partial M}{\partial y} - N\dfrac{\partial N}{\partial y}}{M^2 + N^2} \\[4mm]
\qquad\quad = \dfrac{\partial}{\partial x}\tan^{-1}\dfrac{N}{M} - \dfrac{1}{2}\dfrac{\partial}{\partial y}\log\,(M^2 + N^2).
\end{cases}
$$

Equations (44) are interesting, not only because they enable one to find μ by a quadrature, but also because they lead to the condition that the integral curves of the differential equation (17) be isothermal. For, differentiating the first of (44) with respect to y and the second with respect to x, and equating

$$(45) \qquad \left(\frac{\partial^2}{\partial x^2} + \frac{\partial^2}{\partial y^2}\right)\tan^{-1}\frac{N}{M} \equiv \nabla^2\tan^{-1}\frac{N}{M} = 0.$$

The general solution of this is *

$$(46) \qquad \frac{N}{M} = \tan\left[\Phi(x+iy) + \Psi(x-iy)\right],$$

where Φ and Ψ are arbitrary functions.

The condition (45) is not only necessary that (17) be the differential equation of a family of isothermal curves, but it is also sufficient. For, when M and N satisfy (45), equations (44) are consistent, hence a common integrating factor for (17) and (17') can be found. But the sum of the squares of the coefficients of dx and dy is the same for these two differential equations. Hence, remembering the form (42), δn must be the same (to within a constant factor, which may be made unity by a proper choice of neighboring curves) in the two cases at any point. Hence the integral curves of (17) are isothermal curves.

Remark. — The condition for isothermal curves in terms of their finite equation and that of their orthogonal trajectories is obtained in Note III of the Appendix.

1° In the case of the family of concentric circles, $x^2 + y^2 = const.$, the differential equation is $x\,dx + y\,dy = 0$. Hence (45) is satisfied, since $\nabla^2\tan^{-1}\frac{y}{x} = 0$.

While the solution of this differential equation, as well as that of the differential equation of the orthogonal trajectories, $y\,dx - x\,dy = 0$, is very simple, it is interesting to note that (44) give very readily

$$d\log\mu = -\frac{2\,x\,dx + 2\,y\,dy}{x^2 + y^2} = -d\log(x^2 + y^2). \quad \therefore \mu = \frac{1}{x^2 + y^2}.$$

This is the common integrating factor for the two equations.

* See *El. Dif. Eq.* § 90.

2° The family of circles tangent to the axis of y at the origin $x^2 + y^2 - cx = 0$ has for differential equation $(x^2 - y^2)dx + 2xy\, dy = 0$. It is readily seen that $\nabla^2 \tan^{-1} \dfrac{2xy}{x^2 - y^2} = 0$; hence these circles form an isothermal system. The differential equation of the orthogonal trajectories is $2xy\, dx - (x^2 - y^2)dy = 0$. While this is easy to integrate, it is worth noting that (44) give $\mu = \dfrac{1}{(x^2 + y^2)^2}$. Moreover, since the differential equation is " homogeneous," it is invariant under the group $Uf \equiv x\dfrac{\partial f}{\partial x} + y\dfrac{\partial f}{\partial y}$ (IV, § 19). Hence, a second integrating factor is (§ 12) $\mu_2 \equiv \dfrac{1}{y(x^2 + y^2)}$. The solution of the equation is therefore (§ 16)

$$\frac{\mu_1}{\mu_2} \equiv \frac{x^2 + y^2}{y} = const. \text{ or } x^2 + y^2 - cy = 0,$$

the equation of the family of circles tangent to the axis of x at the origin.

Show that the following curves are isothermal, and find their orthogonal trajectories :

Ex. 1. The equilateral hyperbolas $xy = const.$

Ex. 2. The similar conics $ax^2 + by^2 = const.$, when and only when $b = \pm a$.

Ex. 3. The coaxial circles through the points $(1, 0)$ and $(-1, 0)$, $\dfrac{x^2 + y^2 - 1}{y} = const.$

25. Further Application of the Theorem of § 23. — An obvious corollary of the theorem of § 23 enables one to find an integrating factor, by means of a quadrature, for an interesting set of differential equations. This corollary is : *If the ratio of the integrating factors of two differential equations is a known function, the integrating factors can be found by a single quadrature.* For, suppose that

(47) $$\frac{\mu_2}{\mu_1} \equiv \phi(x, y)$$

is a known function, where μ_1 and μ_2 are the integrating factors of

$$M_1\, dx + N_1\, dy = 0 \text{ and } M_2\, dx + N_2\, dy = 0$$

respectively.   If the second equation be written in the form

$$\phi M_2\, dx + \phi N_2\, dy = 0,$$

its integrating factor is also μ_1.   Hence it and the first equation have a common integrating factor and, by the theorem of § 23, this can be found by a quadrature.

Suppose, now, that it is known that the solutions of three differential equations of the first order

$$M_1\, dx + N_1\, dy = 0, \quad M_2\, dx + N_2\, dy = 0, \quad M_3\, dx + N_3\, dy = 0$$

can be made to assume such forms, $\phi_1 = const.$, $\phi_2 = const.$, $\phi_3 = const.$, that

(48) $$\phi_3 \equiv \phi_1 + \phi_2.$$

If μ_1, μ_2, μ_3 are their respective integrating factors,

$$d\phi_1 \equiv \mu_1(M_1\, dx + N_1\, dy), \quad d\phi_2 \equiv \mu_2(M_2\, dx + N_2\, dy),$$

$$d\phi_3 \equiv \mu_3(M_3\, dx + N_3\, dy).$$

Because of the identity (48)

$$d\phi_3 \equiv d\phi_1 + d\phi_2,$$

or

(49) $$\mu_3 M_3 = \mu_1 M_1 + \mu_2 M_2, \quad \mu_3 N_3 = \mu_1 N_1 + \mu_2 N_2 \;;$$

whence $$\mu_3 = \frac{\mu_1 M_1 + \mu_2 M_2}{M_3} = \frac{\mu_1 N_1 + \mu_2 N_2}{N_3}, \text{ and}$$

(47′) $$\frac{\mu_2}{\mu_1} = -\frac{M_1 N_3 - M_3 N_1}{M_2 N_3 - M_3 N_2}.$$

By the corollary above, μ_1 can be found by a quadrature ; and μ_2 is then known from (47′).   After finding ϕ_1 and ϕ_2 by a single quadrature each, ϕ_3 is given immediately by (48).   Hence the

THEOREM. — *If it is known that the solutions of three differential equations of the first order can be put in such forms $\phi_1 = const.$, $\phi_2 = const.$, $\phi_3 = const.$ that* $\phi_3 \equiv \phi_1 + \phi_2$,

these solutions can be found by means of three quadratures.

This theorem has some interesting applications in the theory of surfaces [*] :

A. If the rectangular coördinates of any point $(x, y, z,)$ on a surface are expressed in terms of the parameters u and v, the expression for the element of length of arc is, using the usual Gauss notation,

$$ds^2 = E\,du^2 + 2\,F\,du\,dv + G\,dv^2,$$

where

$$E \equiv \left(\frac{\partial x}{\partial u}\right)^2 + \left(\frac{\partial y}{\partial u}\right)^2 + \left(\frac{\partial z}{\partial u}\right)^2, \quad F \equiv \frac{\partial x}{\partial u}\frac{\partial x}{\partial v} + \frac{\partial y}{\partial u}\frac{\partial y}{\partial v} + \frac{\partial z}{\partial u}\frac{\partial z}{\partial v},$$

$$G \equiv \left(\frac{\partial x}{\partial v}\right)^2 + \left(\frac{\partial y}{\partial v}\right)^2 + \left(\frac{\partial z}{\partial v}\right)^2.$$

The differential equation of the lines of zero length, usually called *minimal lines,* is then

(50) $$E\,du^2 + 2\,F\,du\,dv + G\,dv^2 = 0.$$

This differential equation, being of the second degree, is equivalent to the two

(51) $$\begin{cases} E\,du + (F + \sqrt{F^2 - EG})\,dv = 0, \\ E\,du + (F - \sqrt{F^2 - EG})\,dv = 0, \end{cases}$$

which are essentially distinct, since it is always presupposed that $EG - F^2$ is different from zero. Let $\alpha(u, v) = const.$ and $\beta(u, v) = const.$ be the solutions of (51). These are the equations of the minimal lines. Choosing them for parametric curves, equation (50)

---

[*] These applications will be of interest to those only who have, at least, a slight acquaintance with the elements of Differential Geometry. They have been taken from Lie's *Vorlesungen über Differentialgleichungen*, Chap. 9.

takes the form $d\alpha\, d\beta = 0$, *i.e.* $E(\alpha, \beta) = G(\alpha, \beta) = 0$, and the expression for the element of length of arc is

$$ds^2 = 2\, F(\alpha, \beta)\, d\alpha\, d\beta.$$

Introducing the new parameters u_1 and v_1 defined by

$$\phi(\alpha) = u_1 + iv_1, \quad \psi(\beta) = u_1 - iv_1\,{}^*$$

where ϕ and ψ are any desired functions of their respective arguments, $\quad ds^2 = \lambda(u_1, v_1)(du_1{}^2 + dv_1{}^2),$

since $d\alpha\, d\beta = \dfrac{1}{\phi'(\alpha)\psi'(\beta)}(du_1{}^2 + dv_1{}^2)$. This form of the expression for the element of length is characteristic of isothermal parametric curves. (Compare Note III of the Appendix). Hence,

$$2\, u_1 \equiv U = \phi(\alpha) + \psi(\beta) = \textit{const.}$$

and $\qquad\quad 2\, iv_1 \equiv V = \phi(\alpha) - \psi(\beta) = \textit{const.}$

are the equations of the isothermal curves and their orthogonal trajectories, respectively. Since $\phi(\alpha) = \textit{const.}$ and $\psi(\beta) = \textit{const.}$ are equally well the equations of the minimal lines, it is evident that the identity (48) is satisfied by the equation of any isothermal system and those of the minimal lines. It follows then from the theorem above that *the differential equation of a family of isothermal curves on any known † surface can be integrated by means of quadratures. Besides, the knowledge of a family of isothermal lines on a known*

---

* In the case of a real surface, α and β may be selected as conjugate complex functions of u and v, when the original parametric curves are real. Real isothermal curves are then obtained by choosing ϕ and ψ conjugate functions of α and β respectively.

† A surface is said to be known if the values of x, y, z in terms of the parameters u, v are known, or if the forms of E, F, G, and of D, D', D'' (to be introduced below) are given in terms of u, v. In this particular case E, F, G only need be known, minimal and isothermal lines not depending upon D, D', D''.

surface. enables one to integrate the differential equations of the minimal lines (51) *by means of two quadratures.*

Remark 1. — For surfaces of the second order, surfaces of revolution, and minimal surfaces, the lines of curvature (see **B** below) are known to be isothermal lines. Hence, in the case of these surfaces the differential equation of the lines of curvature can be integrated by means of quadratures.

Remark 2. — In the case of a minimal surface the asymptotic lines are also isothermals. Hence, on such a surface the differential equation of these lines can also be integrated by means of quadratures.

B. The tangent plane to a surface at a given point cuts the surface in a curve which has a double point at that point. In general, the directions of the tangents to the two branches of the curve at that point are distinct. In this way two directions (in general) are determined at every point on the surface. A curve on the surface whose direction at every point coincides with one of these directions is called an *asymptotic line*. So that, in general, through each point on the surface there pass two asymptotic lines. The differential equation of the asymptotic lines is

$$(52) \qquad D \, du^2 + 2 \, D' du \, dv + D'' dv^2 = 0,$$

where

$$D \equiv \begin{vmatrix} \dfrac{\partial^2 x}{\partial u^2} & \dfrac{\partial x}{\partial u} & \dfrac{\partial x}{\partial v} \\ \dfrac{\partial^2 y}{\partial u^2} & \dfrac{\partial y}{\partial u} & \dfrac{\partial y}{\partial v} \\ \dfrac{\partial^2 z}{\partial u^2} & \dfrac{\partial z}{\partial u} & \dfrac{\partial z}{\partial v} \end{vmatrix}, \quad D' \equiv \begin{vmatrix} \dfrac{\partial^2 x}{\partial u \, \partial v} & \dfrac{\partial x}{\partial u} & \dfrac{\partial x}{\partial v} \\ \dfrac{\partial^2 y}{\partial u \, \partial v} & \dfrac{\partial y}{\partial u} & \dfrac{\partial y}{\partial v} \\ \dfrac{\partial^2 z}{\partial u \, \partial v} & \dfrac{\partial z}{\partial u} & \dfrac{\partial z}{\partial v} \end{vmatrix}, \quad D'' \equiv \begin{vmatrix} \dfrac{\partial^2 x}{\partial v^2} & \dfrac{\partial x}{\partial u} & \dfrac{\partial x}{\partial v} \\ \dfrac{\partial^2 y}{\partial v^2} & \dfrac{\partial y}{\partial u} & \dfrac{\partial y}{\partial v} \\ \dfrac{\partial^2 z}{\partial v^2} & \dfrac{\partial z}{\partial u} & \dfrac{\partial z}{\partial v} \end{vmatrix}.$$

In case $DD'' - D'^2 = 0$, the two curves coincide. This happens at every point of a surface where the Gauss measure of curvature is zero.

Another system of curves playing an important rôle in the theory of surfaces is that of *lines of curvature*, which have the property, that along them consecutive normals to the surface intersect. Their differential equation is given most conveniently in the determinant form

$$(53) \qquad \begin{vmatrix} dv^2 - du\,dv & du^2 \\ E & F & G \\ D & D' & D'' \end{vmatrix} = 0.$$

This differential equation is again of the second degree, so that through each point pass two lines of curvature. These are mutually orthogonal, and besides their directions are harmonic conjugates with respect to those of the asymptotic lines through the same point, as may be seen readily from the forms of equations (50), (52), and (53).

Suppose that on a certain surface the asymptotic lines are known to cut out rhombuses.* This can be expressed analytically in the following way :

The selection of the asymptotic lines as parametric curves does not affect the appearance of the expression for the element of length of arc. But since $u = const.$ and $v = const.$ must then be the solutions of (52), it follows that $D = D'' = 0$. Hence the differential equation of the lines of curvature (53) reduces to

$$(53') \qquad\qquad E\,du^2 - G\,dv^2 = 0.$$

The elements of length along the parametric curves are $\sqrt{E}\,du$ and $\sqrt{G}\,dv$. These will be equal at every point on the surface, and the surface will therefore be divided into rhombuses, if $\sqrt{E} = \lambda(u, v)\phi(u)$ and $\sqrt{G} = \lambda(u, v)\psi(v)$. (See corresponding argument in the case of isothermal lines in Note III of the Appendix.) Letting

---

* This is known to be the case for surfaces of constant Gauss curvature, for example.

$\int \phi(u)\, du \equiv U,\ \int \psi(v)\, dv \equiv V$, the expression for the element of length takes the form

$$ds^2 = \Lambda(U,\ V)(dU^2 + dV^2) + 2\, F(U,\ V)\, dU\, dV.$$

The differential equation of the lines of curvature takes the form

$$dU^2 - dV^2 = 0\ ;$$

whence the equations of the lines of curvature are

$$U + V = const. \text{ and } U - V = const.$$

Since the identity (48) holds, it follows that *if the asymptotic lines divide a surface into rhombuses, the asymptotic lines and lines of curvature can be obtained by means of quadratures.*

CHAPTER IV

DIFFERENTIAL EQUATIONS OF THE SECOND AND HIGHER ORDERS

26. Twice-extended, n-times-extended Group. — A transformation of the variables x and y carries with it a transformation of the various derivatives of y with respect to x. Thus, just as the point transformation

$$x_1 = \phi(x, y), \quad y_1 = \psi(x, y)$$

carries with it (§ 13)

$$\frac{dy_1}{dx_1} \equiv y_1' = \frac{\frac{\partial \psi}{\partial x} + \frac{\partial \psi}{\partial y} y'}{\frac{\partial \phi}{\partial x} + \frac{\partial \phi}{\partial y} y'} \equiv \chi(x, y, y'),$$

so it also implies

$$\frac{dy_1'}{dx_1} \equiv y_1'' = \frac{\frac{\partial \chi}{\partial x} + \frac{\partial \chi}{\partial y} y' + \frac{\partial \chi}{\partial y'} y''}{\frac{\partial \phi}{\partial x} + \frac{\partial \phi}{\partial y} y'} \equiv \omega(x, y, y', y'').$$

The transformation

$$x_1 = \phi(x, y), \quad y_1 = \psi(x, y), \quad y_1' = \chi(x, y, y'), \quad y_1'' = \omega(x, y, y', y'')$$

affecting the four variables x, y, y', y'' which is implied by the point transformation is known as a *twice-extended point transformation.*[*]

Starting with the one-parameter group of point transformations

$$(1) \qquad x_1 = \phi(x, y, a), \quad y_1 = \psi(x, y, a),$$

---

[*] In precisely the same way we are led to the *n-times-extended transformation*

$$x_1 = \phi(x, y), \quad y_1 = \psi(x, y), \quad y_1' = \chi(x, y, y'), \quad y_1'' = \omega(x, y, y', y''), \quad \cdots,$$

$$y_1^{(n)} \equiv \frac{dy_1^{(n-1)}}{dx_1} = \theta(x, y, y', y'', \cdots, y^{(n)}).$$

by employing the method of reasoning in § 13, the corresponding twice-extended transformations

$$(54) \quad x_1 = \phi(x, y, a), \quad y_1 = \psi(x, y, a), \quad y_1' = \frac{dy_1}{dx_1} \equiv \chi(x, y, y', a),$$

$$y_1'' = \frac{dy_1'}{dx_1} \equiv \omega(x, y, y', y'', a),$$

are seen to constitute a one-parameter group in the four variables x, y, y', y''. This group is known as the *twice-extended group* corresponding to (1).

Writing as the symbol of the infinitesimal transformation of the twice-extended group

$$(55) \quad U''f \equiv \xi \frac{\partial f}{\partial x} + \eta \frac{\partial f}{\partial y} + \eta' \frac{\partial f}{\partial y'} + \eta'' \frac{\partial f}{\partial y''},$$

where as before

$$\xi \equiv \frac{\delta x}{\delta a}, \quad \eta \equiv \frac{\delta y}{\delta a}, \quad \eta' \equiv \frac{\delta y'}{\delta a} = \frac{d\eta}{dx} - y' \frac{d\xi}{dx} \ [(23), \ \S \ 13],$$

η'', which is $\dfrac{\delta y''}{\delta a}$, may be found in exactly the same way as η' was; thus

$$\eta'' = \frac{\delta}{\delta a}\left(\frac{dy'}{dx}\right) = \frac{\frac{\delta}{\delta a}(dy')}{dx} - \frac{dy' \frac{\delta}{\delta a}(dx)}{dx^2} = \frac{d\left(\frac{\delta y'}{\delta a}\right)}{dx} - \frac{dy'}{dx}\frac{d\left(\frac{\delta x}{\delta a}\right)}{dx}.$$

$$(56) \qquad\qquad \therefore \eta'' = \frac{d\eta'}{dx} - y'' \frac{d\xi}{dx}.$$

Reasoning as before we have the *n-times-extended group*

$$x_1 = \phi(x, y, a), \quad y_1 = \psi(x, y, a,), \quad y_1' = \frac{dy_1}{dx_1} \equiv \chi(x, y, y', a),$$

$$y_1'' = \frac{dy_1'}{dx_1} \equiv \omega(x, y, y', y'', a), \ \cdots, \ y_1^{(n)} = \frac{dy_1^{(n-1)}}{dx_1} \equiv \theta(x, y, \cdots, y^{(n)}, a),$$

the symbol of whose infinitesimal transformation may be written

$$U^{(n)}f \equiv \xi \frac{\partial f}{\partial x} + \eta \frac{\partial f}{\partial y} + \eta' \frac{\partial f}{\partial y'} + \cdots + \eta^{(k)} \frac{\partial f}{\partial y^{(k)}} + \cdots + \eta^{(n)} \frac{\partial f}{\partial y^{(n)}},$$

where

$$(57) \quad \eta^{(k)} \equiv \frac{\delta y^{(k)}}{\delta a} = \frac{d\eta^{(k-1)}}{dx} - y^{(k)}\frac{d\xi}{dx} \quad (k = 1, 2, 3, \cdots, n).$$

Remark.— While η' is a quadratic polynomial in y' ([24], § 13), it is seen, on expanding (56),

$$(58) \qquad \eta'' = \frac{\partial \eta'}{\partial x} + \frac{\partial \eta'}{\partial y}y' + \left(\frac{\partial \eta'}{\partial y'} - \frac{\partial \xi}{\partial x} - \frac{\partial \xi}{\partial y}y'\right)y''$$

that η'' is linear in y''. In the same way $\eta^{(k)}$ is seen to be linear in $y^{(k)}$ for $k > 1$, since

$$(59) \quad \eta^{(k)} = \frac{\partial \eta^{(k-1)}}{\partial x} + \frac{\partial \eta^{(k-1)}}{\partial y}y' + \frac{\partial \eta^{(k-1)}}{\partial y'}y'' + \cdots + \frac{\partial \eta^{(k-1)}}{\partial y^{(k-2)}}y^{(k-1)}$$

$$+ \left(\frac{\partial \eta^{(k-1)}}{\partial y^{(k-1)}} - \frac{\partial \xi}{\partial x} - \frac{\partial \xi}{\partial y}y'\right)y^{(k)}.$$

In I, $Uf \equiv \frac{\partial f}{\partial y}$, $\xi \equiv 0$, $\eta \equiv 1$. $\therefore \eta' \equiv 0$, $\eta'' \equiv 0$, $\cdots$, $\eta^{(n)} \equiv 0$.

Hence, $$U^{(n)}f \equiv \frac{\partial f}{\partial y}.$$

In II, $Uf \equiv -y\frac{\partial f}{\partial x} + x\frac{\partial f}{\partial y}$, $\xi \equiv -y$, $\eta \equiv x$. $\therefore \eta' \equiv 1 + y'^2$, $\eta'' \equiv 3y'y''$,

$$\eta''' \equiv 3y''^2 + 4y'y''', \quad \eta^{IV} \equiv 5\,(2y''y''' + y'y^{IV}), \quad \cdots.$$

Hence,

$$U^{IV}f \equiv -y\frac{\partial f}{\partial x} + x\frac{\partial f}{\partial y} + (1 + y'^2)\frac{\partial f}{\partial y'} + 3y'y''\frac{\partial f}{\partial y''} + (3y''^2 + 4y'y''')\frac{\partial f}{\partial y'''}$$

$$+ 5(2y''y''' + y'y^{IV})\frac{\partial f}{\partial y^{IV}}.$$

In III, $Uf \equiv y\frac{\partial f}{\partial y}$, $\xi \equiv 0$, $\eta \equiv y$. $\therefore \eta' \equiv y'$, $\eta'' \equiv y''$, $\cdots$, $\eta^{(n)} \equiv y^{(n)}$.

Hence, $$U^{(n)}f \equiv y\frac{\partial f}{\partial y} + y'\frac{\partial f}{\partial y'} + y''\frac{\partial f}{\partial y''} + \cdots + y^{(n)}\frac{\partial f}{\partial y^{(n)}}.$$

In IV, $Uf \equiv x\dfrac{\partial f}{\partial x} + y\dfrac{\partial f}{\partial y}$, $\xi \equiv x$, $\eta \equiv y$. $\therefore \eta' \equiv 0$, $\eta'' \equiv -y''$, $\eta''' \equiv -2y'''$,

..., $\eta^{(n)} \equiv -(n-1)y^{(n)}$.

Hence, $U^{(n)}f \equiv x\dfrac{\partial f}{\partial x} + y\dfrac{\partial f}{\partial y} - y''\dfrac{\partial f}{\partial y''} - 2y'''\dfrac{\partial f}{\partial y'''} - \cdots - (n-1)y^{(n)}\dfrac{\partial f}{\partial y^{(n)}}.$

Extend the following groups:

Ex. 1. $\dfrac{\partial f}{\partial x}.$ **Ex. 2.** $x\dfrac{\partial f}{\partial x}.$ **Ex. 3.** $x\dfrac{\partial f}{\partial x} - y\dfrac{\partial f}{\partial y}.$

Ex. 4. $ax\dfrac{\partial f}{\partial x} + by\dfrac{\partial f}{\partial y}.$ **Ex. 5.** $\phi(x)\dfrac{\partial f}{\partial x}.$ **Ex. 6.** $\phi(x)\dfrac{\partial f}{\partial y}.$

Ex. 7. $x^2\dfrac{\partial f}{\partial x} + r\,xy\dfrac{\partial f}{\partial y}.$

27. Differential Equation of Second Order Invariant under a Given Group. — The effect of any transformation (1) on the variables x and y is to transform the differential equation

(60) $$f(x, y, y', y'') = 0,$$

by the corresponding extended transformation (54). In order that the equation (60) be invariant under the group (54), it is necessary and sufficient that ([12], § 11)

(61) $$U''f = 0 \text{ whenever } f(x, y, y', y'') = 0.$$

Using the same argument as was employed in § 18, it is seen that all the differential equations of the second order invariant under the group are obtained by equating to zero an arbitrary function of three independent solutions of ([9], § 11, footnote)

(62) $$U''f \equiv \xi\frac{\partial f}{\partial x} + \eta\frac{\partial f}{\partial y} + \eta'\frac{\partial f}{\partial y'} + \eta''\frac{\partial f}{\partial y''} = 0.$$

Passing to the corresponding system of ordinary differential equations

(63)
$$\frac{dx}{\xi(x,y)} = \frac{dy}{\eta(x,y)} = \frac{dy'}{\eta'(x,y,y')} = \frac{dy''}{\eta''(x,y,y',y'')},$$

the first three members are seen to be the same as those of (37), § 18. Hence, two of the solutions, $u(x,y) = const.$ and $u'(x,y,y') = const.$, may be found by the methods of that section.

To find a third solution, $u''(x,y,y',y'') = const.$, which must necessarily involve y'', use may be made of the two already found to eliminate y and y' from $\frac{dy''}{dx} = \frac{\eta''}{\xi}$, or x and y' from $\frac{dy''}{dy} = \frac{\eta''}{\eta}$, or x and y from $\frac{dy''}{dy'} = \frac{\eta''}{\eta'}$ (whichever turns out to be the simplest). Each of these differential equations is linear since η'' is of the first degree in y'' (§ 26, Remark). This linear equation can be solved by means of two quadratures. (See *El. Dif. Eq.* § 13).

Lie has given a most ingenious method for finding a form for $u''(x,y,y,'y'')$, without any integration whatever when u and u' are known :

Consider the differential equation

(64)
$$u'(x,y,y') - \alpha\, u(x,y) = \beta,$$

where α and β are constants. Since u and u' are invariants of the once-extended group $U'f$, (64) is invariant under the group Uf; that is, its integral curves are interchanged among themselves by the transformations of this group. Keeping α fixed, an invariant family of a single infinity of integral curves corresponds to each value of β. Still keeping α fixed and allowing β to take successively all possible values, an infinity of such families, constituting a double infinity of integral curves, is determined by (64). This larger aggregate is invariant under the group Uf, since each of the constituent families corresponding to the same value of β is. It is evidently the set of integral curves of the differential equation of the second order obtained by differentiating (64), thereby eliminating β ; viz.

$$(65) \qquad \frac{du'}{dx} - \alpha \frac{du}{dx} = 0, \text{ or } \frac{du'}{du} \equiv \frac{\dfrac{\partial u'}{\partial x} + \dfrac{\partial u'}{\partial y} y' + \dfrac{\partial u'}{\partial y'} y''}{\dfrac{\partial u}{\partial x} + \dfrac{\partial u}{\partial y} y'} = \alpha.$$

Since its integral curves are interchanged among themselves by every transformation (1), it is invariant under the group Uf. Hence, by (61)

$$U''\left(\frac{du'}{du} - \alpha\right) = 0 \text{ whenever } \frac{du'}{du} = \alpha.$$

But α being a constant, $U''\left(\dfrac{du'}{du} - \alpha\right) = U''\left(\dfrac{du'}{du}\right)$; *i.e.* it is independent of α. $U''\left(\dfrac{du'}{du}\right)$ is therefore identically zero ; which is sufficient to make $\dfrac{du'}{du}$ an invariant of (54), ([9], § 11).

Since u' contains y' (§ 18), $\dfrac{\partial u'}{\partial y'} \not\equiv 0$, and $\dfrac{du'}{du}$ must contain y''.*
Hence, $\dfrac{du'}{du} = const.$ may be used as the third solution of (63). The general solution of (62) may then be written in the form

$$(66) \qquad f\left(u, u', \frac{du'}{du}\right) = 0, \text{ or } \frac{du'}{du} = F(u, u').$$

This is the general form of the differential equation of the second order invariant under the group Uf. We have therefore the following most important

THEOREM. — *If $f(x, y, y', y'') = 0$ is a differential equation of the second order invariant under the group Uf,†and if $u(x, y)$ is any*

---

* An invariant of the extended group $U''f$ which involves y'' is known as a *second differential invariant* of the group Uf.

† Attention should be called to the fact that while every differential equation of the first order is invariant under an indefinite number of groups (see §§ 15, 17) a differen-

*invariant and u'(x, y, y') is any first differential invariant of Uf, the
introduction of the new variables*

(67) $$x = u(x, y), \quad y = u'(x, y, y')$$

reduces the differential equation to the form

(66') $$\frac{dy}{dx} = F(x, y),$$

which is of the first order.

In actual practice the introduction of the new variables is usually
most readily effected by noting that

$$\frac{dy}{dx} \equiv \frac{\dfrac{\partial y}{\partial x} + \dfrac{\partial y}{\partial y} y' + \dfrac{\partial y}{\partial y'} y''}{\dfrac{\partial x}{\partial x} + \dfrac{\partial x}{\partial y} y'}$$

is some function of $u \equiv x$, $u' \equiv y$, and u''. When this function is
obvious upon inspection, u'' can be determined in terms of x, y, $\dfrac{dy}{dx}$.
In other cases it may be necessary to solve

$$x = u(x, y), \quad y = u'(x, y, y'), \quad \frac{dy}{dx} = \frac{\dfrac{\partial y}{\partial x} + \dfrac{\partial y}{\partial y} y' + \dfrac{\partial y}{\partial y'} y''}{\dfrac{\partial x}{\partial x} + \dfrac{\partial x}{\partial y} y'}$$

for y, y', y'' in terms of x, y, $\dfrac{dy}{dx}$, x. Substituting these in the differential equation, x must disappear, and the resulting equation must
take the form (66').

After having solved (66'), its solution

(68) $$\phi(u, u', c) = 0$$

is a differential equation of the first order. But owing to the invariance of u and u' (68) is invariant under Uf, so that it may be
solved by the method of § 12 or that of § 20.

tial equation of the second (or higher) order is in general not invariant under any
group. (See Note IV of the Appendix.) On the other hand, a large number of them,
including most of the known forms, are, and these will be considered in this chapter.

28. Illustrations and Applications. —

I. $Uf \equiv \dfrac{\partial f}{\partial y}$. $\xi \equiv 0,\ \eta \equiv 1.$ $\therefore\ \eta' \equiv 0,\ \eta'' \equiv 0$ (§ 26). Equations (63) are

$$\frac{dx}{0} = \frac{dy}{1} = \frac{dy'}{0} = \frac{dy''}{0}\cdot$$

$\therefore u \equiv x,\ u' \equiv y',\ u'' \equiv y''.$ Hence, *the general type of differential equation of the second order invariant under $Uf \equiv \dfrac{\partial f}{\partial y}$ is $f(x, y', y'') = 0$ or $y'' = F(x, y')$.* This equation is characterized by the absence of y.

Note. — The transformation of variables $x = x,\ y = y'$ (§ 27) reduces the differential equation to

$$(66') \qquad\qquad \frac{dy}{dx} = F(x, y).$$

This is precisely the usual method for solving an equation of this type. (See *El. Dif. Eq.* § 57). Solving the solution of (66') for y, it takes the form

$$y \equiv \frac{dy}{dx} = f(x, c),$$

in which the variables are separated, as must be the case (I, § 19), since this equation is invariant under the same group (§ 27).

I'. $Uf \equiv \dfrac{\partial f}{\partial x}$. It is readily seen that *the general type of differential equation of the second order invariant under this group is $f(y, y', y'') = 0$, or $y'' = F(y, y')$.* This equation is characterized by the absence of x.

Note. — The transformation $x = y,\ y = y'$ (§ 27) reduces the differential equation to one of the first order (66'). Its solution

$$y = f(x, c),\ \text{or}\ \frac{dy}{dx} = f(y, c)$$

is a differential equation with x absent again, as must be the case (I', § 19 and § 27). This is also the usual method for solving an equation of this type. (See *El. Dif. Eq.*, § 58.)

Remark. — Owing to the simple form of an equation invariant under either of the groups $Uf \equiv \dfrac{\partial f}{\partial x}$ or $Uf \equiv \dfrac{\partial f}{\partial y}$, it is frequently desirable to introduce canonical variables in case a given differential equation of the second order is known to be invariant under some group. When the introduction of canonical variables is not practicable, other changes of variables reducing the group and equation to known forms may prove desirable. (Compare § 20.)

II. $Uf \equiv -y\dfrac{\partial f}{\partial x} + x\dfrac{\partial f}{\partial y}$. $\xi \equiv -y,\ \eta = x.\ \therefore\ \eta' \equiv 1 + y'^2,\ \eta'' \equiv 3\,y'y''$, (§ 26). Equations (63) are

$$(63')\qquad \frac{dx}{-y} = \frac{dy}{x} = \frac{dy'}{1 + y'^2} = \frac{dy''}{3\,y'y''}.$$

$\therefore\ u \equiv x^2 + y^2,\ u' \equiv \dfrac{y - xy'}{x + yy'}$ (§ 19). Using the last two members of equations $(63')$, $u'' \equiv \dfrac{y''^2}{(1 + y'^2)^3}$. Hence *the general type of differential equation of the second order invariant under* $Uf \equiv -y\dfrac{\partial f}{\partial x} + x\dfrac{\partial f}{\partial y}$ *is*

$$\frac{y''^2}{(1 + y'^2)^3} = F\!\left(x^2 + y^2,\ \frac{y - xy'}{x + yy'}\right).$$

Note. — The form of this differential equation is obvious from geometrical considerations, since u is the square of the radius vector to any point on an integral curve, u' is the tangent of the angle between the radius vector and the tangent to the curve, while u'' is the square of the curvature, all of which are left unaltered by the group of rotations about the origin. (Compare § 29.) In order to integrate such an equation the method of I', Remark, requiring the introduction of canonical variables (polar coördinates in this case) will usually be found desirable.

Making use of the fact that $\dfrac{x + yy'}{\sqrt{1 + y'^2}}$ and $\dfrac{y - xy'}{\sqrt{1 + y'^2}}$ are also first differential invariants of the group of rotations (II, Note, § 19) other possible forms of the invariant differential equation of the second order are

$$\frac{y''^2}{(1+y'^2)^3} = F\left(x^2+y^2, \frac{x+yy'}{\sqrt{1+y'^2}}\right) \text{ and } \frac{y''^2}{(1+y'^2)^3} = F\left(x^2+y^2, \frac{y-xy'}{\sqrt{1+y'^2}}\right).$$

III. $Uf \equiv y\dfrac{\partial f}{\partial y}.$ $\xi \equiv 0, \ \eta \equiv y.$ $\therefore \eta' \equiv y', \ \eta'' \equiv y''$ (§ 26).   Equations (63) are

$$\frac{dx}{0} = \frac{dy}{y} = \frac{dy'}{y'} = \frac{dy''}{y''}.$$

$\therefore u \equiv x, \ u' \equiv \dfrac{y'}{y}, \ u'' \equiv \dfrac{y''}{y}.$*   Hence *the general type of differential equation of the second order invariant under* $Uf \equiv y\dfrac{\partial f}{\partial y}$ *is*

$$f\left(x, \frac{y'}{y}, \frac{y''}{y}\right) = 0, \text{ or } y'' = yF\left(x, \frac{y'}{y}\right).$$

This equation is characterized by being homogeneous in y, y', y''. It is evident, at once, that an equation of this type is left unaltered by the affine group $Uf \equiv y\dfrac{\partial f}{\partial y}$, since the finite transformations of the extended group are $x_1 = x, \ y_1 = ay, \ y_1' = ay', \ y_1'' = ay''$.

Note. — An interesting equation of this type is the homogeneous (or abridged) linear differential equation

(59) $$y'' + P(x)y' + Q(x)y = 0.$$

The transformation $x = x, \ y = \dfrac{y'}{y}$ (§ 27) reduces the equation to

$$\frac{dy}{dx} + y^2 + Py + Q = 0,$$

a Riccati equation.   (Compare *El. Dif. Eq.* § 73, 6°).

---

* The Lie method of § 27 gives $u'' = \dfrac{du'}{du} = \dfrac{yy''-y'^2}{y^2} = \dfrac{y''}{y} - \left(\dfrac{y'}{y}\right)^2$, and the differential equation $\dfrac{y''}{y} = \left(\dfrac{y'}{y}\right)^2 + F\left(x, \dfrac{y'}{y}\right)$, which is, of course, the same in form as that found in the body of the text.

VI. $Uf \equiv x\dfrac{\partial f}{\partial x} + ny\dfrac{\partial f}{\partial y}.$ $\xi \equiv x,\ \eta \equiv ny.$ $\therefore \eta' \equiv (n-1)y',$

$\eta'' \equiv (n-2)y''.$ Equations (63) are

$$\frac{dx}{x} = \frac{dy}{ny} = \frac{dy'}{(n-1)y'} = \frac{dy''}{(n-2)y''}.$$

$$\therefore u \equiv \frac{y}{x^n},\ u' \equiv \frac{y'}{x^{n-1}},\ u'' \equiv \frac{y''}{x^{n-2}}.$$

Hence *the general type of differential equation of the second order invariant under* $Uf \equiv x\dfrac{\partial f}{\partial x} + ny\dfrac{\partial f}{\partial y}$ *is* $f\left(\dfrac{y}{x^n}, \dfrac{y'}{x^{n-1}}, \dfrac{y''}{x^{n-2}}\right) = 0.$

This equation is characterized by being homogeneous in x, y, y', y'' when these elements are given the weights $1, n, n-1, n-2$ respectively.

Note. — Boole called an equation of this type *homogeneous,* and gave as a method for solving it the transformation $\boldsymbol{x} = \log x,\ \boldsymbol{y} = \dfrac{y}{x^n}.$ (See Boole, *Treatise on Differential Equations,* p. 215; Forsyth, *Treatise on Differential Equations,* § 55). The new variables in this transformation are a set of canonical variables. (Compare I', Remark.)

III'. $Uf \equiv x\dfrac{\partial f}{\partial x}$ is a special case of VI. Here $n = 0$, and *the invariant differential equation is of the form* $f(y, xy', x^2y'') = 0.$

This equation is homogeneous in x, y', y'' when these elements have the weights $1, -1, -2$ respectively; the weight of y being zero, the manner in which this variable enters plays no rôle.

III. $Uf \equiv y\dfrac{\partial f}{\partial y}$ may also be looked upon as a special case of VI, corresponding to the value $n = \infty$. Boole deduced a special method for this case (see Boole, p. 220; Forsyth, § 55) which is exactly that of § 27 for this case.

IV. $Uf \equiv x\dfrac{\partial f}{\partial x} + y\dfrac{\partial f}{\partial y}$ is the special case of VI for $n = 1$. *The invariant differential equation is of the form* $f\left(\dfrac{y}{x}, y', xy''\right) = 0.$

V. $Uf = x\dfrac{\partial f}{\partial x} - y\dfrac{\partial f}{\partial y}$ is the special case of VI for $n = -1$. *The invariant differential equation is of the form* $f(xy,\ x^2y',\ x^3y'') = 0.$

VII. $Uf \equiv \phi(x)\dfrac{\partial f}{\partial y}.$ $\xi \equiv 0,\ \eta \equiv \phi(x).$ $\therefore\ \eta' \equiv \phi'(x),\ \eta'' \equiv \phi''(x).$
It is readily seen that

$$u \equiv x,\quad u' \equiv \phi(x)y' - \phi'(x)y,\quad u'' \equiv \phi(x)y'' - \phi''(x)y.$$

Hence *the general type of differential equation of the second order invariant under* $Uf \equiv \phi(x)\dfrac{\partial f}{\partial y}$ *is* $f(x,\ \phi y' - \phi'y,\ \phi y'' - \phi''y) = 0,$ *or*
$$\phi y'' - \phi''y = F(x,\ \phi y' - \phi'y).$$

Note.— An interesting equation of this type is the complete linear equation

(70) $$y'' + P(x)y' + Q(x)y = X(x),$$

which is obtained from the general form by letting F be linear in $u' \equiv \phi y' - \phi'y$. Bearing this fact in mind, it is clear that $y = \phi(x)$ satisfies the abridged equation (69), obtained from (70) by replacing $X(x)$ by 0. Conversely it is readily seen (and will be left as an exercise to prove) that if $y = y_0$ is a solution of (69), (70) is invariant under the group $Uf \equiv y_0\dfrac{\partial f}{\partial y}$. The transformation $x = x,\ y = y_0y' - y_0'y$ (§ 27) reduces the equation to the linear equation of the first order

(71) $$\dfrac{dy}{dx} + P(x)y = y_0(x)X(x).$$

This property of the complete linear differential equation of the second order of reducing to one of the first order by a transformation that is known when a particular integral of the corresponding abridged linear equation is known is not new. (See *El. Dif. Eq.* § 53, 1°.) The transformation employed above yields an equation bearing a more striking resemblance to the original equation than the transformation,

$$x = x, \quad y = \frac{y}{y_0},$$

usually employed.   The new variables in this transformation are a set of canonical variables (I', Remark).

Other groups whose invariant differential equations are readily found are the following :

VII'. $Uf \equiv \psi(y)\dfrac{\partial f}{\partial x}$. $\qquad f\left(y, \dfrac{1}{y'} - \dfrac{\psi'}{\psi}x, \dfrac{y''}{y'^3} + \dfrac{\psi''}{\psi'y'}\right) = 0.$

VIII. $Uf \equiv \psi(y)\dfrac{\partial f}{\partial y}$. $\qquad f\left(x, \dfrac{y'}{\psi}, \dfrac{y''}{\psi} - \dfrac{y'^2\psi'}{\psi^2}\right) = 0.$

VIII'. $Uf \equiv \phi(x)\dfrac{\partial f}{\partial x}$. $\qquad f(y, \phi y', \phi^2 y'' + \phi\phi' y') = 0.$

X. $Uf \equiv \phi(x)\left(x\dfrac{\partial f}{\partial x} + ny\dfrac{\partial f}{\partial y}\right)$.

$$f\left(\frac{y}{x^n}, \frac{xy' - ny}{x^n}\phi, \frac{x^2 y'' + (1-n)xy'}{xy' - ny}\phi - n\phi + x\phi'\right) = 0.$$

XII. $Uf \equiv a\dfrac{\partial f}{\partial x} + b\dfrac{\partial f}{\partial y}$. $\qquad f(bx - ay, y', y'') = 0.$

In Table II of the Appendix will be found a list of the more commonly occurring and readily recognizable classes of equations of higher order than the first invariant under known groups.

Ex. 1. $xyy'' + xy'^2 - yy' = 0$.

This equation is invariant under the group IV : $Uf \equiv x\dfrac{\partial f}{\partial x} + y\dfrac{\partial f}{\partial y}$. Introducing the new variables

$$x = \frac{y}{x}, \quad y = y'$$

the equation takes the simple form

$$\frac{dy}{dx} + \frac{y}{x} = 0.$$

Integrating $\qquad xy = a$, or $\dfrac{yy'}{x} = a.$

Integrating again $\qquad ax^2 - y^2 = b.$

Note. — Inspection shows that this equation is also invariant under
III : $Uf \equiv y\,\dfrac{\partial f}{\partial y}$, and III' : $Uf \equiv x\,\dfrac{\partial f}{\partial x}.$

Ex. 2. $\qquad (x^2 + y^2)y'' + 2(y - xy')(1 + y'^2) = 0.$

This equation is invariant under the group II :

$$Uf \equiv -y\,\frac{\partial f}{\partial x} + x\,\frac{\partial f}{\partial y}.$$

Introducing the canonical variables (in this case, polar coördinates)

$$x = \tan^{-1}\frac{y}{x}, \quad y = \sqrt{x^2 + y^2},$$

the equation takes the form $\dfrac{d^2y}{dx^2} + y = 0.$

Here the independent variable is absent, but, instead of using the method indicated by the general method of § 27, it will be simpler to solve this linear equation with constant coefficients by the usual method for such an equation. (See *El. Dif. Eq.* § 45.)

$$y = a \cos x + b \sin x.$$

To pass back to the original variables, multiply by y, whence

$$x^2 + y^2 = ax + by.$$

Note. — This differential equation is also invariant under IV.

Ex. **3.** $x^2yy'' - (xy' - y)^2 = 0.$ (Invariant under III, IV, ...)

Ex. **4.** $x^3y'' + (xy' - y)^2 = 0.$ Ex. **5.** $x^2y'' = xy' - y.$

Other equations invariant under known groups appear in §§ 39 and 40.

29. Further Applications. — Besides being able to recognize a group under which a given differential equation is invariant from the characteristic properties given in § 28 and enumerated in Table II of the Appendix, it is possible at times, to find such a group from the nature of the problem giving rise to the differential equation. As examples, the following may be noted :

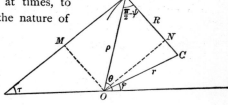

FIG. 4

1° The group of rotations about the origin

$$Uf \equiv -y\frac{\partial f}{\partial x} + x\frac{\partial f}{\partial y} \quad \text{leaves unaltered}$$

$R \equiv$ the radius of curvature of a curve at any point,

$\rho \equiv$ the radius vector to any point on the curve,

$r \equiv$ the radius vector to the centre of curvature,

the distance from the origin to any line (such as the tangent or normal) connected with the curve, thus OM and ON,

$PM \equiv$ the polar subtangent, $= ON$,

$PN \equiv$ the polar subnormal, $= OM$,

$\psi \equiv$ the angle between the radius vector and the tangent,

the remaining angles of the triangle OCP.

Hence a family of curves defined by a relation between any or all of these is unaltered by this group ; the differential equation of the family is therefore invariant under it.   Passing to polar coördinates (the canonical variables) will usually be found desirable in this case.

2° The similitudinous group $Uf \equiv x \dfrac{\partial f}{\partial x} + y \dfrac{\partial f}{\partial y}$ leaves unaltered

$\theta \equiv$ the angle between the initial line and the radius vector,

$\tau \equiv$ the angle between the initial line and the tangent to the curve,

$\phi \equiv$ the angle between the initial line and the radius vector to the centre of curvature,

$\psi \equiv$ the angle between the radius vector and the tangent to the curve,

the ratio of certain lines connected with the curve, such as radius vector, radius of curvature, radius vector to the centre of curvature, intercepts of the tangent, normal, or of the curve itself, subtangent, subnormal, length of tangent or normal from a point on the curve to one of the axes, and the like.

Hence this group leaves unaltered the differential equation of a family of curves defined by a relation between any of the above invariant configurations.   Passing to canonical variables, or to polar coördinates (thereby reducing the group to III') may simplify the problem of solving the differential equation.

3° Certain configurations could be enumerated as invariant under the groups of translations $Uf \equiv \dfrac{\partial f}{\partial x}$ and $Uf \equiv \dfrac{\partial f}{\partial y}$.   But as in either case one of the variables is absent in the resulting differential equation, the latter will suggest the group without considering the definition of the integral curves.

Ex.   Find the family of curves for which the radius vector to any point of a curve is perpendicular to the radius vector drawn to the centre of curvature of the curve at that point.

The differential equation of this family must be invariant under the group of rotations II and also the similitudinous group IV.

Noting in Fig. 4 that the triangle POC is right-angled at O,

$$\frac{OP}{PC} = \cos P, \quad \text{or} \quad \frac{\rho}{R} = \sin \psi.$$

Here $\rho = \sqrt{x^2 + y^2}$, $R = \dfrac{(1 + y'^2)^{\frac{3}{2}}}{y''}$, $\tan \psi = \dfrac{y - xy'}{x + yy'}$.   Hence the differential equation is

$$(x^2 + y^2)y'' - (1 + y'^2)(y - xy') = 0.$$

30. Differential Equation of Order Higher than the Second Invariant under a Given Group. — The method of § 27 can be extended without change to differential equations of higher order:

A differential equation of the nth order

$$(72) \qquad f(x, y, y', y'', \cdots, y^{(n)}) = 0$$

is invariant under the group Uf, if and only if

$$(73) \qquad U^{(n)}f = 0 \text{ whenever } f = 0.$$

All the differential equations of the nth order invariant under the group are obtained by equating to zero an arbitrary function of $n + 1$ independent solutions of

$$(74) \quad U^{(n)}f \equiv \xi \frac{\partial f}{\partial x} + \eta \frac{\partial f}{\partial y} + \eta' \frac{\partial f}{\partial y'} + \eta'' \frac{\partial f}{\partial y''} + \cdots + \eta^{(n)} \frac{\partial f}{\partial y^{(n)}} = 0.$$

These independent solutions may be obtained from the corresponding system of ordinary equations

$$(75) \qquad \frac{dx}{\xi} = \frac{dy}{\eta} = \frac{dy'}{\eta'} = \frac{dy''}{\eta''} = \cdots = \frac{dy^{(n)}}{\eta^{(n)}}.$$

It was seen in § 27 that if $u(x, y)$ is an invariant of Uf, and $u'(x, y, y')$ is a first differential invariant, then $\dfrac{du'}{du}$ is a second differential invariant.   Hence,

$$(76) \qquad \frac{du'}{du} - \alpha u = \beta$$

is an invariant differential equation of the second order for all values
of the constants α and β.   Its integral curves constitute an invariant
family of ∞^2 curves.   The ∞^1 differential equations of the second
order obtained by keeping α fixed and giving to β all possible values
have for integral curves ∞^1 such invariant families of ∞^2 curves.
Grouping all these curves into one aggregate of ∞^3 curves, this aggregate is invariant under the group since each of the families is.   The
differential equation of this family is, therefore, invariant.   It is obtained by differentiating (76), thus eliminating β,

$$(77) \qquad \frac{d}{dx}\left(\frac{du'}{du}\right) - \alpha\frac{du}{dx} = 0, \text{ or } \frac{d^2u'}{du^2} - \alpha = 0.$$

In order that (77) be invariant, we must have from (73)

$$U'''\left(\frac{d^2u'}{du^2} - \alpha\right) = 0, \text{ whenever } \frac{d^2u'}{du^2} = \alpha.$$

But
$$U'''\left(\frac{d^2u'}{du^2} - \alpha\right) = U'''\frac{d^2u'}{du^2} ;$$

i.e. it is independent of α.   Hence, if (77) is to be invariant, $U'''\frac{d^2u'}{du^2}$
must vanish identically.   So that $\frac{d^2u'}{du^2}$ is a solution of (74).   Since it
contains y''' (as may be seen readily), it is independent of u, u', $\frac{du'}{du}$

In the same way it can be shown, step by step, that a set of independent solutions of (74) is

$$u, \quad u', \quad \frac{du'}{du}, \quad \frac{d^2u'}{du^2}, \quad \cdots, \quad \frac{d^{n-1}u'}{du^{n-1}}.$$

Hence the general type of differential equation of order n invariant
under the group Uf is

$$(78) \qquad \frac{d^{n-1}u'}{du^{n-1}} = F\left(u, u', \frac{du'}{du}, \frac{d^2u'}{du^2}, \cdots, \frac{d^{n-2}u'}{du^{n-2}}\right).$$

We have then as an extension of the theorem of § 27 the following

THEOREM. — *If $f(x, y, y', y'', \cdots, y^{(n)}) = 0$ is invariant under the group Uf, and if $u(x, y)$ is any invariant, and $u'(x, y, y')$ is any first differential invariant of Uf, the introduction of the new variables*

$$(79) \qquad\qquad x = u(x, y), \quad y = u'(x, y, y')$$

reduces the differential equation to

$$(78') \qquad\qquad \frac{d^{n-1}y}{dx^{n-1}} = F\left(x, y, \frac{dy}{dx}, \cdots, \frac{d^{n-2}y}{dx^{n-2}}\right),$$

which is of order $n - 1$.

After having integrated $(78')$, its solution

$$f(u, u', c_1, c_2, \cdots, c_{n-1}) = 0$$

is a differential equation, also invariant under Uf, since u and u' are. Hence it may be solved by the method of § 12 or of § 20.

Many of the arguments of § 28 can be used here, almost without a single change. Consequently, the results only will be given, it being left as an exercise for the student to fill in the steps.

I. *The general type of differential equation of the nth order invariant under $Uf \equiv \dfrac{\partial f}{\partial y}$ is $f(x, y', y'', \cdots, y^{(n)}) = 0$,* which is characterized by the absence of y.

The transformation $y = y'$, reducing the differential equation to one of order $n - 1$ constitutes the usual method for solving an equation of this type. (*El. Dif. Eq.* § 57.)

I'. *The general type of differential equation of the nth order invariant under $Uf \equiv \dfrac{\partial f}{\partial x}$ is $f(y, y', y'', \cdots, y^{(n)}) = 0$,* which is characterized by the absence of x.

The transformation $x = y$, $y = y'$, reducing the differential equation to one of order $n - 1$ constitutes the usual method for solving an equation of this type. (*El. Dif. Eq.* § 58.)

The remark of I', § 28 with reference to the introduction of canonical or other variables when a group is known under which a given differential equation is invariant applies equally well here.

I. *The general type of differential equation of the nth order invariant under* $Uf \equiv y\dfrac{\partial f}{\partial y}$ *is* $f\left(x, \dfrac{y'}{y}, \dfrac{y''}{y}, \cdots, \dfrac{y^{(n)}}{y}\right) = 0$, which is characterized by being homogeneous in $y, y', y'', \cdots, y^{(n)}$.

VI. *The general type of differential equation of the nth order invariant under* $Uf \equiv x\dfrac{\partial f}{\partial x} + ry\dfrac{\partial f}{\partial y}$ *is* $f\left(\dfrac{y}{x^r}, \dfrac{y'}{x^{r-1}}, \dfrac{y''}{x^{r-2}}, \cdots, \dfrac{y^{(n)}}{x^{r-n}}\right) = 0$, which is characterized by being homogeneous in $x, y, y', y'', \cdots, y^{(n)}$, when these elements are given the weights $1, r, r-1, r-2, \cdots, r-n$ respectively.

As special cases of this group may be mentioned

IV: $r = 1$, $f\left(\dfrac{y}{x}, y', xy'', \cdots, x^{n-1}y^{(n)}\right) = 0$,

V: $r = -1$, $f(xy, x^2y', x^3y'', \cdots, x^{n+1}y^{(n)}) = 0$,

III': $r = 0$, $f(y, xy', x^2y'', \cdots, x^ny^{(n)}) = 0$,

III: $r = \infty$. The invariant equation in this case is more readily recognized by the other characterization given under III above.

VII. *The general type of differential equation of the nth order invariant under*

$$Uf \equiv \phi(x)\dfrac{\partial f}{\partial y} \text{ is } f(x, \phi y' - \phi'y, \phi y'' - \phi''y, \cdots, \phi y^{(n)} - \phi^{(n)}y) = 0,$$

or $\phi y^{(n)} - \phi^{(n)}y = F(x, \phi y' - \phi'y, \phi y'' - \phi''y, \cdots, \phi y^{(n-1)} - \phi^{(n-1)}y)$.

Note. — An interesting equation of this type is the complete linear equation

(80) $y^{(n)} + P_1 y^{(n-1)} + P_2 y^{(n-2)} + \cdots + P_{n-2}y'' + P_{n-1}y' + P_n y = X$.

If $y = y_0$ is a particular solution of the abridged equation obtained by replacing X by zero, (80) is invariant under $Uf \equiv y_0 \dfrac{\partial f}{\partial y}$.

The transformation (79) $y = y_0 y' - y_0' y$ (or $y = y_0 y$, resulting from the introduction of canonical variables) reduces (80) to a linear equation of order $n - 1$ (*El. Dif. Eq.* § 59), but the resemblance of the resulting equation to the original one is not as striking as in the case of the linear equation of the second order (VII, Note, § 28).

XII. *The general type of differential equation of the nth order invariant under* $Uf \equiv a \dfrac{\partial f}{\partial x} + b \dfrac{\partial f}{\partial y}$ *is* $f(bx - ay, y', y'', \cdots, y^{(n)}) = 0$.

CHAPTER V

LINEAR PARTIAL DIFFERENTIAL EQUATIONS OF THE FIRST ORDER

31. Complete System.*

THEOREM I. — *If $\phi(x, y, z)$ is a solution of the two independent†
linear homogeneous equations*

$$A_1 f \equiv P_1(x, y, z) \frac{\partial f}{\partial x} + Q_1(x, y, z) \frac{\partial f}{\partial y} + R_1(x, y, z) \frac{\partial f}{\partial z} = 0,$$

$$A_2 f \equiv P_2(x, y, z) \frac{\partial f}{\partial x} + Q_2(x, y, z) \frac{\partial f}{\partial y} + R_2(x, y, z) \frac{\partial f}{\partial z} = 0,$$

it is also a solution of

$$(A_1 A_2) f \equiv (A_1 P_2 - A_2 P_1) \frac{\partial f}{\partial x} + (A_1 Q_2 - A_2 Q_1) \frac{\partial f}{\partial y}$$

$$+ (A_1 R_2 - A_2 R_1) \frac{\partial f}{\partial z} = 0,$$

where $(A_1 A_2)$ is the alternant of the operators A_1 and A_2 (§ 14).

For $(A_1 A_2)\phi \equiv A_1(A_2\phi) - A_2(A_1\phi) = 0$, since $A_1\phi = 0$ and $A_2\phi = 0$.

* Only so much of the theory of complete systems and only such methods for their
solution as seem necessary for our immediate purpose are given here. For an excel-
lent detailed treatment of this subject the student is referred to Goursat-Bourlet, *Inté-
gration des èquations aux derivées partielles du premier ordre.*

† r equations of this type in n variables are said to be *independent* if it is impossible
to find r functions $\sigma_1, \sigma_2, \cdots, \sigma_r$ of the variables such that

$$\sigma_1 A_1 f + \sigma_2 A_2 f + \cdots + \sigma_r A_r f \equiv 0.$$

In the case of $r = 2$, this amounts to saying that the equations are independent if
one of them is not a multiple of the other.

If three linear equations in three variables $A_1 f = 0$, $A_2 f = 0$, $A_3 f = 0$ have a common solution $\phi(x, y, z)$ other than a constant, $\dfrac{\partial \phi}{\partial x}$, $\dfrac{\partial \phi}{\partial y}$, $\dfrac{\partial \phi}{\partial z}$ satisfy the three homogeneous linear relations

$$A_1 \phi \equiv P_1 \frac{\partial \phi}{\partial x} + Q_1 \frac{\partial \phi}{\partial y} + R_1 \frac{\partial \phi}{\partial z} = 0,$$

$$A_2 \phi \equiv P_2 \frac{\partial \phi}{\partial x} + Q_2 \frac{\partial \phi}{\partial y} + R_2 \frac{\partial \phi}{\partial z} = 0,$$

$$A_3 \phi \equiv P_3 \frac{\partial \phi}{\partial x} + Q_3 \frac{\partial \phi}{\partial y} + R_3 \frac{\partial \phi}{\partial z} = 0.$$

Since $\phi(x, y, z)$ is not a constant, $\dfrac{\partial \phi}{\partial x}$, $\dfrac{\partial \phi}{\partial y}$, $\dfrac{\partial \phi}{\partial z}$ cannot all be identically zero. Hence

$$\Delta \equiv \begin{vmatrix} P_1 & Q_1 & R_1 \\ P_2 & Q_2 & R_2 \\ P_3 & Q_3 & R_3 \end{vmatrix} \equiv 0.$$

It follows that three functions $\sigma_1(x, y, z)$, $\sigma_2(x, y, z)$, $\sigma_3(x, y, z)$ can be found * such that

$$(81) \qquad \sigma_1 A_1 f + \sigma_2 A_2 f + \sigma_3 A_3 f \equiv 0 ;$$

i.e. the three equations are not independent. Hence follows

THEOREM II. *If the three equations in three variables* $A_1 f = 0$, $A_2 f = 0$, $A_3 f = 0$ *have a common solution, other than a constant, they are not independent;* or stated otherwise, *three independent linear homogeneous partial differential equations in three variables cannot have a common solution, other than a constant.*

From Theorems I and II, it follows at once that *if* $A_1 f = 0$ *and* $A_2 f = 0$ *have a common solution,*

$$(82) \qquad (A_1 A_2) f \equiv \rho_1(x, y, z) A_1 f + \rho_2(x, y, z) A_2 f.$$

---

* Thus, for example, one may take for σ_1, σ_2, σ_3 any three functions proportional to the cofactors of the corresponding elements of any column in Δ.

Clebsch gave the name of *complete system* to a pair of independent equations $A_1f = 0$ and $A_2f = 0$, which are connected by the relation (82). The last statement may therefore be put into the form

THEOREM III. *If $A_1f = 0$ and $A f = 0$ have a common solution, they form a complete system.*

Conversely, we shall prove the very important

THEOREM IV. *If $A_1f = 0$ and $A_2f = 0$ form a complete system, they have a common solution.*

In order to do this it is necessary to prove two lemmas.

LEMMA I. *If $A_1f = 0$ and $A_2f = 0$ form a complete system, any pair of equations formed of independent linear combinations of these also form a complete system.*

The equations

$$(83) \quad \begin{cases} \boldsymbol{A}_1f \equiv \lambda_1(x, y, z)A_1f + \mu_1(x, y, z)A_2f = 0 \\ \boldsymbol{A}_2f \equiv \lambda_2(x, y, z)A_1f + \mu_2(x, y, z)A_2f = 0 \end{cases}$$

are independent if $\lambda_1\mu_2 - \lambda_2\mu_1 \not\equiv 0$. Then A_1f and A_2f can be found as linear functions of $\boldsymbol{A}_1f$ and $\boldsymbol{A}_2f$ from (83).

Since $A_1f = 0$ and $A_2f = 0$ are supposed to form a complete system, $(\boldsymbol{A}_1\boldsymbol{A}_2)f \equiv (\lambda_1\mu_2 - \lambda_2\mu_1)(A_1A_2)f + (\boldsymbol{A}_1\lambda_2 - \boldsymbol{A}_2\lambda_1)A_1f + (\boldsymbol{A}_1\mu_2 - \boldsymbol{A}_2\mu_1)A_2f$ is seen to be a linear function of A_1f and A_2f, and therefore of $\boldsymbol{A}_1f$ and $\boldsymbol{A}_2f$, which proves the lemma.

Moreover, any common solution of $A_1f = 0$ and $A_2f = 0$ must be such for $\boldsymbol{A}_1f = 0$ and $\boldsymbol{A}_2f = 0$, and *vice versa*. Hence the two systems are said to be *equivalent*, or each is said to be equivalent to the other.

A system equivalent to the original system is obtained if the equations of the latter are solved for two of the three partial derivatives $\frac{\partial f}{\partial x}, \frac{\partial f}{\partial y}, \frac{\partial f}{\partial z}$. This can always be done, since all three of the determinants in the matrix $\begin{Vmatrix} P_1 & Q_1 & R_1 \\ P_2 & Q_2 & R_2 \end{Vmatrix}$

do not vanish identically, $A_1 f = 0$ and $A_2 f = 0$ being independent equations. If, in particular $P_1 Q_2 - P_2 Q_1 \equiv D \not\equiv 0$, the equations may be solved for $\dfrac{\partial f}{\partial x}$ and $\dfrac{\partial f}{\partial y}$, thus giving

$$(83')\qquad A_1 f \equiv \frac{\partial f}{\partial x} + R_1 \frac{\partial f}{\partial z} = 0, \quad A_2 f \equiv \frac{\partial f}{\partial y} + R_2 \frac{\partial f}{\partial z} = 0,$$

where $R_1 = \dfrac{Q_2 R_1 - Q_1 R_2}{D}$, $R_2 = \dfrac{-P_2 R_1 + P_1 R_2}{D}$. Here $\lambda_1 = \dfrac{Q_2}{D}$, $\mu_1 = -\dfrac{Q_1}{D}$, $\lambda_2 = -\dfrac{P_2}{D}$, $\mu_2 = \dfrac{P_1}{D}$, and $\lambda_1 \mu_2 - \lambda_2 \mu_1 = \dfrac{1}{D} \not\equiv 0$, since all functions involved are supposed to be generally analytic. Hence equations $(83')$ are independent. This fact is also obvious upon inspection, since the first equation is free of $\dfrac{\partial f}{\partial y}$, while the second does not contain $\dfrac{\partial f}{\partial x}$. Moreover

$$(84)\qquad\qquad (A_1 A_2) f \equiv 0.$$

For, since $A_1 f = 0$ and $A_2 f = 0$ form a complete system

$$(82)\qquad\qquad (A_1 A_2) f \equiv \rho_1 A_1 f + \rho_2 A_2 f.$$

In the case of equations $(83')$

$$(A_1 A_2) f \equiv (A_1 R_2 - A_2 R_1) \frac{\partial f}{\partial z}$$

which is free of both $\dfrac{\partial f}{\partial x}$ and $\dfrac{\partial f}{\partial y}$. Hence ρ_1 and ρ_2 in (82) must both be zero, and the form (84) follows.

A complete system for which $\rho_1 \equiv \rho_2 \equiv 0$ is called a *Jacobian* complete system.* We have thus established

* Originally this term was applied only to a complete system in the special form $(83')$. Lie and other mathematicians, however, used it, as above, to apply to the more general class of complete systems; (see Lie, *Differentialgleichungen*, p. 202; Goursat-Bourlet, *loc. cit.*, p. 347; also *Encyklopädie der Mathematischen Wissenschaften*, Band II$_1$, p. 315).

LEMMA II. — *A Jacobian complete system can always be found equivalent to a given complete system.*

Remark. — It should be noted that this equivalent Jacobian system is not unique, since starting with such a one, the system obtained by taking any pair of independent linear combinations of these equations with constant multipliers is another system of the same sort.

It is easy to show that a Jacobian complete system has a solution. Suppose that $A_1 f = 0$ and $A_2 f = 0$ form such a system.   Then

$$(84) \qquad (A_1 A_2) f \equiv A_1(A_2 f) - A_2(A_1 f) \equiv 0.$$

If $u(x, y, z)$ and $v(x, y, z)$ are two independent solutions of one of the equations, say $A_1 f = 0$, any function of u and v will equally well satisfy this equation.   It remains to find such a function of them, $F(u, v)$, that it shall also be a solution of the other equation $A_2 f = 0$; that is,

$$(85) \qquad A_2 F(u, v) \equiv \frac{\partial F}{\partial u} A_2 u + \frac{\partial F}{\partial v} A_2 v = 0.$$

Replacing f in (84) by u and v successively,

$$A_1(A_2 u) - A_2(A_1 u) = 0 \ \text{ and } \ A_1(A_2 v) - A_2(A_1 v) = 0.$$

Since $A_1 u = 0$ and $A_1 v = 0$, it follows that

$$A_1(A_2 u) = 0 \ \text{ and } \ A_1(A_2 v) = 0.$$

Hence $A_2 u$ and $A_2 v$ are functions of u and v, say $\phi(u, v)$ and $\psi(u, v)$ respectively, and the equation (85) to determine $F(u, v)$ is

$$(85') \qquad \phi(u, v)\frac{\partial F}{\partial u} + \psi(u, v)\frac{\partial F}{\partial v} = 0.$$

The solution of this equation (which is known to exist by the general existence theorem) is a solution of the Jacobian system $A_1 f = 0$, $A_2 f = 0$, and consequently of the equivalent complete system $A_1 f = 0$ and $A_2 f = 0$.   Theorem IV is thus proved.

All that has gone before can be extended at once to homogeneous linear equations in n variables.

Without changing a word in the proof of Theorem I we have: *If $\phi(x_1, x_2, \cdots, x_n)$ is a solution of the two equations*

$$A_1 f \equiv P_{11}(x_1, x_2, \cdots, x_n)\frac{\partial f}{\partial x_1} + P_{12}(x_1, x_2, \cdots, x_n)\frac{\partial f}{\partial x_2} + \cdots$$

$$+ P_{1n}(x_1, x_2, \cdots, x_n)\frac{\partial f}{\partial x_n} = 0,$$

$$A_2 f \equiv P_{21}(x_1, x_2, \cdots, x_n)\frac{\partial f}{\partial x_1} + P_{22}(x_1, x_2, \cdots, x_n)\frac{\partial f}{\partial x_2} + \cdots$$

$$+ P_{2n}(x_1, x_2, \cdots, x_n)\frac{\partial f}{\partial x_n} = 0,$$

it is also a solution of $(A_1 A_2)f = 0$.

As before, *if n equations have a common solution, other than a constant, the equations cannot be independent.* For the determinant of the coefficients

$$\begin{vmatrix} P_{11} & P_{12} & \cdots & P_{1n} \\ P_{21} & P_{22} & \cdots & P_{2n} \\ & \cdot & \cdot & \cdot & \cdot \\ P_{n1} & P_{n2} & \cdots & P_{nn} \end{vmatrix}$$

must vanish.   Hence a relation of the form

$$\sigma_1 A_1 f + \sigma_2 A_2 f + \cdots + \sigma_n A_n f \equiv 0$$

must exist.

Starting with r independent equations

$$A_1 f = 0, \quad A_2 f = 0, \quad \cdots, \quad A_r f = 0 \ (2 \lessgtr r < n)$$

with a common solution, all the equations

$$(A_i A_\kappa)f = 0, \quad (i, \kappa = 1, 2, 3, \cdots, r),$$

will also have this solution.   Some or all of these equations may be independent of the original equations.   Adjoining these to the latter, the process may be repeated as long as independent equations can be found.   This process must come to an end before the total number of equations reaches n.   For it has just been seen that there cannot be n independent linear equations in n variables having a common solution, other than a constant. We have thus obtained a system of s equations

$$A_1f = 0, \quad A_2f = 0, \quad \cdots, \quad A_sf = 0 \ (r \lessgtr s < n)$$

such that

$$(A_iA_\kappa)f \equiv \rho_1A_1f + \rho_2A_2f + \cdots + \rho_sA_sf,$$

$$(i, \kappa = 1, 2, 3, \cdots, s).$$

Such a system constitutes a *complete system*. We have thus shown that *if r equations have a common solution, every member of the complete system determined by them has that solution.*

It will be left as an exercise for the student to show that starting with any complete system an equivalent Jacobian system* can be found. The method is identical with that given above for three variables.

That a Jacobian complete system (and, therefore, any complete system) of s equations in n variables has $n - s$ independent solutions may be proved in a manner entirely analogous to that used above for $s = 2, n = 3$. To illustrate, the case for $s = 3, n = 5$ will be given without detail:

The equation

$$A_1f \equiv P_{11}\frac{\partial f}{\partial x_1} + P_{12}\frac{\partial f}{\partial x_2} + P_{13}\frac{\partial f}{\partial x_3} + P_{14}\frac{\partial f}{\partial x_4} + P_{15}\frac{\partial f}{\partial x_5} = 0,$$

has four independent solutions u_1, u_2, u_3, u_4 (*El. Dif. Eq.* § 79). The problem is now to show that some function $F(u_1, u_2, u_3, u_4)$ of these will satisfy both $A_2f = 0$ and $A_3f = 0$.

Since u_i for $i = 1, 2, 3, 4$ satisfies $A_1f = 0$, it follows on replacing f by u_i in the identity

$$(A_1A_2)f \equiv A_1(A_2f) - A_2(A_1f) \equiv 0$$

that A_2u_i is also a solution of $A_1f = 0$. Hence A_2u_i must be some function of u_1, u_2, u_3, u_4 say $\phi_i(u_1, u_2, u_3, u_4)$, for $i = 1, 2, 3, 4$. If F is any solution of the equation involving the four variables u_1, u_2, u_3, u_4,

$$A_2F \equiv \phi_1\frac{\partial F}{\partial u_1} + \phi_2\frac{\partial F}{\partial u_2} + \phi_3\frac{\partial F}{\partial u_3} + \phi_4\frac{\partial F}{\partial u_4} = 0,$$

it will be a solution of $A_1f = 0$ and $A_2f = 0$.

---

* A *Jacobian complete system* of s equations is one for which

$$(A_iA_\kappa)f \equiv 0 \ (i, \kappa = 1, 2, 3, \cdots, s).$$

See previous footnote.

This equation has three independent solutions v_1, v_2, v_3. Any function of these will be a solution of $A_1 f = 0$ and $A_2 f = 0$; and conversely, every solution common to $A_1 f = 0$ and $A_2 f = 0$ must be a function of v_1, v_2, v_3. It remains to show that some function, $\Phi(v_1, v_2, v_3)$, of them will satisfy $A_3 f = 0$.

As before, it follows on replacing f by v_i in the identities

$$(A_1 A_3)f \equiv A_1(A_3 f) - A_3(A_1 f) \equiv 0 \text{ and } (A_2 A_3)f \equiv A_2(A_3 f) - A_3(A_2 f) \equiv 0,$$

that $A_3 v_i$ is a solution of both $A_1 f = 0$ and $A_2 f = 0$. Hence $A_3 v_i$ must be some function of v_1, v_2, v_3, say $\psi_i(v_1, v_2, v_3)$, for $i = 1, 2, 3$. The function Φ may then be any solution of the equation

$$A_3 \Phi \equiv \psi_1 \frac{\partial \Phi}{\partial v_1} + \psi_2 \frac{\partial \Phi}{\partial v_2} + \psi_3 \frac{\partial \Phi}{\partial v_3} = 0.$$

This is known to have two independent solutions. Each of these is therefore a solution of the complete system, and there can be no others.

32. Method of Solution of Complete System. — To actually find the solution common to the members of a complete system $A_1 f = 0$ and $A_2 f = 0$ it is not necessary to pass to an equivalent Jacobian system. If u and v are two independent solutions of one of the equations, $A_1 f = 0$, it is known that some function $F(u, v)$ is a solution of the other; i.e.

$$(85) \qquad A_2 F(u, v) \equiv A_2 u \frac{\partial F}{\partial u} + A_2 v \frac{\partial F}{\partial v} = 0.$$

or

$$(86) \qquad \frac{\partial F}{\partial u} + \frac{A_2 v}{A_2 u} \frac{\partial F}{\partial v} = 0.$$

Knowing that some form of $F(u, v)$ must satisfy this equation, whence $\dfrac{\partial F}{\partial u}$ and $\dfrac{\partial F}{\partial v}$ are also functions of u and v, $\dfrac{A_2 v}{A_2 u}$ must be a function of u and v.* Hence (86) may be written as an equation in these two variables only, and the usual method of solution for such an equation may then be followed.

* It should be noted that in this case, unlike in the case of a Jacobian complete system, $A_2 u$ and $A_2 v$ need not be functions of u and v, although they may be.

Ex. 1. $A_1 f \equiv \dfrac{\partial f}{\partial x} = 0, \quad A_2 f \equiv x\dfrac{\partial f}{\partial x} + y\dfrac{\partial f}{\partial y} + z\dfrac{\partial f}{\partial z} = 0.$

Since $(A_1 A_2)f \equiv A_1 f$, these form a complete system.

Here $u \equiv y$, $v \equiv z$ are solutions of $A_1 f = 0$. Then $A_2 u = y = u$, $A_2 v = z = v$, and equation (85) may be used to determine F; thus

$$u\frac{\partial F}{\partial u} + v\frac{\partial F}{\partial v} = 0.$$

The general solution of this is any function of $\dfrac{v}{u}$. Hence the common solution of the complete system is any function of $\dfrac{z}{y}$.

Or starting with $u \equiv \dfrac{x}{y}$, $v \equiv \dfrac{x}{z}$, the solutions of $A_2 f = 0$, and noting that $A_1 u = \dfrac{1}{y}$, $A_1 v = \dfrac{1}{z}$, whence $\dfrac{A_1 v}{A_1 u} = \dfrac{y}{z} = \dfrac{v}{u}$, equation (86) is

$$\frac{\partial F}{\partial u} + \frac{v}{u}\frac{\partial F}{\partial v} = 0.$$

Its solution is $\dfrac{v}{u} \equiv \dfrac{y}{z}$, giving the common solution of the system or equations.

Ex. 2. $A_1 f \equiv x\dfrac{\partial f}{\partial x} + y\dfrac{\partial f}{\partial y} + z\dfrac{\partial f}{\partial z},$

$$A_2 f \equiv (x^2 + y^2 + yz)\frac{\partial f}{\partial x} + (x^2 + y^2 - xz)\frac{\partial f}{\partial y} + (xz + yz)\frac{\partial f}{\partial z} = 0.$$

These form a complete system, since $(A_1 A_2)f \equiv A_2 f$.

Here $u \equiv \dfrac{x}{z}$, $v \equiv \dfrac{y}{z}$ are solutions of $A_1 f = 0$. $A_2 u = \dfrac{y^2 + yz - xy}{z}$, $A_2 v = \dfrac{x^2 - xz - xy}{z}$. $\therefore \dfrac{A_2 v}{A_2 u} = -\dfrac{x}{y} = -\dfrac{u}{v}$, and equation (86) is

$$\frac{\partial F}{\partial u} - \frac{u}{v}\frac{\partial F}{\partial v} = 0.$$

Its solution is $u^2 + v^2$. Hence the common solution of the complete system is any function of $\dfrac{x^2 + y^2}{z^2}$.

Ex. 3. $A_1f \equiv y\dfrac{\partial f}{\partial x} - x\dfrac{\partial f}{\partial y} = 0, \ A_2f \equiv \dfrac{\partial f}{\partial z} = 0.$

Ex. 4. $A_1f \equiv x\dfrac{\partial f}{\partial x} + z\dfrac{\partial f}{\partial z} = 0, \ A_2f \equiv y\dfrac{\partial f}{\partial y} + z\dfrac{\partial f}{\partial z} = 0.$

Ex. 5. $A_1f \equiv a\dfrac{\partial f}{\partial x} + b\dfrac{\partial f}{\partial y} + c\dfrac{\partial f}{\partial z} = 0, \ A_2f \equiv x\dfrac{\partial f}{\partial x} + y\dfrac{\partial f}{\partial y} + z\dfrac{\partial f}{\partial z} = 0.$

Ex. 6. $A_1f \equiv (x - y + z)\dfrac{\partial f}{\partial x} - 2y\dfrac{\partial f}{\partial y} + (x - y + z)\dfrac{\partial f}{\partial z} = 0,$

$A_2f \equiv (y - z)\dfrac{\partial f}{\partial x} + (z - x)\dfrac{\partial f}{\partial y} + (x - y)\dfrac{\partial f}{\partial z} = 0.$

Ex. 7. $A_1f \equiv (xz - y)\dfrac{\partial f}{\partial x} + (yz - x)\dfrac{\partial f}{\partial y} + (1 - z^2)\dfrac{\partial f}{\partial z} = 0,$

$A_2f \equiv (x^2 + y^2)\dfrac{\partial f}{\partial x} + 2xy\dfrac{\partial f}{\partial y} - y(1 - z^2)\dfrac{\partial f}{\partial z} = 0.$

33. Second Method of Solution. — If $\phi(x, y, z)$ is a solution of the complete system $A_1f = 0$ and $A_2f = 0$, the equations

$$A_1\phi \equiv P_1\frac{\partial \phi}{\partial x} + Q_1\frac{\partial \phi}{\partial y} + R_1\frac{\partial \phi}{\partial z} = 0,$$

$$A_2\phi \equiv P_2\frac{\partial \phi}{\partial x} + Q_2\frac{\partial \phi}{\partial y} + R_2\frac{\partial \phi}{\partial z} = 0$$

give $\quad \dfrac{\partial \phi}{\partial x} : \dfrac{\partial \phi}{\partial y} : \dfrac{\partial \phi}{\partial z} = Q_1R_2 - Q_2R_1 : R_1P_2 - R_2P_1 : P_1Q_2 - P_2Q_1.$

Since the total differential equation which has $\phi(x, y, z) = const.$ for solution is

$$\frac{\partial \phi}{\partial x}dx + \frac{\partial \phi}{\partial y}dy + \frac{\partial \phi}{\partial z}dz = 0,$$

or differs from it by a factor involving x, y, z only, this equation may take the form

$$(87) \quad (Q_1R_2 - Q_2R_1)dx + (R_1P_2 - R_2P_1)dy + (P_1Q_2 - P_2Q_1)dz = 0.*$$

The problem of solving a complete system is thus reduced to that of solving a total differential equation (87). At times the actual work involved in solving (87) turns out to be simpler than that required by the method of the previous section.

Besides the usual methods for integrating total differential equations (see *El. Dif. Eq.* Chapter VI) the following method due to Dubois-Reymond may be mentioned.

Instead of letting one of the variables, say z, be a constant temporarily, as is usually done, let it be a linear function of the other two, thus

$$z = x + ay$$

where a is an arbitrary constant. This relation carries with it

$$dz = dx + a\,dy.$$

Eliminating z and dz from these two and the total differential equation, there results an ordinary differential equation

$$M(x, y, a)dx + N(x, y, a)dy = 0 \dagger$$

whose solution $\qquad \psi(x, y, a) = const.$

---

* Equation (87) may be put in the convenient determinant form

$$\begin{vmatrix} dx & dy & dz \\ P_1 & Q_1 & R_1 \\ P_2 & Q_2 & R_2 \end{vmatrix} = 0$$

which expresses the condition that the above three homogeneous linear equations in $\dfrac{\partial\phi}{\partial x}$, $\dfrac{\partial\phi}{\partial y}$, $\dfrac{\partial\phi}{\partial z}$ are consistent.

† If it happens that this differential equation does not contain a, some other linear relation among the three variables containing an arbitrary constant should be tried leading to a differential equation in two of the variables only and containing the arbitrary constant.

gives, on replacing a by its value in terms of x, y, z,

$$\psi\left(x, y, \frac{z-x}{y}\right) = const.,$$

which is the solution of the total differential equation.

This method requires the solution of only one ordinary differential equation instead of two, as in the usual method, when an integrating factor is not known. But in actual practice, this theoretically simpler method may not prove as desirable as the other.

Ex. The examples of § 32 should be solved by the methods of this section.

Thus for Ex. 1 the total differential equation to be solved is

$$\begin{vmatrix} dx & dy & dz \\ 1 & 0 & 0 \\ x & y & z \end{vmatrix} = z\,dy - y\,dz = 0.$$

Its solution is $\frac{y}{z} = const.$

For Ex. 2

$$\begin{vmatrix} dx & dy & dz \\ x & y & z \\ x^2+y^2+yz & x^2+y^2-xz & z(x+y) \end{vmatrix} = 0$$

becomes, on multiplying the second row by $x + y$ and subtracting from the third row,

$$(y + z - x)\begin{vmatrix} dx & dy & dz \\ x & y & z \\ y & -x & 0 \end{vmatrix} = 0$$

or

$$xz\,dx + yz\,dy - (x^2 + y^2)dz = 0.$$

An obvious integrating factor is $\dfrac{1}{z(x^2+y^2)}$, and the solution is $\dfrac{x^2+y^2}{z^2} = const.$

34. Linear Partial Differential Equation Invariant under a Group.—

The homogeneous linear partial differential equation of the first order,

$$(88) \qquad Af \equiv P\frac{\partial f}{\partial x} + Q\frac{\partial f}{\partial y} + R\frac{\partial f}{\partial z} = 0,$$

has two independent solutions $\phi_1(x, y, z)$ and $\phi_2(x, y, z)$.   Every other solution is some function of these.

The result of transforming (88) by the transformation

$$(89) \qquad x_1 = \phi(x, y, z), \quad y_1 = \psi(x, y, z), \quad z_1 = \chi(x, y, z)$$

is ([15], § 11) the new equation

$$(90) \qquad A\phi \frac{\partial f}{\partial x_1} + A\psi \frac{\partial f}{\partial y_1} + A\chi \frac{\partial f}{\partial z_1} = 0,$$

where $A\phi$, $A\psi$, $A\chi$ are to be expressed in terms of x_1, y_1, z_1.   If (90) is the same equation in the new variables as (88) is in the old ones, or differs from it by a factor, the transformation (89) is said to leave the differential equation (88) unaltered.   In this case it must transform both ϕ_1 and ϕ_2 into solutions again; that is, they are either left unaltered by (89) or they are transformed into some functions of themselves by it.

Let us find under what condition (88) is left unaltered by every transformation of the group

$$Uf \equiv \xi \frac{\partial f}{\partial x} + \eta \frac{\partial f}{\partial y} + \zeta \frac{\partial f}{\partial z}.$$

We have seen ([7], § 11),

$$\phi_i(x_1, y_1, z_1) = \phi_i(x, y, z) + U\phi_i \frac{t}{1} + U^2\phi_i \frac{t^2}{2!} + \cdots,$$
$$(i = 1, 2).$$

In order that this be a function of $\phi_1(x, y, z)$ and $\phi_2(x, y, z)$ for all transformations of the group, *i.e.* for all values of t, it is necessary that

$$(91) \qquad U\phi_i = F_i(\phi_1, \phi_2), \quad (i = 1, 2).$$

It is readily seen that this is also a sufficient condition.   For

$$U^2\phi_i = UU\phi_i = UF_i(\phi_1, \phi_2) = \frac{\partial F_i}{\partial \phi_1} U\phi_1 + \frac{\partial F_i}{\partial \phi_2} U\phi_2 = \frac{\partial F_i}{\partial \phi_1} F_1 + \frac{\partial F_i}{\partial \phi_2} F_2,$$

which is again a function of ϕ_1 and ϕ_2. In the same way it can be shown that if $U^k\phi_i$ is a function of ϕ_1 and ϕ_2, $U^{k+1}\phi_i$ is. Hence, (91) is the necessary and sufficient condition that the equation* whose solutions are ϕ_1 and ϕ_2 shall be invariant under the group.

It is desirable to have a condition expressed in terms of the differential equation itself. The linear equation

$$(92) \quad (UA)f \equiv (UP - A\xi)\frac{\partial f}{\partial x} + (UQ - A\eta)\frac{\partial f}{\partial y} + (UR - A\zeta)\frac{\partial f}{\partial z} = 0$$

has ϕ_1 and ϕ_2 for solutions when $Af = 0$ is invariant under Uf. For

$$(UA)\phi_i \equiv UA\phi_i - AU\phi_i = U(0) - AF_i(\phi_1, \phi_2) = 0$$
$$(i = 1, 2).$$

Since (88) and (92) have the same solutions, they must be the same equation, to within a possible factor, by the previous footnote.

---

* A unique linear differential equation of the form (88) (to within a possible factor involving the variables only) is determined by two independent solutions. For if ϕ_1 and ϕ_2 are the solutions of

$$Af \equiv P\frac{\partial f}{\partial x} + Q\frac{\partial f}{\partial y} + R\frac{\partial f}{\partial z} = 0,$$

then

$$A\phi_1 \equiv P\frac{\partial \phi_1}{\partial x} + Q\frac{\partial \phi_1}{\partial y} + R\frac{\partial \phi_1}{\partial z} = 0,$$

$$A\phi_2 \equiv P\frac{\partial \phi_2}{\partial x} + Q\frac{\partial \phi_2}{\partial y} + R\frac{\partial \phi_2}{\partial z} = 0,$$

whence
$$P : Q : R = \frac{\partial \phi_1}{\partial y}\frac{\partial \phi_2}{\partial z} - \frac{\partial \phi_1}{\partial z}\frac{\partial \phi_2}{\partial y} : \frac{\partial \phi_1}{\partial z}\frac{\partial \phi_2}{\partial x} - \frac{\partial \phi_1}{\partial x}\frac{\partial \phi_2}{\partial z} : \frac{\partial \phi_1}{\partial x}\frac{\partial \phi_2}{\partial y} - \frac{\partial \phi_1}{\partial y}\frac{\partial \phi_2}{\partial x}.$$

So that the differential equation having ϕ_1 and ϕ_2 for solutions may be written in the convenient form

$$\begin{vmatrix} \dfrac{\partial f}{\partial x} & \dfrac{\partial f}{\partial y} & \dfrac{\partial f}{\partial z} \\[2mm] \dfrac{\partial \phi_1}{\partial x} & \dfrac{\partial \phi_1}{\partial y} & \dfrac{\partial \phi_1}{\partial z} \\[2mm] \dfrac{\partial \phi_2}{\partial x} & \dfrac{\partial \phi_2}{\partial y} & \dfrac{\partial \phi_2}{\partial z} \end{vmatrix} = 0.$$

Hence *when* $Af = 0$ *is invariant under* Uf

[31] $(UA)f \equiv \lambda(x, y, z)Af.$

Conversely, when [31] holds, (88) and (92)* have the same solutions; then $(UA)\phi_i \equiv UA\phi_i - AU\phi_i = 0, \quad (i = 1, 2).$

Since $A\phi_i = 0$, it follows that $A(U\phi_i) = 0$; hence $U\phi_i$ is a solution of (88), and must be a function of ϕ_1 and ϕ_2.

Therefore [31] *is both the necessary and sufficient condition that* Uf *leave* $Af = 0$ *unaltered.*†

Thus, the group $Uf \equiv x\frac{\partial f}{\partial x} + y\frac{\partial f}{\partial y} + z\frac{\partial f}{\partial z}$ leaves $Af \equiv \frac{\partial f}{\partial x} + \frac{\partial f}{\partial y} + \frac{\partial f}{\partial z} = 0$ unaltered, since $(UA)f \equiv -\left(\frac{\partial f}{\partial x} + \frac{\partial f}{\partial y} + \frac{\partial f}{\partial z}\right) = -Af.$

Similarly the same group leaves $Af \equiv y\frac{\partial f}{\partial x} - x\frac{\partial f}{\partial y} + z\frac{\partial f}{\partial z} = 0$ unaltered, since $(UA)f \equiv 0$.

It also follows from this that the group $Uf \equiv y\frac{\partial f}{\partial x} - x\frac{\partial f}{\partial y} + z\frac{\partial f}{\partial z}$ leaves the equation $Af \equiv x\frac{\partial f}{\partial x} + y\frac{\partial f}{\partial y} + z\frac{\partial f}{\partial z} = 0$ unaltered.

Remark. — From the form of the condition [31] it is obvious that if an equation $Af = 0$ is invariant under each of a number of groups $U_1f, U_2f, \cdots, U_rf$, it is invariant under $Uf \equiv a_1U_1f + a_2U_2f + \cdots + a_rU_rf$, where $a_1, a_2, \cdots, a_r$ are any constants.

---

* If $\lambda(x, y, z)$ is identically zero, in other words if $(UA)f \equiv 0$ for all functions f, [31] is still a sufficient condition that Uf leave $Af = 0$ unaltered. In this case one cannot speak of the equation (92); but writing the identity $(UA)f \equiv 0$ in the form $UAf \equiv AUf$, it follows that $AU\phi_i = 0$ since $UA\phi_i = U(0) = 0$. Hence $U\phi_i$ is a function ϕ_1 and ϕ_2 as above.

† Using the method of the previous footnote, it can be shown that a homogeneous linear equation in n variables is determined, to within a factor by its $n - 1$ independent solutions. The argument of this section therefore applies without change to such an equation. Hence [31] *is the condition that* $Af = 0$, *involving n variables, shall be invariant under the group* $Uf \equiv \xi_1\frac{\partial f}{\partial x_1} + \xi_2\frac{\partial f}{\partial x_2} + \cdots + \xi_n\frac{\partial f}{\partial x_n}$. In § 15 essentially the same method for the case of two variables was carried out.

Ex.   Determine which of the equations below are left unaltered by each of the following groups :

1. $Uf \equiv x\dfrac{\partial f}{\partial x} + y\dfrac{\partial f}{\partial y} + \dfrac{\partial f}{\partial z}.$

2. $Uf \equiv y\dfrac{\partial f}{\partial x} - x\dfrac{\partial f}{\partial y}.$

3. $Uf \equiv x^2\dfrac{\partial f}{\partial x} + (xy + xz - yz)\dfrac{\partial f}{\partial y} + (2\,xy - y^2)\dfrac{\partial f}{\partial z}.$

4. $Uf \equiv x\dfrac{\partial f}{\partial x} + y\dfrac{\partial f}{\partial y} + z\dfrac{\partial f}{\partial z}.$

a. $Af \equiv x\dfrac{\partial f}{\partial x} + y\dfrac{\partial f}{\partial y} = 0.$

b. $Af \equiv x^2\dfrac{\partial f}{\partial x} + y^2\dfrac{\partial f}{\partial y} - xy\dfrac{\partial f}{\partial z} = 0.$

c. $Af \equiv \dfrac{\partial f}{\partial x} + \dfrac{\partial f}{\partial y} + \dfrac{\partial f}{\partial z} = 0.$

d. $Af \equiv xy\dfrac{\partial f}{\partial x} - x^2\dfrac{\partial f}{\partial y} + (x + y)\dfrac{\partial f}{\partial z} = 0.$

35. Method of Solution of Linear Partial Differential Equation Invariant under a Group. — If the equation $Af = 0$ is invariant under Uf,*

[31] $(UA)f \equiv \lambda Af,$

i.e. $Uf = 0$ and $Af = 0$ form a complete system.   Hence the methods of §§ 32 and 33 are available for finding one of the solutions of $Af = 0$.

---

* While $Uf = \rho(x, y, z)\,Af$ leaves $Af = 0$ unaltered for all forms of $\rho(x, y, z)$, such a group is said to be *trivial* because it is of no service in solving $Af = 0$.   We shall presuppose that the group Uf under consideration here is not trivial.

Having thus found $\phi(x, y, z)$, a common solution of $Uf = 0$ and $Af = 0$, a second solution of $Af = 0$ may be found in the following way :

Since $\phi(x, y, z)$ is not a constant, it must involve at least one of the variables, say z. Replacing z by the new variable

$$z = \phi(x, y, z),$$

the equation and the group take the forms ([15], § 11),

$$Af \equiv P(x, y, z)\frac{\partial f}{\partial x} + Q(x, y, z)\frac{\partial f}{\partial y} = 0,$$

$$Uf \equiv \xi(x, y, z)\frac{\partial f}{\partial x} + \eta(x, y, z)\frac{\partial f}{\partial y},$$

since $A\phi = 0$ and $U\phi = 0$.

Here P, Q, ξ, η are what P, Q, ξ, η respectively become when in them z is replaced by its value in terms of x, y, z obtained from $z = \phi(x, y, z)$. Here z plays the rôle of a constant since the coefficients of $\frac{\partial f}{\partial z}$ in Af and Uf are both zero. To solve $Af = 0$ we proceed to the corresponding ordinary differential equation

$$Q\,dx - P\,dy = 0.$$

This is invariant under Uf. Hence the methods of §§ 12 and 20 may be employed.

Remark. — When the usual Lagrange method (see *El. Dif. Eq.* § 79) is practicable, it will, as a rule, prove simpler than the method of this section. As an exercise it may be desirable to solve the examples below by both methods. But the Lie method is of interest theoretically and may prove valuable when the other method cannot be carried out.

Ex. 1. $Af \equiv 2\,xy^2 \dfrac{\partial f}{\partial x} - 2\,x^2 y \dfrac{\partial f}{\partial y} + (y^2 - x^2)z \dfrac{\partial f}{\partial z} = 0.$

The coefficients are homogeneous and of the same degree. Hence this equation is left unaltered by the group $Uf \equiv x\dfrac{\partial f}{\partial x} + y\dfrac{\partial f}{\partial y} + z\dfrac{\partial f}{\partial z}$; as a matter of fact, $(UA)f \equiv 2\,Af.$

By the method of § 32 or that of § 33, $\frac{xy}{z^2}$ is readily found to be the common solution of $Af = 0$ and $Uf = 0$.

The transformation $z = \frac{xy}{z^2}$ reduces $Af = 0$ and Uf to

$$Af \equiv 2\,xy^2\frac{\partial f}{\partial x} - 2\,x^2y\frac{\partial f}{\partial y} = 0 \text{ and } Uf \equiv x\frac{\partial f}{\partial x} + y\frac{\partial f}{\partial y}$$

respectively. The corresponding ordinary differential equation is

$$2\,x^2y\,dx + 2\,xy^2\,dy = 0.$$

Lie's integrating factor $\dfrac{1}{2\,xy(x^2+y^2)}$ $\left(\text{or the obvious integrating factor } \dfrac{1}{xy}\right)$ leads at once to the solution $x^2 + y^2 = const.$ Hence two independent solutions of $Af = 0$ are $\frac{xy}{z^2}$ and $x^2 + y^2$.

Ex. 2. $Af \equiv (x^2 + y^2 + yz)\dfrac{\partial f}{\partial x} + (x^2 + y^2 - xz)\dfrac{\partial f}{\partial y} + (xz + yz)\dfrac{\partial f}{\partial z} = 0.$

Ex. 3. $Af \equiv (x + y)\dfrac{\partial f}{\partial x} + (x + y)\dfrac{\partial f}{\partial y} - (x + y + 2\,z)\dfrac{\partial f}{\partial z} = 0.$

$\left[\text{Invariant under } Uf \equiv (x+y)\dfrac{\partial f}{\partial x} + (x+y)\dfrac{\partial f}{\partial y} + 2\,z\,\dfrac{\partial f}{\partial z}, \text{ as well as under } Uf \equiv x\dfrac{\partial f}{\partial x} + y\dfrac{\partial f}{\partial y} + z\,\dfrac{\partial f}{\partial z}\right].$

Ex. 4. $Af \equiv (xz - y)\dfrac{\partial f}{\partial x} + (yz - x)\dfrac{\partial f}{\partial y} + (1 - z^2)\dfrac{\partial f}{\partial z} = 0.$

$\left[\text{Invariant under } Uf \equiv x\dfrac{\partial f}{\partial x} + y\dfrac{\partial f}{\partial y}\right].$

36. Jacobi's Identity. — For further development of the theory it will be necessary to have available a certain identity first noted by Jacobi and known by his name :

If A_1f, A_2f, A_3f are three homogeneous linear partial differential expressions in any number of variables,

(93) $((A_1A_2)A_3)f + ((A_2A_3)A_1)f + ((A_3A_1)A_2)f \equiv 0.$

This may be verified directly in the case of three special forms, and also in the general case for two variables. This is suggested as an exercise to the student.

Probably the simplest way to prove the theorem is the following, due to Engel:

Since $\qquad (A_1A_2)f \equiv A_1A_2f - A_2A_1f,$

$$((A_1A_2)A_3)f \equiv A_1A_2A_3f - A_3A_1A_2f - A_2A_1A_3f + A_3A_2A_1f,$$

$$((A_2A_3)A_1)f \equiv A_2A_3A_1f - A_1A_2A_3f - A_3A_2A_1f + A_1A_3A_2f,$$

$$((A_3A_1)A_2)f \equiv A_3A_1A_2f - A_2A_3A_1f - A_1A_3A_2f + A_2A_1A_3f.$$

The sum of these is obviously identically zero. Hence the identity (93) is established.

37. Linear Partial Differential Equation Invariant under Two Groups. — If the equation $Af = 0$ is invariant under two distinct* groups U_1f and U_2f,

$$[31'] \qquad (U_1A)f \equiv \lambda_1Af, \quad (U_2A)f \equiv \lambda_2Af.$$

Jacobi's identity (93) for U_1f, U_2f, Af is

$$((U_1U_2)A)f + ((U_2A)U_1)f + ((AU_1)U_2)f \equiv 0.$$

Using $[31']$ and obvious properties of alternants (§ 14), this becomes

$$((U_1U_2)A)f \equiv \mu Af,$$

where $\mu \equiv U_1\lambda_2 - U_2\lambda_1$. Hence the

THEOREM. — *If $Af = 0$ is invariant under U_1f and U_2f, it is also invariant under $(U_1U_2)f$.*†

---

* Two groups U_1f and U_2f are said to be *distinct* with respect to the equation $Af = 0$, provided no relation of the form

(94) $\qquad a_1U_1f + a_2U_2f + \rho(x, y, z)Af \equiv 0$

exists, where a_1 and a_2 are constants and ρ is any function of the variables. For it is obvious that if U_1f leaves $Af = 0$ unaltered, $U_2f \equiv cU_1f + \rho Af$ will also do so for all choices of the constant c and of the function $\rho(x, y, z)$.

† This theorem holds, and is proved in exactly the same way, for n variables.

If $(U_1U_2)f$ is not of the form

$$(95) \qquad a_1U_1f + a_2U_2f + \rho(x, y, z)Af,$$

where a_1 and a_2 are any constants and ρ is any function of the variables, it is said to be *distinct* from U_1f and U_2f with respect to the equation $Af = 0$. In this case the theorem gives a new group under which the equation is invariant. The theorem may then be applied to this new group and one of the original ones. And so on.

Remark. — It is important to note that there always exists a linear relation between four homogeneous linear partial differential expressions of the first order in three variables.* For eliminating $\frac{\partial f}{\partial x}$, $\frac{\partial f}{\partial y}$, $\frac{\partial f}{\partial z}$ from the four identities

$$U_1f \equiv \xi_1 \frac{\partial f}{\partial x} + \eta_1 \frac{\partial f}{\partial y} + \zeta_1 \frac{\partial f}{\partial z},$$

$$U_2f \equiv \xi_2 \frac{\partial f}{\partial x} + \eta_2 \frac{\partial f}{\partial y} + \zeta_2 \frac{\partial f}{\partial z},$$

$$U_3f \equiv \xi_3 \frac{\partial f}{\partial x} + \eta_3 \frac{\partial f}{\partial y} + \zeta_3 \frac{\partial f}{\partial z},$$

$$U_4f \equiv \xi_4 \frac{\partial f}{\partial x} + \eta_4 \frac{\partial f}{\partial y} + \zeta_4 \frac{\partial f}{\partial z}$$

the linear relation

$$\begin{vmatrix} U_1f & \xi_1 & \eta_1 & \zeta_1 \\ U_2f & \xi_2 & \eta_2 & \zeta_2 \\ U_3f & \xi_3 & \eta_3 & \zeta_3 \\ U_4f & \xi_4 & \eta_4 & \zeta_4 \end{vmatrix} \equiv 0$$

is obtained. In general the coefficients are functions of the variables.

---

* Similarly, there is always a linear relation between $n + 1$ such expressions in n variables.

As a consequence we always have

$$(96) \qquad (U_1U_2)f \equiv \alpha_1(x, y, z)\, U_1f + \alpha_2(x, y, z)\, U_2f + \rho(x, y, z)\, Af.$$

If it turns out that α_1 and α_2 are constants, this is of the form (95), in which case $(U_1U_2)f$ is not distinct from U_1f and U_2f.

Thus the equation $Af \equiv \dfrac{\partial f}{\partial x} + \dfrac{\partial f}{\partial y} + \dfrac{\partial f}{\partial z} = 0$ is left unaltered by

$$U_1f \equiv (y - z)\frac{\partial f}{\partial y} \text{ and } U_2f \equiv x^2\frac{\partial f}{\partial x} + x^2\frac{\partial f}{\partial y} + (2\,xy - y^2)\frac{\partial f}{\partial z},$$

since $\qquad (U_1A)f \equiv 0, \quad (U_2A)f \equiv -2\,x\,Af.$

Moreover $\quad (U_1U_2)f \equiv -(x - y)^2\dfrac{\partial f}{\partial y} + 2(y - z)(x - y)\dfrac{\partial f}{\partial z}$

also leaves $Af = 0$ unaltered, since $((U_1U_2)A)f \equiv 0$. It is readily seen that

$$(U_1U_2)f \equiv -\frac{(x - y)^2}{y - z}\,U_1f - \frac{2(y - z)}{x - y}\,U_2f + \frac{2\,x^2(y - z)}{x - y}\,Af.$$

Again

$$(U_1(U_1U_2))f \equiv \left[4(y - z)(x - y) + (x - y)^2\right]\frac{\partial f}{\partial y} + 2(y - z)(x - 2\,y + z)\frac{\partial f}{\partial z}$$

$$\equiv \left[4(x - y) + \frac{(x - y)^2}{y - z}\right]U_1f + 2\left[\frac{z - y}{x - y} + \left(\frac{z - y}{x - y}\right)^2\right]U_2f$$

$$- 2\,x^2\left[\frac{z - y}{x - y} + \left(\frac{z - y}{x - y}\right)^2\right]Af$$

also leaves $Af = 0$ unaltered, as is readily verified. And so on.

38. Methods of Solution of Linear Partial Differential Equation Invariant under Two Distinct Groups. — Two important cases are to be distinguished:

A. If a relation of the form

$$(97) \qquad U_2f \equiv \alpha(x, y, z)\, U_1f + \rho(x, y, z)\, Af$$

exists,* where α is not a constant, $U_2 f$ is still considered distinct from $U_1 f$. In this case $\alpha(x, y, z)$ is a solution of $Af = 0$. For, since $Af = 0$ is invariant under $U_2 f$, $(U_2 A) f$ must be a multiple of Af. But

$$(\alpha U_1 + \rho A, A)f \equiv \alpha(U_1 A)f - A\alpha\ U_1 f - A\rho\ Af$$
$$\equiv (\alpha\lambda_1 - A\rho)Af - A\alpha\ U_1 f.$$

Since $U_1 f$ is supposed to be not trivial, *i.e.* not a multiple of Af (§ 35), the only way in which $(U_2 A)f$ can be a multiple of Af is by having $A\alpha = 0$. Hence α is one of the two independent solutions of $Af = 0$ to be found. †

To find a second solution of $Af = 0$, several possibilities may arise which will be mentioned in the order of desirability :

1° Since $Af = 0$ is invariant under $U_1 f$, $U_1 \alpha$ is also a solution of $Af = 0$ [(91), § 34]. If $U_1 \alpha$ turns out to be distinct from α, it may be taken as the second solution necessary to give the general solution of $Af = 0$.

2° If $U_1 \alpha$ ‡ is a function of α or a constant other than zero, two methods are possible :

* A linear relation between Af, $U_1 f$, $U_2 f$ will show itself by the vanishing of the determinant of their coefficients, thus

$$\Delta \equiv \begin{vmatrix} P & Q & R \\ \xi_1 & \eta_1 & \zeta_1 \\ \xi_2 & \eta_2 & \zeta_2 \end{vmatrix} \equiv 0.$$

Here $$\alpha = \frac{Q\zeta_2 - R\eta_2}{Q\zeta_1 - R\eta_1} = \frac{R\xi_2 - P\zeta_2}{R\xi_1 - P\zeta_1} = \frac{P\eta_2 - Q\xi_2}{P\eta_1 - Q\xi_1}.$$

† Conversely, if α is a solution of $Af=0$ and $U_1 f$ is a group that leaves the equation unaltered,

[35] $$U_2 f \equiv \alpha U_1 f + \rho Af$$

will also leave it unaltered no matter what be the form of $\rho(x, y, z)$. For

$$(U_2 A)f \equiv (\alpha U_1 + \rho A, A)f = (\alpha\lambda_1 - A\rho)Af,$$

since $A\alpha=0$. [Compare (35) § 17.]

‡ Since $U_2 \alpha \equiv \alpha U_1 \alpha + \rho A\alpha = \alpha U_1 \alpha$, it is sufficient to consider $U_1 \alpha$ only.

(a) The solution common to $Af = 0$ and $U_1f = 0$ (or $U_2f = 0$) may be found by either the method of § 32 or that of § 33. Since $U_1\alpha \neq 0$, this common solution will be independent of α.

(b) Since α must contain at least one of the variables, say z, the introduction of the new variable $z = \alpha\,(x, y, z)$ in place of z reduces $Af = 0$ to one in two variables,

$$P(x, y, z)\frac{\partial f}{\partial x} + Q(x, y, z)\frac{\partial f}{\partial y} = 0,$$

z appearing as a constant since the coefficient of $\dfrac{\partial f}{\partial z}$ is zero. (Compare § 35.) But since $U_1\alpha \neq 0$, the above equation must be integrated, without any further assistance from the groups U_1f and U_2f.

3°. If $U_1\alpha = 0$, the method of § 35 is available; thus the introduction of the new variable z gives the same differential equation as above, but now the transformed group

$$\xi_1(x, y, z)\frac{\partial f}{\partial x} + \eta_1(x, y, z)\frac{\partial f}{\partial y}$$

under which it is invariant also leaves z unaltered. Hence the methods of §§ 12 and 20 are available for solving the corresponding ordinary differential equation

$$Q\,dx - P\,dy = 0.$$

B. If no relation of the type (97) exists between Af, U_1f, U_2f, the relation

$$(96)\quad (U_1U_2)f \equiv \alpha_1(x, y, z)\,U_1f + \alpha_2(x, y, z)\,U_2f + \rho\,(x, y, z)Af,$$

which always exists (Remark § 37), will prove of service if α_1 and α_2 are not both constants; for α_1 and α_2 are solutions of $Af = 0$, as may be seen from the following consideration : *

---

* By exactly the same kind of reasoning as that employed here, the following general theorem can be established. (It is suggested that the student carry out the proof.)
  If the equation in n variables

By the Theorem of § 37, $(U_1 U_2)f$ leaves $Af = 0$ unaltered. Hence

$$((U_1 U_2)A)f \equiv \mu A f.$$

But

$$(\alpha_1 U_1 + \alpha_2 U_2 + \rho A, A)f \equiv \alpha_1(U_1 A)f + \alpha_2(U_2 A)f - A\alpha_1 U_1 f$$
$$- A\alpha_2 U_2 f - A\rho A f$$
$$\equiv (\alpha_1 \lambda_1 + \alpha_2 \lambda_2 - A\rho)Af - A\alpha_1 U_1 f - A\alpha_2 U_2 f.$$

Since no linear relation is supposed to exist between Af, $U_1 f$, $U_2 f$, the only way in which $((U_1 U_2)A)f$ can be a multiple of Af is by having $A\alpha_1 = 0$ and $A\alpha_2 = 0$. Hence α_1 and α_2 are solutions of $Af = 0$.*

1° If α_1 and α_2 are two independent functions of the variables, the general solution of $Af = 0$ is known without any further work.

2° If one of them, say α, is a function of the variables, while the other, α_2, is either a function of α_1 or a constant, use may be made of the fact that $U_1 \alpha_1$ and $U_2 \alpha_1$ are also solutions of $Af = 0$ [(91), § 34]. If either of these turns out to be a function distinct from α_1, it may be used as the second solution.

$$Af \equiv P_1 \frac{\partial f}{\partial x_1} + P_2 \frac{\partial f}{\partial x_2} + \cdots + P_n \frac{\partial f}{\partial x_n} = 0$$

is invariant under $r + 1$ *distinct groups* $U_1 f$, $U_2 f$, $\cdots$, $U_{r+1} f$, *and if no linear relation of the type*

$$\sigma_1 U_1 f + \sigma_2 U_2 f + \cdots + \sigma_r U_r f + \rho Af \equiv 0$$

exists between Af *and* r *of the* Uf's, *but*

$$U_{r+1} f \equiv \alpha_1 U_1 f + \alpha_2 U_2 f + \cdots + \alpha_r U_r f + \rho Af,$$

then α_1, α_2, $\cdots$, α_r *are solutions of* $Af = 0$.

---

* The student should have no difficulty in showing that, conversely, if α_1 and α_2 are solutions of $Af = 0$, and $U_1 f$ and $U_2 f$ are two groups that leave the equation unaltered, the group

[35'] $U_3 f \equiv \alpha_1 U_1 f + \alpha_2 U_2 f + \rho Af$

will also leave it unaltered no matter what be the form of $\rho(x, y, z)$. (Compare [35] above.)

3°. If both $U_1\alpha_1$ and $U_2\alpha_1{}^*$ are either functions of α_1 or constants, either of the methods (a) and (b) of **A**, $2°$ may be employed.

Or,

(a) if one of $U_1\alpha_1$ and $U_2\alpha_1$ is zero, the method of **A**, $3°$ is available,

(b) if neither is zero, the group $Vf \equiv U_2\alpha_1 U_1 f - U_1\alpha_1 U_2 f$ leaves $Af = 0$ unaltered, and $V\alpha_1 = 0$; hence case (a) exists.

4°. If both α_1 and α_2 are constants, say a_1 and a_2, the solution common to $Af = 0$ and $U_1 f = 0$, and that common to $Af = 0$ and $U_2 f = 0$ may be found by either of the methods of §§ 32 and 33. Moreover, these solutions will be independent since there is no linear relation connecting Af, $U_1 f$, $U_2 f$. (Theorem II, § 31.) We shall show, by a method due to Lie, that an integrating factor for at least one, and sometimes for both, of the total differential equations arising in the method of § 33 can be found in this case. (But it is possible, at times, to find by inspection, an integrating factor that is simpler than the one given by the following method) :

In $(U_1 U_2)f \equiv a_1 U_1 f + a_2 U_2 f + \rho A f$ either a_1 and a_2 are both zero or they are not.

(a) If $a_1 = a_2 = 0$, $(U_1 U_2)f \equiv \rho A f.$

Since $Af = 0$ is invariant under $U_2 f$,

$$(U_2 A)f \equiv \lambda_2 A f.$$

If $\phi(x, y, z)$ is the common solution of $Af = 0$ and $U_1 f = 0$,

$U_1 U_2 \phi \equiv 0$, since $(U_1 U_2)\phi \equiv U_1 U_2 \phi - U_2 U_1 \phi \equiv \rho A \phi \equiv 0$;

$A U_2 \phi \equiv 0$, since $(U_2 A)\phi \equiv U_2 A \phi - A U_2 \phi \equiv \lambda_2 A \phi \equiv 0.$

These identities can hold only provided $U_2\phi$ is a solution of both $U_1 f = 0$ and $Af = 0$; i.e. $U_2\phi$ must be a function of ϕ, say $F(\phi)$.

---

* In this case $(U_1 U_2)\alpha_1$ will also be a function of α_1 or a constant, including zero, because of (96).

Moreover $F(\phi) \not\equiv 0$, for, as noted above, $Af = 0$, $U_1 f = 0$, $U_2 f = 0$ cannot have a common solution, since they are independent. As was done in an analogous case in § 12, ϕ, the common solution of $Af = 0$ and $U_1 f = 0$, may be chosen in such a form that $U_2\phi \equiv 1$. It must then satisfy the three equations

$$A\phi \equiv P\frac{\partial\phi}{\partial x} + Q\frac{\partial\phi}{\partial y} + R\frac{\partial\phi}{\partial z} = 0,$$

$$U_1\phi \equiv \xi_1\frac{\partial\phi}{\partial x} + \eta_1\frac{\partial\phi}{\partial y} + \zeta_1\frac{\partial\phi}{\partial z} = 0,$$

$$U_2\phi \equiv \xi_2\frac{\partial\phi}{\partial x} + \eta_2\frac{\partial\phi}{\partial y} + \zeta_2\frac{\partial\phi}{\partial z} = 1.$$

These equations determine $\dfrac{\partial\phi}{\partial x}, \dfrac{\partial\phi}{\partial y}, \dfrac{\partial\phi}{\partial z}$; whence ϕ is obtained from

$$d\phi = \frac{\partial\phi}{\partial x}dx + \frac{\partial\phi}{\partial y}dy + \frac{\partial\phi}{\partial z}dz$$

by the quadrature

$$\phi = \int \frac{\begin{vmatrix} dx & dy & dz \\ P & Q & R \\ \xi_1 & \eta_1 & \zeta_1 \end{vmatrix}}{\Delta}, \text{ where } \Delta \equiv \begin{vmatrix} P & Q & R \\ \xi_1 & \eta_1 & \zeta_1 \\ \xi_2 & \eta_2 & \zeta_2 \end{vmatrix}.$$

In exactly the same way, ψ, that form of the common solution of $Af = 0$ and $U_2 f = 0$ for which $U_1\psi \equiv -1$, may be obtained by the quadrature

$$\psi = \int \frac{\begin{vmatrix} dx & dy & dz \\ P & Q & R \\ \xi_2 & \eta_2 & \zeta_2 \end{vmatrix}}{\Delta}.$$

The determinant Δ is thus seen to be an integrating factor for each of the total differential equations arising in the method of § 33 for finding the two independent solutions of $Af = 0$.

(*b*) If only one of a_1 and a_2 is zero, let $a_2 = 0$. Then

$$(U_1U_2)f \equiv a_1U_1f + \rho Af.$$

In precisely the same way as before, it is seen that, if ϕ is the common solution of $Af = 0$ and $U_1f = 0$, $U_2\phi \equiv F(\phi) \not\equiv 0$. Hence that form of ϕ for which $U_2\phi \equiv 1$ is given by the quadrature

$$\phi = \int \frac{\begin{vmatrix} dx & dy & dz \\ P & Q & R \\ \xi_1 & \eta_1 & \zeta_1 \end{vmatrix}}{\Delta}.$$

To find a second solution of $Af = 0$, independent of ϕ, either the method of **A**, 3° may be employed, or the common solution of $Af = 0$ and $U_2f = 0$ may be found by one of the methods of §§ 32 and 33.

(*c*) If both a_1 and a_2 are different from zero, consider the two groups
$$Vf \equiv a_1U_1f + a_2U_2f \text{ and } U_2f.$$

These are obviously distinct and leave $Af = 0$ unaltered. Moreover
$$(VU_2)f \equiv a_1Vf + a_1\rho Af.$$

We are thus under case (*b*) and the method for that case may be employed.

Note.— For practical purposes it may be worth noting, that the choice of the groups U_1f and $Vf \equiv a_1U_1f + a_2U_2f$ also leads to case (*b*).

Remark 1.— A hasty survey of the processes involved in the methods to be employed in the various cases considered in this section, brings out the fact that when two distinct groups are known under which the equation $Af = 0$ is invariant, the solution of the latter can be obtained by means of quadratures only, except in the case of **A**, 2°, where one ordinary differential equation of the first order must be solved. In certain cases, such as **A**, 1° and **B**, 1° and 2°, no integration whatever is required. In the above scheme, certain alternative methods involving the solution of differential equations have also been suggested, for in certain cases these processes may prove simpler of execution than those involved in carrying out quadratures.

Remark 2. — It is easy to prove the existence of a pair of groups $U_1 f$ and $U_2 f$ under which $Af = 0$ is invariant, and for which no linear relation of the form (97) holds. For $Af = 0$ has two independent solutions ϕ_1 and ϕ_2. These are independent with respect to at least two of the variables, say x and y. Introducing the new variables

$$x = \phi_1(x, y, z), \quad y = \phi_2(x, y, z), \quad z = z,$$

$Af = 0$ takes the form

$$Af \equiv Ax\,\frac{\partial f}{\partial x} + Ay\,\frac{\partial f}{\partial y} + Az\,\frac{\partial f}{\partial z} = 0,$$

or

$$\frac{\partial f}{\partial z} = 0.$$

By inspection $U_1 f \equiv \dfrac{\partial f}{\partial x}$ and $U_2 f \equiv \dfrac{\partial f}{\partial y}$ are seen to leave the differential equation unaltered. Moreover there is obviously no linear relation between $\dfrac{\partial f}{\partial x}, \dfrac{\partial f}{\partial y}, \dfrac{\partial f}{\partial z}$. Passing back to the original variables, $Af = 0$ will be invariant under the groups $U_1 f$ and $U_2 f$ into which $U_1 f$ and $U_2 f$ are transformed, and no linear relation can exist now.

Ex. 1. $Af \equiv (x+y)\dfrac{\partial f}{\partial x} + (x+y)\dfrac{\partial f}{\partial y} - (x+y+2z)\dfrac{\partial f}{\partial z} = 0.$

This equation is invariant under

$$U_1 f \equiv (x+y)\frac{\partial f}{\partial x} + (x+y)\frac{\partial f}{\partial y} + 2z\frac{\partial f}{\partial z} \text{ and}$$

$$U_2 f \equiv z(x+y)^2\frac{\partial f}{\partial x} + z(x+y)^2\frac{\partial f}{\partial y} + [(xy+2z^2)(x+y) + 4xyz]\frac{\partial f}{\partial z},$$

as may be verified easily.

Here $\Delta \equiv 0$, and $U_2 f \equiv (yz + zx + xy)U_1 f - xy Af$, (**A**).

$\therefore yz + zx + xy$ is a solution of $Af = 0$.

Moreover $U_1(yz + zx + xy) \equiv 4(yz + zx + xy) + (x - y)^2$ is also a solution (**A**, 1°).

Taking account of the first solution, the second one may be replaced by $x - y$. Hence the general solution of $Af = 0$ is

$$\Phi(yz + zx + xy, \, x - y) = 0.$$

Ex. 2. $Af \equiv (xz - y)\dfrac{\partial f}{\partial x} + (yz - x)\dfrac{\partial f}{\partial y} + (1 - z^2)\dfrac{\partial f}{\partial z} = 0.$

This equation is invariant under

$$U_1 f \equiv x \frac{\partial f}{\partial x} + y \frac{\partial f}{\partial y} \text{ and}$$

$$U_2 f \equiv (x^2 + y^2)\frac{\partial f}{\partial x} + 2xy \frac{\partial f}{\partial y} - y(1 - z^2)\frac{\partial f}{\partial z}.$$

$$\Delta \equiv 0, \text{ and } U_2 f \equiv (x + yz)U_1 f - yAf.$$

$\therefore x + yz$ is a solution of $Af = 0$.

Moreover $\qquad U_1(x + yz) = x + yz \not\equiv 0$ (**A**, 2°).

To find the solution common to $Af = 0$ and $U_1 f = 0$ the method of § 33 requires the solution of the total differential equation

$$y(1 - z^2)dx - x(1 - z^2)dy + (y^2 - x^2)dz = 0.$$

An obvious integrating factor is $\dfrac{1}{(y^2 - x^2)(1 - z^2)}$, leading to the solution

$$\log\left(\frac{x + y}{x - y}\frac{1 + z}{1 - z}\right) = const.$$

or $\qquad\qquad \dfrac{x + yz + y + xz}{x + yz - (y + xz)} = const.$

The left-hand member of this is, therefore, a second solution of $Af = 0$.

Taking account of the first solution, the second one may be replaced by $y + zx$. Hence the general solution of $Af = 0$ is

$$\Phi(x + yz, \, y + zx) = 0.$$

Ex. 3. $Af \equiv (x+y)\dfrac{\partial f}{\partial x} + (x+y)\dfrac{\partial f}{\partial y} - (x+y+2\,z)\dfrac{\partial f}{\partial z} = 0.$

$$U_1 f \equiv (x+y)\frac{\partial f}{\partial x} + (x+y)\frac{\partial f}{\partial y} + 2\,z\,\frac{\partial f}{\partial z}.$$

$$U_2 f \equiv (x-y)(x+y+4\,z)\frac{\partial f}{\partial z}.$$

Ex. 4. $Af \equiv (x+y)\dfrac{\partial f}{\partial x} + (x+y)\dfrac{\partial f}{\partial y} - (x+y+2\,z)\dfrac{\partial f}{\partial z} = 0.$

$$U_1 f \equiv (x+y)\frac{\partial f}{\partial x} + (x+y)\frac{\partial f}{\partial y} + 2\,z\,\frac{\partial f}{\partial z}.$$

$$U_2 f \equiv x\,\frac{\partial f}{\partial x} + y\,\frac{\partial f}{\partial y} + z\,\frac{\partial f}{\partial z}.$$

Ex. 5. $Af \equiv \dfrac{\partial f}{\partial x} + \dfrac{\partial f}{\partial y} + \dfrac{\partial f}{\partial z} = 0.$

$$U_1 f \equiv (y-z)\frac{\partial f}{\partial y}.$$

$$U_2 f \equiv x^2\,\frac{\partial f}{\partial x} + x^2\frac{\partial f}{\partial y} + (2\,xy - y^2)\frac{\partial f}{\partial z}.$$

Ex. 6. $Af \equiv (xz - y)\dfrac{\partial f}{\partial x} + (yz - x)\dfrac{\partial f}{\partial y} + (1 - z^2)\dfrac{\partial f}{\partial z} = 0.$

$$U_1 f \equiv y\frac{\partial f}{\partial x} + x\frac{\partial f}{\partial y}.$$

$$U_2 f \equiv (x^2 + y^2)\frac{\partial f}{\partial x} + 2xy\frac{\partial f}{\partial y} - y(1 - z^2)\frac{\partial f}{\partial z}.$$

CHAPTER VI

ORDINARY DIFFERENTIAL EQUATIONS OF THE SECOND ORDER

39. Differential Equation of the Second Order Invariant under a Group. — The differential equation of the second order

(98) $$y'' = F(x, y, y')$$

is equivalent to the system of equations of the first order *

(99) $$\frac{dx}{1} = \frac{dy}{y'} = \frac{dy'}{F(x, y, y')}.$$

If the solutions of the latter are

(100) $$u(x, y, y') = a, \quad v(x, y, y') = b,$$

the solution of (98) may be obtained by eliminating y' from the two equations (100).†

Instead of solving (99), one may find u and v as two independent solutions of the corresponding linear partial differential equation ‡

(101) $$Af \equiv \frac{\partial f}{\partial x} + y' \frac{\partial f}{\partial y} + F(x, y, y') \frac{\partial f}{\partial y'} = 0.$$

The problem of solving (98) is thus reduced to that of finding two independent solutions of (101).

If (98) is invariant under a group Uf, the equivalent system (99), involving the three variables x, y, y', is invariant under the extended

---

* *El. Dif. Eq.* § 68.

† The equations (100) are two independent first integrals of (98). (See § 52, Theorem IV.) ‡ *El. Dif. Eq.* § 79.

group $U'f$. The effect of $U'f$ on u and v is, therefore, to transform them into some functions of themselves ; *i.e.* $U'u = \phi(u, v)$, $U'v = \psi(u, v)$. Hence the linear partial differential equation (101) having u and v for solutions is also invariant under $U'f$ (§ 34). Consequently the method of § 35 may be employed to find u and v.

Remark. — Since the invariance of (98) under Uf implies the invariance of (101) under the extended group, and conversely, it follows from the remark of § 34 that if (98) is invariant under each of a number of groups $U_1 f$, $U_2 f$, $\cdots$, $U_r f$, it is invariant under the group $Uf \equiv a_1 U_1 f + a_2 U_2 f + \cdots + a_r U_r f$, where a_1, a_2, $\cdots$, a_r are any constants.

This remark applies without modification to a differential equation of any order, because the form of the condition [31], § 34 is independent of the number of variables appearing in the linear partial differential equation $Af = 0$.

Ex. 1. $xyy'' + xy'^2 - yy' = 0.$

This equation is invariant under $Uf \equiv x \dfrac{\partial f}{\partial x} + ny \dfrac{\partial f}{\partial y}$ for any value of n (VI, § 28). In particular it is left unaltered by $Uf \equiv x \dfrac{\partial f}{\partial x} + y \dfrac{\partial f}{\partial y}$.

Here
$$Af \equiv \frac{\partial f}{\partial x} + y' \frac{\partial f}{\partial y} + \frac{y'(y - xy')}{xy} \frac{\partial f}{\partial y'} = 0.$$

$$U'f \equiv x \frac{\partial f}{\partial x} + y \frac{\partial f}{\partial y}. \quad (U'A)f \equiv - Af.$$

For the method of § 32 * use may be made of the fact that $u \equiv \dfrac{y}{x}$, $v \equiv y'$ are solutions of $U'f = 0$.

---

* The method of § 33 requires the solution of

$$\begin{vmatrix} dx & dy & dy' \\ 1 & y' & \dfrac{y'(y - xy')}{xy} \\ x & y & 0 \end{vmatrix} = 0, \quad \text{or} \quad (y - xy')\left(-\frac{y' dx}{x} + \frac{y' dy}{y} + dy'\right) = 0.$$

The evident integrating factor $\dfrac{1}{y'(y - xy')}$ leads to the solution $\dfrac{yy'}{x} = const.$

$$Au = \frac{xy' - y}{x^2}, \quad Av = \frac{y'(y - xy')}{xy}. \quad \therefore \frac{Av}{Au} = -\frac{xy'}{y} = -\frac{v}{u}.$$

Equation (86), § 32 is $\quad \dfrac{\partial F}{\partial u} - \dfrac{v}{u}\dfrac{\partial F}{\partial v} = 0. \quad \therefore F \equiv uv = \dfrac{yy'}{x}.$

Introducing the new variable

$$y' = \frac{yy'}{x}, \quad \text{whence } y' = \frac{xy'}{y},$$

$$Af \equiv \frac{\partial f}{\partial x} + \frac{xy'}{y}\frac{\partial f}{\partial y} = 0, \quad Uf \equiv x\frac{\partial f}{\partial x} + y\frac{\partial f}{\partial y}.$$

$x^2y' - y^2$ or $xyy' - y^2$ is readily found to be the solution.

Eliminating y' from $\dfrac{yy'}{x} = a$ and $xyy' - y^2 = b$ gives

$$ax^2 - y^2 = b$$

as the solution of the original equation.

Compare this method with that of § 27 or of § 28, I', Remark.

Ex. 2. $yy'' + y'^2 = 1.$

Since x is absent, this equation is invariant under $Uf \equiv \dfrac{\partial f}{\partial x}$ (I', § 28). Here

$$Af \equiv \frac{\partial f}{\partial x} + y'\frac{\partial f}{\partial y} + \frac{1 - y'^2}{y}\frac{\partial f}{\partial y'} = 0, \quad U'f \equiv \frac{\partial f}{\partial x}, \quad (U'A)f \equiv 0.$$

By either of the methods of §§ 32 and 33, the solution common to $Af = 0$ and $U'f = 0$ is easily found to be $y\sqrt{1 - y'^2}$. Introducing the new variable

$$y' = y\sqrt{1 - y'^2}, \quad \text{whence } y' = \frac{\sqrt{y^2 - y'^2}}{y},$$

$$Af \equiv \frac{\partial f}{\partial x} + \frac{\sqrt{y^2 - y'^2}}{y}\frac{\partial f}{\partial y} = 0, \quad U'f \equiv \frac{\partial f}{\partial x}.$$

The corresponding ordinary differential equation

$$dx = \frac{y \, dy}{\sqrt{y^2 - y'^2}}$$

has for solution $x - \sqrt{y^2 - y'^2} = const.$ Passing back to the original variables this becomes $x - yy' = const.$ Eliminating y' from

$$y\sqrt{1 - y'^2} = a \text{ and } x - yy' = b,$$

gives as the solution of the original equation

$$y^2 - (x - b)^2 = a^2.$$

Ex. 3. $y'' = y'^2 + 1.$ Ex. 4. $x^2 yy'' + (xy' - y)^2 = 0.$
Solve examples of § 28 by the method of this section.

40. Differential Equation of the Second Order Invariant under Two Groups. — Since, if the two groups $U_1 f$ and $U_2 f$ leave

$$(98) \qquad\qquad y'' = F(x, y, y')$$

unaltered,[*] the corresponding partial differential equation

$$(\text{101}) \qquad Af \equiv \frac{\partial f}{\partial x} + y'\frac{\partial f}{\partial y} + F(x, y, y')\frac{\partial f}{\partial y'} = 0$$

is invariant under the extended groups $U_1' f$ and $U_2' f$, the methods of § 38 may be employed to solve (98).

Ex. 1. $xyy'' + xy'^2 - yy' = 0$ (Ex. 1, § 39).

This equation is invariant under $U_1 f \equiv x\frac{\partial f}{\partial x} + y\frac{\partial f}{\partial y}$ and $U_2 f \equiv y\frac{\partial f}{\partial y}.$

Here $$Af \equiv \frac{\partial f}{\partial x} + y'\frac{\partial f}{\partial y} + \frac{y'(y - xy')}{xy}\frac{\partial f}{\partial y'} = 0.$$

$$U_1' f \equiv x\frac{\partial f}{\partial x} + y\frac{\partial f}{\partial y}, \quad U_2' f \equiv y\frac{\partial f}{\partial y} + y'\frac{\partial f}{\partial y'}.$$

---

[*] Then (98) is also invariant under $Uf \equiv a_1 U_1 f + a_2 U_2 f$ (Remark, § 39). It is possible that Uf may assume simpler forms than $U_1 f$ or $U_2 f$ for certain choices of the constants a_1 and a_2.

$$\Delta \equiv \begin{vmatrix} 1 & y' & \dfrac{y'(y-xy')}{xy} \\ x & y & 0 \\ 0 & y & y' \end{vmatrix} = 2\,y'(y-xy') \not\equiv 0.$$

$$(U_1'U_2')f \equiv 0.$$

Hence the method of **B**, 4, (*a*), § 38 applies. The solution common to $Af = 0$ and $U_1'f = 0$ is

$$\phi = \int \dfrac{\begin{vmatrix} dx & dy & dy' \\ 1 & y' & \dfrac{y'(y-xy')}{xy} \\ x & y & 0 \end{vmatrix}}{\tfrac{1}{2}\Delta} = \int -\dfrac{dx}{x} + \dfrac{dy}{y} + \dfrac{dy'}{y'} = \log \dfrac{yy'}{x}.$$

The solution common to $Af = 0$ and $U_2'f = 0$ is

$$\psi = \int \dfrac{\begin{vmatrix} dx & dy & dy' \\ 1 & y' & \dfrac{y'(y-xy')}{xy} \\ 0 & y & y' \end{vmatrix}}{\tfrac{1}{2}\Delta}$$

$$= \int \left(\dfrac{y'}{y-xy'} - \dfrac{1}{x} \right) dx - \dfrac{y'dy}{y'(y-xy')} + \dfrac{y\,dy'}{y'(y-xy')}$$

$$= \log \dfrac{y'}{x(y-xy')}.^{*}$$

The general solution of the original differential equation of the second order is found by eliminating y' from $\dfrac{yy'}{x} = a$ and $\dfrac{x(y-xy')}{y'} = b$ to be $ax^2 - y^2 = c$, where $c = ab$.

---

* The method of § 32 is also available for finding these common solutions.

Ex. 2. $y'' = P(x)y' + Q(x)y + X(x)$.

If $y = y_1$ and $y = y_2$ are particular solutions of the abridged linear equation $y'' = Py' + Qy$, the general linear equation is invariant under $U_1 f \equiv y_1 \dfrac{\partial f}{\partial y}$ and $U_2 f \equiv y_2 \dfrac{\partial f}{\partial y}$ (§ 28, VII, Note). Here

$$Af \equiv \frac{\partial f}{\partial x} + y' \frac{\partial f}{\partial y} + (Py' + Qy + X)\frac{\partial f}{\partial y'} = 0,$$

$$U_1'f \equiv \qquad y_1 \frac{\partial f}{\partial y} + \qquad\qquad y_1' \frac{\partial f}{\partial y'},$$

$$U_2'f \equiv \qquad y_2 \frac{\partial f}{\partial y} + \qquad\qquad y_2' \frac{\partial f}{\partial y'},$$

where y_1' and y_2' stand for $\dfrac{dy_1}{dx}$ and $\dfrac{dy_2}{dx}$ respectively.

$\Delta \equiv y_1 y_2' - y_2 y_1' \not\equiv 0$, since the two particular solutions are supposed to be independent.

$(U_1' U_2')f \equiv 0$. Hence method of **B**, 4°, (a), § 38 applies.

Since $y = y_1$ and $y = y_2$ are solutions of the abridged linear equation,

$$y_1'' = Py_1' + Qy_1 \text{ and } y_2'' = Py_2' + Q_2,$$

whence $\quad P = \dfrac{y_1 y_2'' - y_2 y_1''}{\Delta} = \dfrac{\Delta'}{\Delta}, \quad Q = \dfrac{y_2' y_1'' - y_1' y_2''}{\Delta}.$

Introducing these values in the expression for the solution common to $Af = 0$ and $U_1'f = 0$,

$$\phi = \int \frac{\begin{vmatrix} dx & dy & dy' \\ 1 & y' & Py' + Qy + X \\ 0 & y_1 & y_1' \end{vmatrix}}{\Delta},$$

we have

$$\phi = \int \frac{[y_1' y' \Delta - y_1 y' \Delta' - y_1 y (y_2' y_1'' - y_1' y_2'')]\,dx - y_1' \Delta dy + y_1 \Delta dy'}{(y_1 y_2' - y_2 y_1')^2}$$

$$- \int \frac{y_1 X}{y_1 y_2' - y_2 y_1'}\,dx.$$

Noting that $-y_1 y(y_2'y_1'' - y_1'y_2'') = -y_1''y\Delta + y_1'y\Delta'$, the first quadrature is readily effected, thus giving

$$\phi = \frac{y_1 y' - y_1' y}{y_1 y_2' - y_2 y_1'} - \int \frac{y_1 X}{y_1 y_2' - y_2 y_1'} \, dx.$$

Similarly, the solution common to $Af = 0$ and $U_2'f = 0$ is

$$\psi = \frac{y_2 y' - y_2' y}{y_2 y_1' - y_1 y_2'} - \int \frac{y_2 X}{y_2 y_1' - y_1 y_2'} \, dx.$$

The general solution of the original equation is found by eliminating y' from $\phi = c_2$ and $\psi = c_1$ to be

$$y = c_1 y_1 + c_2 y_2 - y_1 \int \frac{y_2 X}{y_1 y_2' - y_2 y_1'} \, dx + y_2 \int \frac{y_1 X}{y_1 y_2' - y_2 y_1'} \, dx.$$

Note. — It is an interesting fact that this form of the solution is exactly that obtained by the method of variation of parameters (*El. Dif. Eq.* § 49) from the complementary function $y = c_1 y_1 + c_2 y_2$, as may be easily verified.

Ex. 3. $y'' = Py' + Qy.$

This equation being homogeneous in y, y', y'', it is invariant under $U_1 f \equiv y \frac{\partial f}{\partial y}$ (III, § 28).   Moreover, if $y = y_1(x)$ is a particular solution, the equation is also invariant under $U_2 f \equiv y_1 \frac{\partial f}{\partial y}$ (§ 28, VIII, Note).

Here
$$Af \equiv \frac{\partial f}{\partial x} + y' \frac{\partial f}{\partial y} + (Py' + Qy) \frac{\partial f}{\partial y'} = 0,$$

$$U_1'f \equiv y \frac{\partial f}{\partial y} + y' \frac{\partial f}{\partial y'},$$

$$U_2'f \equiv y_1 \frac{\partial f}{\partial y} + y_1' \frac{\partial f}{\partial y'}.$$

$$\Delta \equiv yy_1' - y'y_1 \not\equiv 0, \quad (U_1' U_2')f \equiv -U_2'f.$$

Hence the method of **B**, 4°, (*b*), § 38 applies.

The solution common to $Af = 0$ and $U_2'f = 0$ is given by that method in the form

$$\phi = \int \frac{(y'y_1' - Py_1y' - Q\,yy_1)dx - y_1'dy + y_1dy'}{yy_1' - y'y_1}.$$

Replacing Qy_1 by its value $y_1'' - P_1y_1'$, this quadrature is readily effected, giving

$$\phi = -\log(y'y_1 - yy_1') + \int P dx.$$

A more convenient form for the solution is

$$e^{-\phi} \equiv \Phi = e^{-\int P dx}(y'y_1 - yy_1').$$

To find a second solution of $Af = 0$, introduce the new variable

$$y' = e^{-\int P dx}(y'y_1 - yy_1'), \text{ whence } y' = \frac{yy_1' + y'e^{\int P dx}}{y_1},$$

and $Af = 0$ takes the form

$$Af \equiv \frac{\partial f}{\partial x} + \frac{yy_1' + y'e^{\int P dx}}{y_1} \frac{\partial f}{\partial y} = 0.^*$$

The corresponding ordinary differential equation

$$\frac{dy}{dx} - \frac{y_1'}{y_1} y - \frac{y'e^{\int P dx}}{y_1} = 0$$

is linear with the obvious integrating factor $\dfrac{1}{y_1}$. Its solution is

$$\frac{y}{y_1} - y' \int \frac{e^{\int P dx}}{y_1^2} dx = const.$$

---

* Here y' appears as a constant, (§ 35).

The general solution of the original differential equation is found by eliminating y' from

$$\Phi = a \text{ and } \frac{y}{y_1} - \Phi \int \frac{e^{\int P dx}}{y_1{}^2} \, dx = b$$

to be

$$y = a y_1 \int \frac{e^{\int P dx}}{y_1{}^2} \, dx + b y_1.$$

Note. — This is the same form of the solution as is given by the usual method (*El. Dif. Eq.* § 53, 1°).

Ex. **4.** $yy'' + y'^2 = 1$ (Ex. 2, § 39).

This equation is also invariant under $Uf \equiv x \dfrac{\partial f}{\partial x} + y \dfrac{\partial f}{\partial y}.$

Ex. **5.** $y'' = y'^2 + 1.$

Since x and y are both absent, two available groups are

$$U_1 f \equiv \frac{\partial f}{\partial x}, \ U_2 f \equiv \frac{\partial f}{\partial y}.$$

Ex. **6.** $x^2 y y'' - (xy' - y)^2 = 0$ (Invariant under VI for all values of n; hence under III, III′, IV, etc.).

Ex. **7.** $(x^2 + y^2) y'' + 2(y - xy')(1 + y'^2) = 0$ (Ex. 2, § 28).

Ex. **8.** $x^2 y'' + x^2 y'^2 - 2 xy' + 2 = 0.$

This equation is invariant under I and III′.

41. Other Methods of Solution. — By making use of the properties of what Lie calls r-parameter groups of infinitesimal transformations (§ 43) the method of solving a differential equation of the second order invariant under two groups can be modified so as to be considerably simpler both as to the number of cases to be distinguished and as to the actual processes involved in obtaining the solution. A brief study of these groups will be made in this chapter, leading to the methods of solution in §§ 46 and 47.

42. Number of Linearly Independent Infinitesimal Transformations, that Leave a Differential Equation of the Second Order Unaltered, Limited. — Since a differential equation of the first order always has an integrating factor, in general, (*El. Dif. Eq.* § 5) it is left unaltered by an indefinite number of infinitesimal transformations, the general expression for whose symbols involves two arbitrary functions (§ 15). On the other hand, a differential equation of the second (or higher) order is, in general, not left unaltered by any infinitesimal transformation (see Note IV of the Appendix), although some of them are. We shall prove the

THEOREM. — *A differential equation of the second order cannot be left unaltered by more than eight linearly independent* infinitesimal transformations.*

Suppose that the equation

(98) $$y'' = F(x, y, y')$$

is invariant under the nine linearly independent infinitesimal transformations $U_1 f,\ U_2 f,\ \cdots,\ U_9 f$, it is also invariant under

(102) $$Uf \equiv a_1 U_1 f + a_2 U_2 f + \cdots + a_9 U_9 f \equiv \xi \frac{\partial f}{\partial x} + \eta \frac{\partial f}{\partial y}$$

for all possible choices of the constants $a_1,\ a_2,\ \cdots,\ a_9$ (Remark, § 39).

It is a well-known theorem in the Theory of Functions that, in general, a unique integral curve of a differential equation of the second order and first degree (98) passes through two points, lying within a definite region determined by (98). Suppose that $P_1,\ P_2,\ P_3,\ P_4$ in Fig. 5 are four points such that each of the six pairs that can be formed of them determines a distinct integral curve of (98). The nine constants $a_1,\ a_2,\ \cdots,\ a_9$ can be so chosen that (102) leaves

---

* A set of infinitesimal transformations $U_1 f,\ U_2 f,\ \cdots,\ U_r f$ is said to be *linearly independent* if there is no linear relation, with constant coefficients, connecting their symbols; *i.e.* if it is impossible to find a set of constants $c_1, c_2, \cdots, c_r$ such that

$$c_1 U_1 f + c_2 U_2 f + \cdots + c_r U_r f \equiv 0.$$

each of these four points unaltered. For, if their coördinates are respectively (x_1, y_1), (x_2, y_2), (x_3, y_3), (x_4, y_4), the requirement for this is the simultaneous satisfaction of the eight equations

$$\xi(x_j, y_j) \equiv a_1\xi_1(x_j, y_j) + a_2\xi_2(x_j, y_j) + \cdots + a_9\xi_9(x_j, y_j) = 0,$$

$$\eta(x_j, y_j) \equiv a_1\eta_1(x_j, y_j) + a_2\eta_2(x_j, y_j) + \cdots + a_9\eta_9(x_j, y_j) = 0,$$

$$(j = 1, 2, 3, 4.)$$

These equations determine finite values of the ratios of eight of the a's to the ninth one (excepting possibly for peculiar choices of the four points, which can be avoided) because of the linear independence of the nine transformations.

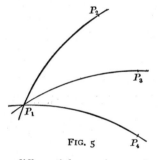

FIG. 5

With the a's thus chosen, the transformation (102) leaves the four points P_1, P_2, P_3, P_4 unaltered and, therefore, also the integral curves determined by any two of the points, since integral curves are transformed into integral curves by a transformation which leaves a differential equation unaltered, and the four points were so chosen that through any two of them passes a unique integral curve. Thus through each one of the points, *e.g.* through P_1, pass three of these invariant integral curves. The point P_1 on these being left unaltered by (102), their slopes at this point, which may be designated by y_{12}', y_{13}', y_{14}', respectively, are also left unaltered by it. Hence if η' is the coefficient of $\dfrac{\partial f}{\partial y'}$ in the extended transformation corresponding to (102), it follows that

$$(103) \qquad \eta' \equiv \frac{\partial \eta}{\partial x} + \left(\frac{\partial \eta}{\partial y} - \frac{\partial \xi}{\partial x}\right)y' - \frac{\partial \xi}{\partial y}y'^2 = 0$$

for $x = x_1$, $y = y_1$, $y' = y_{12}'$, y_{13}', y_{14}'. Letting a, b, c be the values of $\dfrac{\partial \eta}{\partial x}$, $\dfrac{\partial \eta}{\partial y} - \dfrac{\partial \xi}{\partial x}$, $-\dfrac{\partial \xi}{\partial y}$ respectively when $x = x_1$, $y = y_1$, (103) gives the three relations

$$a + by_{12}' + cy_{12}'^2 = 0,$$

$$a + by_{13}' + cy_{13}'^2 = 0,$$

$$a + by_{14}' + cy_{14}'^2 = 0.$$

Since the determinant of the coefficients

$$\begin{vmatrix} 1 & y_{12}' & y_{12}'^2 \\ 1 & y_{13}' & y_{13}'^2 \\ 1 & y_{14}' & y_{14}'^2 \end{vmatrix} \equiv (y_{13}' - y_{14}')(y_{14}' - y_{12}')(y_{12}' - y_{13}')$$

is different from zero, $a = b = c = 0$. Hence $\eta' \equiv 0$ for every integral curve through P_1, whence every integral curve through P_1 is invariant* under (102).

In exactly the same way it can be shown that every integral curve through each of the other points P_2, P_3, P_4 is left unaltered by (102).

If P is any fifth point in the region containing P_1, P_2, P_3, P_4, it will lie upon at least two † integral curves each of which passes through one of those points. These integral curves being invariant, the point P is left unaltered by (102). In this way every point of the plane (with, perhaps, exception of certain points determined by the differential equation) is found to be left unaltered by (102). The latter must therefore be identically zero ; *i.e.*

$$a_1 U_1 f + a_2 U_2 f + \cdots + a_9 U_9 f \equiv 0.$$

---

* This follows from the fact that a unique integral curve of a differential equation of the second order is, in general, determined by the conditions that it pass through a given point (x, y) and have a given slope y' at that point.

† If P does not lie upon any of the six integral curves determined by the four points (which is the general case), this number is *four;* it is *three* if P is on one of these curves, and *two* if it is at the intersection of two of them.

Hence any nine infinitesimal transformations which leave a differential equation of the second order unaltered cannot be linearly independent.   This proves the theorem.

The differential equation $y'' = 0$ is a simple example of an equation that is left unaltered by the maximum number of infinitesimal transformations.   For, since its integral curves are the straight lines of the plane, $y = ax + b$, it is left unaltered by every projective transformation

$$x_1 = \frac{a_1 x + a_2 y + a_3}{a_7 x + a_8 y + a_9}, \quad y_1 = \frac{a_4 x + a_5 y + a_6}{a_7 x + a_8 y + a_9}.$$

In Note VI of the Appendix it will be seen that there are eight linearly independent infinitesimal projective transformations.

Remark. — In the case of a differential equation of higher order than the second, the following theorem holds : *A differential equation of the nth order ($n > 2$) cannot be invariant under more than $n + 4$ linearly independent infinitesimal transformations.*   A proof of this theorem may be found in Lie, *Continuierliche Gruppen*, pp. 296-298.

As in the case where $n = 2$, a differential equation of order $n > 2$ is in general not left unaltered by any infinitesimal transformation. On the other hand the differential equation $y^{(n)} = 0$, $n > 2$ is invariant under each of the $n + 4$ transformations (Examples, § 26)

$$\frac{\partial f}{\partial x}, \ \frac{\partial f}{\partial y}, \ x\frac{\partial f}{\partial x}, \ y\frac{\partial f}{\partial y}, \ x\frac{\partial f}{\partial y}, \ x^2\frac{\partial f}{\partial y}, \ \cdots, \ x^{n-1}\frac{\partial f}{\partial y}, \ x^2\frac{\partial f}{\partial x} + (n-1)xy\frac{\partial f}{\partial y}.$$

43. r-parameter Group of Infinitesimal Transformations. — Starting with a set of infinitesimal transformations $U_1 f, U_2 f, \cdots, U_r f$, the infinitesimal transformations, whose symbols are obtained from these by applying the alternating process to them in pairs, may or may not be linearly independent of them.

Thus, if $\qquad U_1 f \equiv \dfrac{\partial f}{\partial x}, \ \ U_2 f \equiv x\dfrac{\partial f}{\partial y}, \ \ U_3 f \equiv x^2\dfrac{\partial f}{\partial x},$

the transformations $(U_1 U_2)f \equiv \dfrac{\partial f}{\partial y}, \ \ (U_1 U_3)f \equiv 2x\dfrac{\partial f}{\partial x}, \ \ (U_2 U_3)f \equiv -x^2\dfrac{\partial f}{\partial y}$
are all independent of them.

On the other hand, if

$$U_1 f \equiv x\frac{\partial f}{\partial x}, \quad U_2 f \equiv x\frac{\partial f}{\partial y}, \quad U_3 f \equiv (x+y)\frac{\partial f}{\partial x},$$

the transformation

$$(U_2 U_3)f \equiv x\frac{\partial f}{\partial x} - (x+y)\frac{\partial f}{\partial y} \text{ is independent,}$$

while $(U_1 U_2)f \equiv U_2 f, \quad (U_1 U_3)f \equiv U_1 f - U_3 f.$

Finally, if $U_1 f \equiv x\frac{\partial f}{\partial x} - y\frac{\partial f}{\partial y}, \quad U_2 f \equiv x\frac{\partial f}{\partial y}, \quad U_3 f \equiv y\frac{\partial f}{\partial x},$

none of the new transformations are independent of them; for

$$(U_1 U_2)f \equiv 2\, U_2 f, \quad (U_1 U_3)f \equiv -2\, U_3 f, \quad (U_2 U_3)f \equiv U_1 f.$$

The case where none of the new transformations are linearly independent of the old ones is of special interest. If r linearly independent infinitesimal transformations $U_1 f$, $U_2 f$, $\cdots$, $U_r f$ have the property

(104) $(U_i U_j)f \equiv a_{ij1}U_1 f + a_{ij2}U_2 f + \cdots + a_{ijr}U_r f, (i, j = 1, 2, \cdots r),$

where the a's are constants, the aggregate of these and all the transformations $Uf \equiv a_1 U_1 f + a_2 U_2 f + \cdots + a_r U_r f$ where these a's are any constants constitute an *r-parameter group of infinitesimal transformations.**

Remark 1. — An r-parameter group of infinitesimal transformations is determined by *any* r of its transformations which are linearly independent, since the symbols of all its transformations can be expressed linearly with constant coefficients in terms of any r independent ones. Moreover it is readily seen that any set of r linearly independent transformations of the group have the property (104).

---

* In Note VI of the Appendix an *r*-parameter continuous group containing both finite and infinitesimal transformations is defined. The intimate relation between these two classes of groups is brought out in Lie's Principal Theorem at the end of the Note.

Turning our attention now to the transformations which leave a differential equation of the second order unaltered, we shall first prove

THEOREM I. — *If a differential equation of the second order is invariant under $U_1 f$ and $U_2 f$, it is invariant under $(U_1 U_2) f$.*

For, if $U_1 f$ and $U_2 f$ leave

$$(98) \qquad\qquad y'' = F(x, y, y')$$

unaltered, the extended transformations $U_1' f$ and $U_2' f$ leave

$$(101) \qquad Af \equiv \frac{\partial f}{\partial x} + y' \frac{\partial f}{\partial y} + F(x, y, y') \frac{\partial f}{\partial y'} = 0$$

unaltered. By the theorem of § 37, $(U_1' U_2') f$ or its equal $(U_1 U_2)' f$ (see Note V of the Appendix) leaves $Af = 0$ unaltered. Hence Theorem I follows.*

In § 42 it was established that the number of linearly independent infinitesimal transformations that leave any differential equation of the second order unaltered is limited. If in the case of a given differential equation this number is r, all the infinitesimal transformations leaving the differential equation unaltered are linear functions, with constant coefficients, of any set of r linearly independent ones $U_1 f$, $U_2 f$, $\cdots$, $U_r f$. By Theorem I $(U_i U_j) f$, for $i, j = 1, 2, \cdots, r$, must also leave the differential equation unaltered. Hence they, too, are linear functions with constant coefficients of the set $U_1 f$, $U_2 f$, $\cdots$, $U_r f$. The latter therefore have the property (104), and we have thus established

THEOREM II. — *The aggregate of all the infinitesimal transformations leaving a given differential equation of the second order unaltered constitute an r-parameter group. Here $0 \lessgtr r \lessgtr 8$.†*

---

* This theorem is true for a differential equation of any order, and is proved in the same way.

† The same theorem is true for a differential equation of the n-th order, where $n > 2$. In this case $0 \lessgtr r \lessgtr n + 4$.

It is possible that a smaller number than r, say s, of linearly independent infinitesimal transformations in an r-parameter group determine a group ; the latter is known as an s-parameter *subgroup* of the larger group.

The four transformations

$$U_1 f \equiv x \frac{\partial f}{\partial x}, \quad U_2 f \equiv y \frac{\partial f}{\partial x}, \quad U_3 f \equiv x \frac{\partial f}{\partial y}, \quad U_4 f \equiv y \frac{\partial f}{\partial y}$$

determine a four-parameter group ; for they are linearly independent, and besides

$$(U_1 U_2) f \equiv - U_2 f, \ (U_1 U_3) f \equiv U_3 f, \ (U_1 U_4) f \equiv 0,$$
$$(U_2 U_3) f \equiv U_4 f - U_1 f, \ (U_2 U_4) f \equiv - U_2 f, \ (U_3 U_4) f \equiv U_3 f.$$

Of the subgroups of the four-parameter group the following are immediately obvious :

The two-parameter subgroups $U_1 f, \ U_2 f; \ U_1 f, \ U_3 f; \ U_1 f, \ U_4 f; \ U_2 f, \ U_4 f;$ $U_3 f, \ U_4 f.$

The three-parameter subgroups $U_1 f, \ U_2 f, \ U_4 f; \ U_1 f, \ U_3 f, \ U_4 f.$

$Uf \equiv x \dfrac{\partial f}{\partial x} - y \dfrac{\partial f}{\partial y} \equiv U_1 f - U_4 f,$ also a transformation of the four-parameter group, determines with $U_2 f$ and $U_3 f$ a three-parameter subgroup, since

$$(U U_2) f \equiv - 2 U_2 f, \ (U U_3) f \equiv 2 U_3 f, \ (U_2 U_3) f \equiv - U f.$$

Remark 2.— Starting with two or more linearly independent infinitesimal transformations which leave a given differential equation of the second (or higher) order unaltered, a group of infinitesimal transformations is determined which is either the r-parameter group of Theorem II or a subgroup of it.

For, let $U_1 f, U_2 f, \cdots, U_k f, (2 < k < r)$ be a set of linearly independent transformations which leave the differential equation of the second order unaltered. By Theorem I, $(U_i U_j) f, (i, j = 1, 2, \cdots, k)$ also leave the differential equation unaltered. Some or all of these may be linearly independent of the original ones. Let k' of them be such. We know that $k + k' \lessgtr 8$. Adding these to the original set, combine the larger set in pairs by the alternating process as before.

The resulting transformations also leave the differential equation un-altered. If any of these are independent of the members of the larger set, add them to the latter, thus forming a still larger set of linearly independent transformations leaving the differential equation unaltered. Proceed with this set as before. Obviously this process must be a finite one, since the maximum number of members of a set is eight. So that the above process stops when no new transformations independent of the previous ones arise as a result of the alternating process. If the number of independent transformations finally appearing is r, the r-parameter group determined by them is precisely that of Theorem II ; if the number is $s < r$, the s-parameter group determined by them is a subgroup of the other.

We shall prove

THEOREM III. — *Every r-parameter group $(r > 2)$ contains two-parameter subgroups.**

As a matter of fact we shall show that, fixing upon any one of the transformations, say $U_1 f$, a set of $r - 1$ constants $c_2, c_3, \cdots, c_r$ can be found such that

$$U_1 f \text{ and } U f \equiv c_2 U_2 f + c_3 U_3 f + \cdots + c_r U_r f$$

constitute a two-parameter subgroup ; it being understood that the r-parameter group is determined by $U_1 f, U_2 f, \cdots U_r f$, which are, therefore, subject to the conditions

$$(104) \qquad (U_i U_j) f \equiv \sum_{k=1}^{r} a_{ijk} U_k f, \quad (i, j = 1, 2, \cdots, r).$$

In order that this be the case

$$(105) \quad (U_1, c_2 U_2 f + c_3 U_3 f + \cdots + c_r U_r f) \equiv a U_1 f + b(c_2 U_2 f + c_3 U_3 f \\ + \cdots + c_r U_r f).$$

* This theorem and its proof hold, without modification, for groups involving n variables.

Since $\left(U_1, \sum\limits_{j=2}^{r} c_j U_j\right) f \equiv \sum\limits_{j=2}^{r} c_j (U_1 U_j) f \equiv \sum\limits_{j=2}^{r} c_j \sum\limits_{k=1}^{r} a_{ijk} U_k f$, and since $U_1 f, U_2 f, \cdots, U_r f$ are linearly independent, (105) can hold only in case

(106) $\sum\limits_{j=2}^{r} c_j a_{1j1} = a, \quad \sum\limits_{j=2}^{r} c_j a_{1jk} = b c_k, \; (k = 2, 3, \cdots, r).$

Conversely, if $c_2, c_3, \cdots, c_r$ can be found to satisfy r equations of the type (106), where a and b are *any* constants, and not all of the c's zero, the group $Uf \equiv \sum\limits_{j=2}^{r} c_j U_j f$ will determine with $U_1 f$ a two-parameter subgroup; for in this case

$$(U_1 U) f \equiv a U_1 f + b U f.$$

That such a set of c's can always be found may be seen as follows:

The last $r - 1$ equations of (106) are the linear homogeneous equations

(107) $\begin{cases} (a_{122} - b) c_2 + a_{132} c_3 + \cdots + a_{1r2} c_r = 0, \\ a_{123} c_2 + (a_{133} - b) c_3 + \cdots + a_{1r3} c_r = 0, \\ \cdot \quad \cdot \quad \cdot \quad \cdot \quad \cdot \quad \cdot \quad \cdot \quad \cdot \\ a_{12r} c_2 + a_{13r} c_3 + \cdots + (a_{1rr} - b) c_r = 0. \end{cases}$

These can be solved provided b satisfies the equation

(108) $\begin{vmatrix} a_{122} - b & a_{132} & \cdots & a_{1r2}, \\ a_{123} & a_{133} - b & \cdots & a_{1r3}, \\ \cdot & \cdot \quad \cdot \quad \cdot \quad \cdot & \cdot & \cdot \\ a_{12r} & a_{13r} & \cdots & a_{1rr} - b \end{vmatrix} = 0.$

This equation necessarily contains b, since the coefficient of b^{r-1} is $(-1)^{r-1}$. Using any value of b satisfying it, the c's are determined to within a common factor (which is not essential), by solving (107). The value of a is then determined by the first equation of (106). Thus Theorem III is not only proved, but a method for finding the two-parameter subgroup is also given.

The transformations

$$U_1 f \equiv \frac{\partial f}{\partial x}, \quad U_2 f \equiv \frac{\partial f}{\partial y}, \quad U_3 f \equiv y \frac{\partial f}{\partial x} + x \frac{\partial f}{\partial y}$$

determine a three-parameter group, since

$$(U_1 U_2) f \equiv o, \quad (U_1 U_3) f \equiv U_2 f, \quad (U_2 U_3) f \equiv U_1 f.$$

Inspection shows that $U_1 f$ and $U_2 f$ determine a two-parameter subgroup. To find another two-parameter subgroup of which $U_3 f$ is one of the determining elements, the method of this section may be employed. The constants c_1 and c_2 must be so determined that

$$(U_3, c_1 U_1 + c_2 U_2) f \equiv a U_3 f + b(c_1 U_1 f + c_2 U_2 f),$$

i.e. $$- c_1 U_2 f - c_2 U_1 f \equiv a U_3 f + b c_1 U_1 f + b c_2 U_2 f.$$

$$\therefore a = o, \quad b c_1 + c_2 = o, \quad b c_2 + c_1 = o.$$

In order that the last two equations be consistent, b must satisfy the equation

$$b^2 - 1 = o,$$

whence $b = \pm 1$ and $\frac{c_1}{c_2} = \mp 1$. Hence

$$U_3 \equiv y \frac{\partial f}{\partial x} + x \frac{\partial f}{\partial y}, \quad U f \equiv \frac{\partial f}{\partial x} + \frac{\partial f}{\partial y} \text{ and } U_3 f \equiv y \frac{\partial f}{\partial x} + x \frac{\partial f}{\partial y}, \quad U f \equiv \frac{\partial f}{\partial x} - \frac{\partial f}{\partial y}$$

are two two-parameter subgroups of the original group.

44. Classification of Two-parameter Groups. — If a two-parameter group is determined by $U_1 f$ and $U_2 f$,

$$(U_1 U_2) f \equiv a_1 U_1 f + a_2 U_2 f.$$

Either both a_1 and a_2 are zero or they are not. In the latter case it is always possible to find a pair of transformations to determine the two-parameter group for which one of these constants is unity and the other zero. For, if $a_1 \neq o$

$$V_1 f \equiv U_1 f + \frac{a_2}{a_1} U_2 f$$

$$V_2 f \equiv \qquad \frac{1}{a_1} U_2 f$$

are linearly independent and

$$(V_1 V_2)f \equiv V_1 f.*$$

Moreover, if for any pair of linearly independent transformations $U_1 f$ and $U_2 f$ of a two-parameter group

$$(U_1 U_2)f \equiv 0,†$$

this is true for every pair, since

$$(c_1 U_1 + c_2 U_2, \ b_1 U_1 + b_2 U_2)f \equiv (c_1 b_2 - c_2 b_1)(U_1 U_2)f \equiv 0$$

for all choices of constants c_1, c_2, b_1, b_2. Hence *every two-parameter group can be represented by a pair of transformations $U_1 f$ and $U_2 f$ such that either*
$$(U_1 U_2)f \equiv 0 \ \text{or} \ (U_1 U_2)f \equiv U_1 f.$$

These two possibilities are mutually exclusive; any group can come under one head only.

A second mode of classification is suggested by the following:

If a two-parameter group is determined by $U_1 f$ and $U_2 f$ which are connected by a relation of the form

$$(109) \qquad\qquad U_2 f \equiv \rho(x, y) U_1 f$$

where $\rho(x, y)$ is not a constant,‡ every pair of distinct transformations of the group are connected by a relation of the form (109);

---

* If $a_1 = 0$, $a_2 \neq 0$, so that $(U_1 U_2)f \equiv a_2 U_2 f$, the groups
$$V_1 f \equiv U_2 f \ \text{and} \ V_2 f \equiv -\frac{1}{a_2} U_1 f$$
satisfy the condition $\qquad\qquad (V_1 V_2)f \equiv V_1 f.$

† It is interesting to note that $(U_1 U_2)f \equiv 0$ is the necessary and sufficient condition that each transformation of the group generated by $U_1 f$ be commutative with every transformation of the group generated by $U_2 f$. For an elementary proof of this fact, see Lie, *Differentialgleichungen*, p. 305.

‡ While in this case $U_1 f$ and $U_2 f$ are distinct transformations, the one-parameter continuous groups generated by them have the same path-curves.

for if

$$V_1 f \equiv a_1 U_1 f + a_2 U_2 f, \quad V_2 f \equiv b_1 U_1 f + b_2 U_2 f, \quad (a_1 b_2 - a_2 b_1 \neq 0)$$

$$V_2 f \equiv \frac{b_1 + b_2 \rho}{a_1 + a_2 \rho} V_1 f.$$

Hence *all two-parameter groups may be divided into two classes according as their distinct transformations are connected by a relation of the form* (109) *or not.*

These two modes of classification are independent of each other. Hence *four classes of two-parameter groups may be distinguished according as they are representable by a pair of transformations* $U_1 f$ *and* $U_2 f$ *such that*

$$\alpha. \quad (U_1 U_2) f \equiv 0, \qquad U_2 f \not\equiv \rho(x, y) U_1 f,$$

$$\beta. \quad (U_1 U_2) f \equiv 0, \qquad U_2 f \equiv \rho(x, y) U_1 f,$$

$$\gamma. \quad (U_1 U_2) f \equiv U_1 f, \quad U_2 f \not\equiv \rho(x, y) U_1 f,$$

$$\delta. \quad (U_1 U_2) f \equiv U_1 f, \quad U_2 f \equiv \rho(x, y) U_1 f.$$

Classify the following two-parameter groups :

Ex. 1. $(x + y) \dfrac{\partial f}{\partial x} + (y - x) \dfrac{\partial f}{\partial y}, \quad x \dfrac{\partial f}{\partial x} + y \dfrac{\partial f}{\partial y}.$

Ex. 2. $(x + y) \dfrac{\partial f}{\partial x}, \quad x \dfrac{\partial f}{\partial x}.$

Ex. 3. $x(x + y) \dfrac{\partial f}{\partial x} + y(x + y) \dfrac{\partial f}{\partial y}, \quad x(x - y) \dfrac{\partial f}{\partial x} + y(x - y) \dfrac{\partial f}{\partial y}.$

Ex. 4. $y \dfrac{\partial f}{\partial x} - x \dfrac{\partial f}{\partial y}, \quad \sqrt{x^2 + y^2} \left(y \dfrac{\partial f}{\partial x} - x \dfrac{\partial f}{\partial y} \right).$

Ex. 5. $\dfrac{x \dfrac{\partial f}{\partial x} + y \dfrac{\partial f}{\partial y}}{x + y}, \quad \dfrac{x^2 \dfrac{\partial f}{\partial x} + (y^2 + 2xy) \dfrac{\partial f}{\partial y}}{x + y}.$

Ex. 6. $x \dfrac{\partial f}{\partial x} + y \dfrac{\partial f}{\partial y}, \quad x^2 \dfrac{\partial f}{\partial x} + (y^2 + 2xy) \dfrac{\partial f}{\partial y}.$

45. Canonical Forms of Two-parameter Groups. — By a proper choice of variables the various classes of two-parameter groups can be reduced to certain simple forms which Lie called their *canonical forms*. These will now be determined in turn.

a. $$(U_1U_2)f \equiv 0, \quad U_2f \not\equiv \rho(x, y)\, U_1f.$$

By the method of § 9 a set of variables can be determined so that U_1f takes the form

$$U_1f \equiv \frac{\partial f}{\partial x}.$$

If the resulting form of U_2f is

$$U_2f \equiv \xi \frac{\partial f}{\partial x} + \eta \frac{\partial f}{\partial y},$$

$\frac{\partial \xi}{\partial x} \equiv 0$ and $\frac{\partial \eta}{\partial x} \equiv 0$, since $(U_1U_2)f \equiv \frac{\partial \xi}{\partial x} \frac{\partial f}{\partial x} + \frac{\partial \eta}{\partial x} \frac{\partial f}{\partial y} \equiv 0.$ Hence ξ and η are, at most, functions of y; *i.e.*

$$U_2f \equiv \xi(y) \frac{\partial f}{\partial x} + \eta(y) \frac{\partial f}{\partial y},$$

where $\eta(y) \not\equiv 0$, since $U_2f \not\equiv \rho(x, y)\, U_1f.$

The transformation $U_1f \equiv \frac{\partial f}{\partial x}$ remains unaltered by a change of variables of the type

$$\boldsymbol{x} = x - \phi(y), \quad \boldsymbol{y} = \psi(y),$$

where $\phi(y)$ and $\psi(y)$ are at our disposal. This change of variables causes U_2f to take the form $[(15)\ \S\ 9]$

$$\left[\xi(y) - \eta(y)\, \phi'(y) \right] \frac{\partial f}{\partial x} + \eta(y)\, \psi'(y) \frac{\partial f}{\partial y}.$$

If $\phi = \int \frac{\xi(y)}{\eta(y)}\, dy$ and $\psi(y) = \int \frac{dy}{\eta(y)}$, U_2f assumes the form $\frac{\partial f}{\partial \boldsymbol{y}}$.

Hence, *by a proper choice of variables, a pair of transformations
satisfying conditions α can be made to assume the canonical forms*

$$U_1 f \equiv \frac{\partial f}{\partial x}, \quad U_2 f \equiv \frac{\partial f}{\partial y}.$$

Having established the existence of the canonical forms in this
case, the actual finding of the *canonical variables* (which reduce the
transformations to these forms) can be accomplished by two quadratures.   For, starting with a pair of groups

$$U_1 f \equiv \xi_1 \frac{\partial f}{\partial x} + \eta_1 \frac{\partial f}{\partial y} \quad \text{and} \quad U_2 f \equiv \xi_2 \frac{\partial f}{\partial x} + \eta_2 \frac{\partial f}{\partial y}$$

satisfying conditions *α*, the new variables x and y will reduce these
to the forms

$$U_1 f \equiv \frac{\partial f}{\partial x} \quad \text{and} \quad U_2 f \equiv \frac{\partial f}{\partial y}$$

respectively, provided x satisfies

$$\xi_1 \frac{\partial x}{\partial x} + \eta_1 \frac{\partial x}{\partial y} = 1, \quad \xi_2 \frac{\partial x}{\partial x} + \eta_2 \frac{\partial x}{\partial y} = 0,$$

and y satisfies $\xi_1 \dfrac{\partial y}{\partial x} + \eta_1 \dfrac{\partial y}{\partial y} = 0, \quad \xi_2 \dfrac{\partial y}{\partial x} + \eta_2 \dfrac{\partial y}{\partial y} = 1.$

Since such new variables must exist, the equations of each pair
must be consistent.   Because $U_2 f \not\equiv \rho U_1 f$, they can be solved for
$\dfrac{\partial x}{\partial x}, \dfrac{\partial x}{\partial y}$ and $\dfrac{\partial y}{\partial x}, \dfrac{\partial y}{\partial y}$ respectively, whence x and y are determined
by the two quadratures

$$x = \int \frac{\partial x}{\partial x} dx + \frac{\partial x}{\partial y} dy, \quad y = \int \frac{\partial y}{\partial x} dx + \frac{\partial y}{\partial y} dy.$$

The transformations

$$U_1 f \equiv -y \frac{\partial f}{\partial x} + x \frac{\partial f}{\partial y} \quad \text{and} \quad U_2 f \equiv x \frac{\partial f}{\partial x} + y \frac{\partial f}{\partial y}$$

form a pair satisfying conditions α. From

$$-y \frac{\partial x}{\partial x} + x \frac{\partial x}{\partial y} = 1 \text{ and } x \frac{\partial x}{\partial x} + y \frac{\partial x}{\partial y} = 0,$$

$$\frac{\partial x}{\partial x} = \frac{-y}{x^2 + y^2} \text{ and } \frac{\partial x}{\partial y} = \frac{x}{x^2 + y^2},$$

whence

$$x = \int \frac{x \, dy - y \, dx}{x^2 + y^2} = \tan^{-1} \frac{y}{x}.$$

Similarly, from

$$-y \frac{\partial y}{\partial x} + x \frac{\partial y}{\partial y} = 0 \text{ and } x \frac{\partial y}{\partial x} + y \frac{\partial y}{\partial y} = 1,$$

$$\frac{\partial y}{\partial x} = \frac{x}{x^2 + y^2} \text{ and } \frac{\partial y}{\partial y} = \frac{y}{x^2 + y^2},$$

whence

$$y = \int \frac{x \, dx + y \, dy}{x^2 + y^2} = \log \sqrt{x^2 + y^2}.$$

These canonical variables are obvious from geometrical considerations.

β. $(U_1 U_2)f \equiv 0, \quad U_2 f \equiv \rho(x, y) U_1 f.$

As before, $U_1 f$ can be reduced to the form

$$U_1 f \equiv \frac{\partial f}{\partial y}$$

by the choice of canonical variables (§ 10). Then $U_2 f$ assumes the form

$$U_2 f \equiv \sigma(x, y) \frac{\partial f}{\partial y},$$

where $\sigma(x, y)$ is what ρ becomes when the old variables are replaced by the new. Since

$$(U_1 U_2)f \equiv \frac{\partial \sigma}{\partial y} \frac{\partial f}{\partial y} \equiv 0,$$

σ is a function of x only. Taking this as the new x, which change of variables leaves $U_1 f$ unaltered, $U_2 f$ assumes the form $x \frac{\partial f}{\partial y}$. Hence, *by a proper choice of variables a pair of transformations satisfying conditions β can be made to assume the canonical forms*

$$U_1 f \equiv \frac{\partial f}{\partial y}, \quad U_2 f \equiv x \frac{\partial f}{\partial y}.$$

The actual finding of the canonical variables in this case requires a single quadrature.   For, starting with a pair of transformations

$$U_1 f \equiv \xi \frac{\partial f}{\partial x} + \eta \frac{\partial f}{\partial y} \text{ and } U_2 f \equiv \rho \left(\xi \frac{\partial f}{\partial x} + \eta \frac{\partial f}{\partial y} \right),$$

where $(U_1 U_2) f \equiv U_1 \rho \, U_1 f \equiv 0, \text{ i.e. } U_1 \rho \equiv 0,$

the new variables x and y will reduce these to the forms

$$U_1 f \equiv \frac{\partial f}{\partial y} \text{ and } U_2 f \equiv x \frac{\partial f}{\partial y}$$

respectively, if $x = \rho(x, y)$

and y satisfies the equation (§ 10),

$$\xi \frac{\partial y}{\partial x} + \eta \frac{\partial y}{\partial y} = 1.$$

Moreover, since $U_1 \rho \equiv 0$, ρ is a solution of

$$\xi \frac{\partial f}{\partial x} + \eta \frac{\partial f}{\partial y} = 0.$$

Hence, $y = F(x, y)$ is some solution of

$$\frac{dx}{\xi} = \frac{dy}{\eta} = \frac{dy}{1}$$

distinct from $\rho = const.$, which is also a solution of this system of equations.   Among the various ways that will suggest themselves when ξ and η are given in any specific case, a possible method is to solve $\rho(x, y) = c$ for one of the variables, say $x = \phi(y, c)$, whence

$$y = \int \frac{dy}{\eta(\phi, y)}.$$

The transformations

$$U_1 f \equiv xy \frac{\partial f}{\partial x} + 2y^2 \frac{\partial f}{\partial y} \text{ and } U_2 f \equiv x^3 \frac{\partial f}{\partial x} + 2x^2 y \frac{\partial f}{\partial y}$$

form a pair satisfying conditions β.

$$U_2 f \equiv \frac{x^2}{y} U_1 f. \quad \therefore x = \frac{x^2}{y}.$$

y must satisfy

$$xy \frac{\partial y}{\partial x} + 2y^2 \frac{\partial y}{\partial y} = 1.$$

To solve the corresponding system of ordinary equations

$$\frac{dx}{xy} = \frac{dy}{2y^2} = \frac{dy}{1}$$

use may be made of the solution $\dfrac{x^2}{y} = c$ or $y = \dfrac{x^2}{c}$. Then

$$y = c \int \frac{dx}{x^3} = -\frac{c}{2x^2} = -\frac{1}{2y}.$$

γ. $(U_1 U_2) f \equiv U_1 f, \ U_2 f \not\equiv \rho(x, y) \ U_1 f.$

As before, $U_1 f$ can be put in the form

$$U_1 f \equiv \frac{\partial f}{\partial y}$$

by introducing canonical variables.   Taking $U_2 f$ in the **form**

$$U_2 f \equiv \xi(x, y) \frac{\partial f}{\partial x} + \eta(x, y) \frac{\partial f}{\partial y}$$

we must have $\dfrac{\partial \xi}{\partial y} = 0$ and $\dfrac{\partial \eta}{\partial y} = 1$, since

$$(U_1 U_2) f \equiv \frac{\partial \xi}{\partial y} \frac{\partial f}{\partial x} + \frac{\partial \eta}{\partial y} \frac{\partial f}{\partial y} \equiv \frac{\partial f}{\partial y}.$$

Hence, $U_2 f$ must have the form

$$U_2 f \equiv \xi(x) \frac{\partial f}{\partial x} + [X(x) + y] \frac{\partial f}{\partial y},$$

where $\xi(x) \not\equiv 0$, because $U_2f \not\equiv \rho U_1 f$. The introduction of the new variables

$$x = \phi(x),\ y = \psi(x) + y$$

leaves $U_1 f \equiv \dfrac{\partial f}{\partial y}$ unchanged in form, but changes $U_2 f$ into

$$U_2 f \equiv \xi(x)\phi'(x)\frac{\partial f}{\partial x} + [\xi(x)\psi'(x) + X(x) + y]\frac{\partial f}{\partial y}.$$

This takes the form $\qquad U_2 f \equiv x\dfrac{\partial f}{\partial x} + y\dfrac{\partial f}{\partial y}$

when $\xi(x)\phi'(x) = \phi(x)$, or $\phi(x) = e^{\int \frac{dx}{\xi(x)}}$

and $\xi(x)\psi'(x) + X(x) = \psi(x)$, or $\psi(x) = -e^{\int \frac{dx}{\xi(x)}}\int \dfrac{X}{\xi} e^{-\int \frac{dx}{\xi(x)}}\,dx.$

Hence, *by a proper choice of variables a pair of transformations satisfying conditions γ can be made to assume the canonical forms*

$$U_1 f \equiv \frac{\partial f}{\partial y},\ U_2 f \equiv x\frac{\partial f}{\partial x} + y\frac{\partial f}{\partial y}.$$

The actual finding of the canonical variables in this case requires two quadratures. For, starting with a pair of groups

$$U_1 f \equiv \xi_1 \frac{\partial f}{\partial x} + \eta_1 \frac{\partial f}{\partial y} \text{ and } U_2 f \equiv \xi_2 \frac{\partial f}{\partial x} + \eta_2 \frac{\partial f}{\partial y}$$

satisfying the conditions γ, the new variables x and y will reduce these to the forms

$$U_1 f \equiv \frac{\partial f}{\partial y} \text{ and } U_2 f \equiv x\frac{\partial f}{\partial x} + y\frac{\partial f}{\partial y}$$

respectively, provided x satisfies

$$\xi_1 \frac{\partial x}{\partial x} + \eta_1 \frac{\partial x}{\partial y} = 0,\ \ \xi_2 \frac{\partial x}{\partial x} + \eta_2 \frac{\partial x}{\partial y} = x$$

and y satisfies

$$\xi_1 \frac{\partial y}{\partial x} + \eta_1 \frac{\partial y}{\partial y} = 1, \quad \xi_2 \frac{\partial y}{\partial x} + \eta_2 \frac{\partial y}{\partial y} = y.$$

Since such new variables must exist, the equations of each pair must be consistent. Because $U_2 f \not\equiv \rho U_1 f$ they can be solved for $\dfrac{\partial x}{\partial x}$, $\dfrac{\partial x}{\partial y}$ and $\dfrac{\partial y}{\partial x}$, $\dfrac{\partial y}{\partial y}$, giving

(110) $\dfrac{\partial x}{\partial x} = \dfrac{-\eta_1}{\xi_1 \eta_2 - \xi_2 \eta_1} x, \quad \dfrac{\partial x}{\partial y} = \dfrac{\xi_1}{\xi_1 \eta_2 - \xi_2 \eta_1} x,$

(111) $\dfrac{\partial y}{\partial x} = \dfrac{-\eta_1}{\xi_1 \eta_2 - \xi_2 \eta_1} y + \dfrac{\eta_2}{\xi_1 \eta_2 - \xi_2 \eta_1}, \quad \dfrac{\partial y}{\partial y} = \dfrac{\xi_1}{\xi_1 \eta_2 - \xi_2 \eta_1} y - \dfrac{\xi_2}{\xi_1 \eta_2 - \xi_2 \eta_1}.$

Dividing (110) by x, $\dfrac{\partial \log x}{\partial x}$ and $\dfrac{\partial \log x}{\partial y}$ are given, whence $\log x$ is obtained by a quadrature and the form for x follows.

Equations (111) may be solved in various ways. The most general form for y satisfying them is not needed. As a matter of fact, the simpler the form obtainable, the better. One way of proceeding* is to assume that x and y are no longer independent, but that $y = cx$ where c is a constant. Then

(112) $\dfrac{dy}{dx} = \dfrac{\partial y}{\partial x} + c \dfrac{\partial y}{\partial y} = (\lambda + c\mu)y + \nu + c\pi$

where λ, μ, ν, π are what the corresponding coefficients in (111) become when y is replaced by cx. Since (112) is a linear ordinary differential equation of the first order, it may be solved by the usual method, involving two quadratures (*El. Dif. Eq.* § 13). A process, however, by which a single quadrature alone is involved in solving (112) is given by the following:

---

* Special methods will frequently be found simpler, however.

Inspection of equations (110) and (111) shows that $y = x(x, cx)$, which is obtained from $x(x, y)$ by replacing y by cx, satisfies the equation

$$\frac{dy}{dx} = (\lambda + c\mu)y.$$

Hence the transformation $y = vx(x, cx)$ reduces (112) to

$$\frac{dv}{dx} = \frac{v + c\pi}{x(x, cx)},$$

whence v is obtained by a quadrature. Then y follows at once, after replacing c by $\frac{y}{x}$.

The transformations

$$U_1 f \equiv x\frac{\partial f}{\partial y} \text{ and } U_2 f \equiv x^2\frac{\partial f}{\partial x} + (y + xy)\frac{\partial f}{\partial y}$$

form a pair satisfying the conditions γ.   From

$$x\frac{\partial x}{\partial y} = 0 \text{ and } x^2\frac{\partial x}{\partial x} + (y + xy)\frac{\partial x}{\partial y} = x$$

$$\frac{\partial \log x}{\partial x} = \frac{1}{x^2}, \quad \frac{\partial \log x}{\partial y} = 0.$$

$$\therefore \log x = -\frac{1}{x}, \text{ and } x = e^{-\frac{1}{x}}.$$

From

$$x\frac{\partial y}{\partial y} = 1 \text{ and } x^2\frac{\partial y}{\partial x} + (y + xy)\frac{\partial y}{\partial y} = y,$$

$$\frac{\partial y}{\partial x} = \frac{y}{x^2} - \frac{y + xy}{x^3}, \quad \frac{\partial y}{\partial y} = \frac{1}{x}. *$$

Putting $y = cx$

$$\frac{dy}{dx} = \frac{y}{x^2} - \frac{c}{x^2}.$$

* These equations can be solved directly. From the second one $y = \frac{y}{x} + \phi(x)$, where $\phi(x)$ is to be determined. Putting this value of y in the first equation gives

$$\frac{d\phi}{dx} = \frac{\phi}{x^2}, \text{ whence } \phi = ke^{-\frac{1}{x}}.$$

$k = 0$ gives the form for y obtained in the text.

Using the method given above, put $y = ve^{-\frac{1}{x}}$. The linear equation then reduces

to
$$\frac{dv}{dx} = -\frac{c}{x^2}\, e^{\frac{1}{x}}\, ; \quad \text{whence } v = ce^{\frac{1}{x}}.$$

$$\therefore y = c = \frac{y}{x}.$$

δ.
$$(U_1 U_2)f \equiv U_1 f, \quad U_2 f \equiv \rho(x, y)U_1 f.$$

As before, by the introduction of canonical variables $U_1 f$ can be made to assume the form

$$U_1 f \equiv \frac{\partial f}{\partial y}.$$

These variables will cause $U_2 f$ to assume the form

$$U_2 f \equiv \eta(x, y)\, \frac{\partial f}{\partial y}.$$

Since $(U_1 U_2)f \equiv U_1 f$, $\dfrac{\partial \eta}{\partial y} = 1$ and $\eta = X(x) + y$. So that

$$U_2 f \equiv [X(x) + y]\frac{\partial f}{\partial y}.$$

The change of variables $y = X(x) + y$ leaves $U_1 f$ unaltered and changes $U_2 f$ to the form $U_2 f \equiv y\dfrac{\partial f}{\partial y}.$ Hence, by a proper choice of variables a pair of transformations satisfying conditions δ can be made to assume the canonical forms

$$U_1 f \equiv \frac{\partial f}{\partial y}, \quad U_2 f \equiv y\frac{\partial f}{\partial y}.$$

The actual finding of the canonical variables in this case requires the solving of the differential equation of the first order determining the path-curves of the group generated by either of the transformations. For, starting with the pair of transformations,

$$U_1 f \equiv \xi \frac{\partial f}{\partial x} + \eta \frac{\partial f}{\partial y} \text{ and } U_2 f \equiv \rho \left(\xi \frac{\partial f}{\partial x} + \eta \frac{\partial f}{\partial y} \right)$$

where $(U_1 U_2) f \equiv U_1 f$, the new variables x and y will reduce these to the forms

$$U_1 f \equiv \frac{\partial f}{\partial y} \text{ and } U_2 f \equiv y \frac{\partial f}{\partial y}$$

respectively, if
$$y = \rho(x, y) *$$

and x satisfies the equation

$$\xi \frac{\partial x}{\partial x} + \eta \frac{\partial x}{\partial y} = 0.$$

The solution of this equation is usually obtained by first solving

$$\frac{dx}{\xi} = \frac{dy}{\eta},$$

the differential equation of the path-curves of $U_1 f$.

The transformations

$$U_1 f \equiv x^2 \frac{\partial f}{\partial x} - y^2 \frac{\partial f}{\partial y} \text{ and } U_2 f \equiv \frac{x^2}{y} \frac{\partial f}{\partial y} - y \frac{\partial f}{\partial y}$$

form a pair satisfying conditions δ.

$$U_2 f \equiv \frac{1}{y} U_1 f. \quad \therefore y = \frac{1}{y}.$$

The solution of $\quad \frac{dx}{x^2} + \frac{dy}{y^2} = 0$ is $\frac{1}{x} + \frac{1}{y} = const.$

$$\therefore x = \frac{x + y}{xy}.$$

Ex. Determine the canonical variables for the groups at the end of § 44.

* The other requirement of y, viz. $Uy \equiv 1$, follows from the given conditions on $U_1 f$ and $U_2 f$, since $(U_1, \rho U_1) f \equiv U_1 \rho U_1 f$.

46. Differential Equation of the Second Order Invariant under Two Groups. — Starting with two non-trivial infinitesimal transformations [*] which leave a differential equation of the second order

$$(98) \qquad y'' = F(x, y, y')$$

unaltered, an s-parameter group of infinitesimal transformations, leaving (98) unaltered, can be found (Remark 2, § 43), which contains a two-parameter subgroup (Theorem III, § 43) determined by a pair of transformations U_1f and U_2f which satisfy one and only one of the conditions (§ 44),

$$(U_1U_2)f \equiv 0 \text{ and } (U_1U_2)f \equiv U_1f.$$

Moreover, these two transformations can be found by direct and practicable processes from the original two transformations, and they also leave the differential equation (98) unaltered.

We shall now suppose that we have found such a pair of infinitesimal transformations U_1f and U_2f. Passing, as was done in § 39, to the corresponding linear partial differential equation

$$(101) \qquad Af \equiv \frac{\partial f}{\partial x} + y'\frac{\partial f}{\partial y} + F(x, y, y')\frac{\partial f}{\partial y'} = 0,$$

the latter is invariant under the extended transformations $U_1'f$ and $U_2'f$, which are subject to one of the conditions

$$(U_1'U_2')f \equiv 0 \text{ and } (U_1'U_2')f \equiv U_1'f,$$

since $(U_1'U_2')f \equiv (U_1U_2)'f$ (see Note V of the Appendix). Two important cases are to be distinguished :

A. A relation of the form

$$(97') \qquad U_2'f \equiv \alpha U_1'f + \rho Af$$

---

[*] As use is to be made of the properties of groups of infinitesimal transformations, the one-parameter groups under which (98) is invariant will be replaced by their representative infinitesimal transformations in what follows. (Compare Remark, § 6.)

exists.   In this case U_1f and U_2f determine distinct path-curves, that is, no relation of the form

(109) $$U_2f \equiv \sigma(x, y)\, U_1f$$

can connect them.   For, if such a relation did exist, and if

$$U_1'f \equiv \xi_1 \frac{\partial f}{\partial x} + \eta_1 \frac{\partial f}{\partial y} + \eta_1' \frac{\partial f}{\partial y'},$$

$U_2'f$ would have the form

$$U_2'f \equiv \sigma\xi_1 \frac{\partial f}{\partial x} + \sigma\eta_1 \frac{\partial f}{\partial y} + \left(\sigma\eta_1' + \eta_1 \frac{\partial \sigma}{\partial x} + \eta_1 \frac{\partial \sigma}{\partial y} y' - \xi_1 \frac{\partial \sigma}{\partial x} y' - \xi_1 \frac{\partial \sigma}{\partial y} y'^2\right) \frac{\partial f}{\partial y'}.$$

A relation of the form (97′) implies the vanishing of the determinant

$$\Delta \equiv \begin{vmatrix} 1 & y' & F(x, y, y') \\ \xi_1 & \eta_1 & \eta_1' \\ \sigma\xi_1 & \sigma\eta_1 & \sigma\eta_1' + \eta_1 \dfrac{\partial \sigma}{\partial x} + \left(\eta_1 \dfrac{\partial \sigma}{\partial y} - \xi_1 \dfrac{\partial \sigma}{\partial x}\right) y' - \xi_1 \dfrac{\partial \sigma}{\partial y} y'^2 \end{vmatrix}.$$

This reduces at once to

$$(\eta_1 - \xi_1 y') \left[\eta_1 \frac{\partial \sigma}{\partial x} + \left(\eta_1 \frac{\partial \sigma}{\partial y} - \xi_1 \frac{\partial \sigma}{\partial x}\right) y' - \xi_1 \frac{\partial \sigma}{\partial y} y'^2 \right].$$

Since neither $\eta_1 - \xi_1 y'$ nor both ξ_1 and η_1 can be zero identically, Δ can vanish identically only in case $\dfrac{\partial \sigma}{\partial x} \equiv 0$ and $\dfrac{\partial \sigma}{\partial y} \equiv 0$ simultaneously, that is, σ must be a constant.   This would make U_1f and U_2f one and the same transformation.   Hence the relation (109) cannot hold when (97′) does.   Assuming that (97′) holds, two cases must still be considered :

   1° $$(U_1 U_2)f \equiv 0.$$

By means of two quadratures (§ 45, α) canonical variables can be found so as to reduce the two transformations to the forms

$$U_1 f \equiv \frac{\partial f}{\partial x}, \quad U_2 f \equiv \frac{\partial f}{\partial y}$$

respectively. Since the differential equation expressed in terms of these variables must be left unaltered by these two transformations, it must be free of both x and y (I and I′, § 28). Hence it has the form

$$y'' = F(y'),$$

and the corresponding partial differential equation has the form

$$Af \equiv \frac{\partial f}{\partial x} + y' \frac{\partial f}{\partial y} + F(y') \frac{\partial f}{\partial y'} = 0.$$

Moreover, $\quad U_1' f \equiv \dfrac{\partial f}{\partial x}, \quad U_2' f \equiv \dfrac{\partial f}{\partial y}.$

The relation (97′) implies that

$$\begin{vmatrix} 1 & y' & F(y') \\ 1 & 0 & 0 \\ 0 & 1 & 0 \end{vmatrix} \equiv F(y') \equiv 0.$$

Hence *when conditions (97′) and 1° hold, the introduction of canonical variables for the two-parameter group reduces the differential equation to the form*
$$y'' = 0,$$
and the solution is $\quad y = ax + b.$

2° $\quad\quad (U_1 U_2) f \equiv U_1 f.$

By means of two quadratures (§ 45, γ) canonical variables can be found in this case, reducing the transformations to the forms

$$U_1 f \equiv \frac{\partial f}{\partial y}, \quad U_2 f \equiv x \frac{\partial f}{\partial x} + y \frac{\partial f}{\partial y}.$$

The introduction of these variables reduces the differential equation to the form (I and IV, § 28)

$$f(y', xy'') = 0, \text{ or } y'' = \frac{F(y')}{x}.$$

The corresponding linear partial differential equation has the form

$$Af \equiv \frac{\partial f}{\partial x} + y' \frac{\partial f}{\partial y} + \frac{F(y')}{x} \frac{\partial f}{\partial y'} = 0.$$

Moreover, $$U_1'f \equiv \frac{\partial f}{\partial y}, \; U_2'f \equiv x\frac{\partial f}{\partial x} + y\frac{\partial f}{\partial y}.$$

The relation (97′) implies that

$$\begin{vmatrix} 1 & y' & \dfrac{F(y')}{x} \\ 0 & 1 & 0 \\ x & y & 0 \end{vmatrix} \equiv -F(y') \equiv 0.$$

Hence, also, *in the case where conditions* (97′) *and* 2° *hold, the introduction of canonical variables for the two-parameter group reduces the differential equation to the form*

$$y'' = 0$$

and the solution is $$y = ax + b.$$

B. No relation of the type (97′) exists. That is,

$$U_2'f \not\equiv \alpha \, U_1'f + \rho Af.$$

Here the two subcases in **A** are also to be considered.

1° $$(U_1 U_2)f \equiv 0.$$

Since this carries with it

$$(U_1' U_2')f \equiv 0,$$

the conditions of § 38, **B**, 4°, (*a*) exist, and the two solutions of the corresponding linear partial differential equation are given by the two quadratures

$$\int \frac{\begin{vmatrix} dx & dy & dy' \\ 1 & y' & F(x,y,y') \\ \xi_1 & \eta_1 & \eta_1' \end{vmatrix}}{\Delta} = a \text{ and } \int \frac{\begin{vmatrix} dx & dy & dy' \\ 1 & y' & F(x,y,y') \\ \xi_2 & \eta_2 & \eta_2' \end{vmatrix}}{\Delta} = b,$$

where
$$\Delta \equiv \begin{vmatrix} 1 & y' & F(x,y,y') \\ \xi_1 & \eta_1 & \eta_1' \\ \xi_2 & \eta_2 & \eta_2' \end{vmatrix}.$$

Eliminating y' from these gives the solution of the original differential equation.

2°
$$(U_1 U_2)f \equiv U_1 f.$$

Since this carries with it

$$(U_1' U_2')f \equiv U_1' f,$$

the conditions of § 38, **B**, 4°, (*b*) exist. Two solutions of the corresponding linear partial differential equation are obtained by two quadratures, by the method given there. Eliminating y' from these, the solution of the original differential equation follows.

Remark. — It may be noted that in every instance where an ordinary differential equation of the second order is known to be invariant under two distinct groups, of which neither is trivial, its integration can be effected by means of two quadratures.

47. Second Method of Solution for B. — The method in cases **A**, 1° and 2° of the previous section leaves nothing to be desired. For the remaining cases, however, while, theoretically, the reduction of the problem to two quadratures seems sufficiently simple, a method analogous to that employed for **A**, even if involving a larger number of quadratures, or possibly the solution of a differential equation of the first order, may prove simpler in actual practice. Still under the supposition **B**, viz.

$$U_2'f \not\equiv \alpha U_1'f + \rho\, Af,$$

the four possible forms (§ 44) of the two-parameter groups of infinitesimal transformations leaving the differential equation unaltered will be considered :

α. $\qquad (U_1U_2)f \equiv 0, \quad U_2f \not\equiv \rho(x, y)\, U_1f.$

By a process involving two quadratures (§ 45, α) canonical variables x and y can be found, reducing the infinitesimal transformations to the forms

$$U_1f \equiv \frac{\partial f}{\partial x} \text{ and } U_2f \equiv \frac{\partial f}{\partial y}.$$

The differential equation invariant under these has the form (I and I′, § 28)

$$y'' \equiv F(y').$$

An additional quadrature gives

$$\int \frac{dy'}{F(y')} = x + a,$$

or, when solved for y', $\quad y' = \phi(x + a),$

and a final quadrature gives the solution

$$y = \int \phi(x + a)\, dx + b.$$

In this case four quadratures are required.

β. $\qquad (U_1U_2)f \equiv 0, \quad U_2f \equiv \rho(x, y)\, U_1f.$

By a process involving one quadrature (§ 45, β) canonical variables x and y can be found, reducing the infinitesimal transformations
to the forms

$$U_1 f \equiv \frac{\partial f}{\partial y} \text{ and } U_2 f \equiv x \frac{\partial f}{\partial y}.$$

The differential equation invariant under these has the form
(I and VII, § 28)

$$y'' = F(x).$$

Two additional quadratures give the solution

$$y = \int \int F(x) dx^2 + ax + b.$$

In this case three quadratures are required.

γ. $(U_1 U_2) f \equiv U_1 f, \quad U_2 f \not\equiv \rho(x, y) U_1 f.$

By a process involving two quadratures (§ 45, γ) canonical variables x and y can be found, reducing the infinitesimal transformations
to the forms

$$U_1 f \equiv \frac{\partial f}{\partial y} \text{ and } U_2 f \equiv x \frac{\partial f}{\partial x} + y \frac{\partial f}{\partial y}.$$

The differential equation invariant under these has the form (I and
IV, § 28)

$$y'' = \frac{1}{x} F(y').$$

As in the case α, two additional quadratures give the solution.
In this case four quadratures are required.

δ. $(U_1 U_2) f \equiv U_1 f, \quad U_2 f \equiv \rho(x, y) U_1 f.$

By a process (§ 45, δ) involving the finding of the path-curves determined by either infinitesimal transformation, *i.e.* the solution of
the differential equation

$$\frac{dx}{\xi_1} = \frac{dy}{\eta_1},$$

canonical variables x and y can be found, reducing the transformations to the forms

$$U_1 f \equiv \frac{\partial f}{\partial y} \text{ and } U_2 f \equiv y \frac{\partial f}{\partial y}.$$

The differential equation invariant under these has the form (I and
III, § 28)

$$\frac{y''}{y'} = F(x).$$

Two quadratures give the solution

$$y = a \int e^{\int F(x)dx} dx + b.$$

Remark. — The above classification holds equally well for **A**, for
which it is exceedingly simple, cases β and δ never arising (§ 46).
Hence the method of introducing canonical variables applies to all
cases where a differential equation of the second order is invariant
under two groups.   The interest in § 46 lies in the fact that it is there
shown that it is always possible, if desirable, to solve the differential
equation by two quadratures only.

While the classification of § 40 is more complicated, it must be
borne in mind that the two groups employed there need not determine a two-parameter group.   Some of the methods of § 40 are exceedingly simple ; so that they are not to be ignored.   On the other
hand, it is suggested that the method of this section be applied to the
examples of § 40.

Ex. **1.** $xyy'' + xy'^2 - yy' = 0.$ (Ex. 1, § 40).

This equation is invariant under $U_1 f \equiv x \frac{\partial f}{\partial x} + y \frac{\partial f}{\partial y}$ and $U_2 f \equiv y \frac{\partial f}{\partial y}$.
These determine a two-parameter group of the type α.   The canoni-
cal variables are readily found to be $x = \log x$, $y = \log \frac{y}{x}$.   Introducing these, the differential equation takes the form

$$y'' + 2(y'^2 + y') = 0 \text{ or } \frac{dy'}{y'(1 + y')} + 2\,dx = 0.$$

Integrating this, one obtains

$$\log \frac{y'}{1+y'} + 2x = c \text{ or } y' = \frac{1}{c_1 e^{2x} - 1} = \frac{e^{-2x}}{c_1 - e^{-2x}}.$$

Integrating again,

$$2y + c = \log(c_1 - e^{-2x}) \text{ or } c_2 e^{2y} = c_1 - e^{-2x}.$$

Passing back to the original variables,

$$c_1 x^2 - c_2 y^2 = 1.$$

Ex. 2. $y'' = Py' + Qy + X$. (Ex. 2, § 40).

This equation is invariant under $U_1 f \equiv y_1 \dfrac{\partial f}{\partial y}$ and $U_2 f \equiv y_2 \dfrac{\partial f}{\partial y}$, if $y_1'' = Py_1' + Qy_1$ and $y_2'' = Py_2' + Qy_2$. The transformations $U_1 f$ and $U_2 f$ determine a two-parameter group of type β. The canonical variables are $x = \dfrac{y_2}{y_1}$, $y = \dfrac{y}{y_1}$. To introduce these use should be made of the fact that $\dfrac{dy}{dx} = \dfrac{dy}{dx}\dfrac{dx}{dx} = \dfrac{y' \Delta}{y_1^2}$, where $\Delta \equiv y_1 y_2' - y_2 y_1'$, and that $y_1 y_2'' - y_2 y_1'' = P\Delta$. Then

$$y = y_1 y,$$

$$y' = y_1' y + \frac{y' \Delta}{y_1},$$

$$y'' = y_1'' y + \frac{y' P \Delta}{y_1} + \frac{y'' \Delta^2}{y_1^3}.$$

Substituting these values in the differential equation gives

$$\frac{y'' \Delta^2}{y_1^3} = X \text{ or } y'' = \frac{y_1^3 X}{\Delta^2},$$

where the right-hand member must be expressed as a function of x. Integrating twice,

$$y = \int dx \int \frac{y_1^3 X}{\Delta^2} dx + ax + b.$$

Passing back to the original variables,

$$y = y_1 \int d\left(\frac{y_2}{y_1}\right) \int \frac{y_1{}^3 X}{(y_1 y_2{}' - y_2 y_1{}')^2} d\left(\frac{y_2}{y_1}\right) + ay_2 + by_1.$$

Note. — It is an interesting fact that this form of the solution includes as a special case the form obtained by a well-known method in case the coefficients in the linear equation are constants. (See *El. Dif. Eq.* § 47.)

Ex. 3. $y'' = Iy' + Qy.$ (Ex. 3, § 40.)

This equation is invariant under $U_1 f \equiv y_1 \dfrac{\partial f}{\partial y}$ if y_1 is a particular solution of the equation, and also under $U_2 f \equiv y \dfrac{\partial f}{\partial y}$. The transformations $U_1 f$ and $U_2 f$ determine a two-parameter group of type δ. The canonical variables are $x = x, \; y = \dfrac{y}{y_1}$. This change of variables is the one usually employed.   (See *El. Dif. Eq.* § 53, 1°.)

CHAPTER VII

CONTACT TRANSFORMATIONS

48. Union of Elements. — The configuration consisting of a point and a line * through it is known as a *lineal element*. It is obviously self-dualistic. Since a lineal element in the plane is determined by three coördinates,† there are ∞^3 such elements.

Any curve in the plane determines ∞^1 lineal elements, each one consisting of a point of the curve and the tangent line at that point. [In particular a straight line determines ∞^1 lineal elements, all having the same p-coördinate; while a single point (looked upon as a line curve of the first class) determines ∞^1 elements all having the same x- and y-coördinates]. Such a single infinity of lineal elements is said to form a *union of elements*,‡ and successive elements in this case are said to be *united*. In general ∞^1 lineal elements do not form a union; it is easy, however, to find the condition that they do:

Two relations among the three coördinates

$$(113) \qquad \phi(x, y, p) = 0 \text{ and } \psi(x, y, p) = 0$$

---

* At times it is convenient to replace the line by its direction in the above definition.

† We shall use the nonself-dualistic set (x, y, p) where x and y are the rectangular coördinates of the point and p is the slope of the line.

It is almost needless to add that the theory here developed is no more restricted to this choice of coördinates than the general theory of Analytic Geometry is confined to the use of Cartesian coördinates.

‡ In this case the locus of the points of the elements coincides with the envelope of the lines of the elements; and besides, the point of tangency of each line with the envelope is the point of the element to which the line belongs. This locus will be referred to as the *curve of the union*.

determine ∞^1 elements.* The locus of the points of the latter

(114) $$\omega(x, y) = 0$$

is obtained by eliminating p between the two relations (113). A union exists provided the value of p, in terms of x and y, obtained from either of the two relations is the same as that of the slope of the tangent to the curve (114), *i.e.*

$$p = \frac{dy}{dx} = -\frac{\omega_x}{\omega_y},$$

where partial differentiation is indicated by a suffix. *The condition that the lineal elements determined by* (113) *form a union is therefore that*

(115) $$dy - p\,dx = 0.\dagger$$

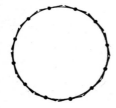

Ex. 1. Starting with the relations

$$x + yp = 0, \quad y^2(1 + p^2) = 1,$$

the point locus is the circle $x^2 + y^2 = 1$. Here

$$\frac{dy}{dx} = -\frac{x}{y} = p.$$

Fig. 6   Hence the elements form a union. (See Fig. 6.)

---

* A single relation $\phi(x, y) = 0$ free of p defines ∞^1 unions, each consisting of the ∞^1 elements having a point of the curve $\phi(x, y) = 0$ in common, p being undetermined.

Hence, if neither of the relations $\phi(x, y) = 0$ and $\psi(x, y) = 0$ involves p, they together determine a finite number of unions, each consisting of the ∞^1 elements having in common a point of intersection of the curves $\phi(x, y) = 0$ and $\psi(x, y) = 0$. (See Ex. 4, below.)

† The same condition obviously holds when the lineal elements are determined parametically

(116) $$x = X(t), \quad y = Y(t), p = P(t).$$

Ex. 2. In the case of

$$y + xp = 0, \quad x + yp = 0$$

the point locus is the pair of lines $x^2 - y^2 = 0$.
Here $\dfrac{dy}{dx} = \dfrac{x}{y}$; while $p = -\dfrac{x}{y}$. Hence there is no

union. (See Fig. 7.)

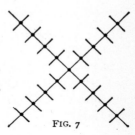

FIG. 7

FIG. 8

Ex. 3. In the case of

$$y = xp + 1, \quad p = a = const.$$

the point locus is the line $y = ax + 1$. **Here**
$\dfrac{dy}{dx} = a = p$. Hence the elements form a union. (See Fig. 8.)

Ex. 4. In the case of

$$x - 3y + 3 = 0, \quad 3x - y + 1 = 0$$

the point locus is the point $x = 0, y = 1$, while p is undetermined. The
elements form a union. (See Fig. 9.)

FIG. 9

FIG. 10

Ex. 5. The elements determined by

$$x = \cos t, \quad y = \sin t, \quad p = \tan t$$

do not form a union, since the point locus is the
circle $x^2 + y^2 = 1$, where

$$\frac{dy}{dx} = -\frac{x}{y} = -\cos t \neq p.$$

(See Fig. 10.)

Ex. 6. In the case of

$$y = xp + 1, \quad y = 1$$

the point locus is the line $y = 1$. Along this $p = 0$.
Hence the elements form a union. (See Fig. 11.)

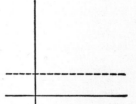

FIG. 11

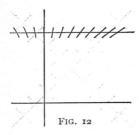

FIG. 12

Ex. **7.** In the case of

$$y = xp + 1, \ y = 3$$

the point locus is the line $y = 3$. Along this $p = 0$. But the elements along this line determined by the first relation have $p = \dfrac{y - 1}{x} \neq 0$. Hence there is no union. (See Fig. 12.)

49. Contact Transformation. — Of the possible transformations on the coördinates of a lineal element

$$(117) \qquad x_1 = X(x, y, p), \ y_1 = Y(x, y, p), \ p_1 = P(x, y, p),$$

those which transform every union of elements into a union play an important rôle and are known as *contact transformations.* The condition that (117) be a contact transformation is readily seen to be

$$(118) \qquad dy_1 - p_1 \, dx_1 \equiv \rho(x, y, p)(dy - p \, dx), \text{ where } \rho \not\equiv 0.$$

For, from the condition (115) it follows that if a union is to be transformed into a union $dy_1 - p_1 \, dx_1$ must vanish whenever $dy - p \, dx$ does; that is, the former must contain the latter as a factor.

Indicating partial differentiation by a subscript, (118) may be written

$$(Y_x - PX_x)dx + (Y_y - PX_y)dy + (Y_p - PX_p)dp \equiv \rho(dy - p \, dx).$$

This is equivalent to

$$(119) \qquad Y_x - PX_x = -\rho p, \ \ Y_y - PX_y = \rho, \ \ Y_p - PX_p = 0;$$

whence

$$(120) \qquad\qquad\qquad P = \frac{Y_p}{X_p}$$

and

(121) $$X_p(Y_x + p\,Y_y) - Y_p(X_x + p\,X_y) = 0.^*$$

The two relations (120) and (121) may be put in the compact form

(122) $$P = \frac{Y_p}{X_p} = \frac{Y_x + p\,Y_y}{X_x + p\,X_y}.$$

These relations, which are necessary conditions that (117) be a contact transformation, are also sufficient, as may be seen as follows: They lead at once to

$$Y_x + p\,Y_y - P(X_x + p\,X_y) = 0,$$

or

$$\frac{Y_x - PX_x}{-p} = \frac{Y_y - PX_y}{1} \equiv \rho.\dagger$$

Equations (119) follow at once, and, therefore, condition (118) is fulfilled.

Conditions (120) and (121), or their equivalents (122), may thus be used instead of (118), when desired.‡

* Introducing the Poissonian symbol

$$[XY] \equiv \begin{vmatrix} X_p & X_x + p\,X_y \\ Y_p & Y_x + p\,Y_y \end{vmatrix},$$

the relation (121) takes the simple form

(121) $$[XY] = 0.$$

When two functions X and Y satisfy the condition (121), they are said to be *in involution*.

† This value of the common ratio ρ cannot be identically zero, for using (122) it may be written

$$\rho = \frac{X_p Y_y - X_y Y_p}{X_p} = \frac{X_x Y_y - X_y Y_x}{X_x + p\,X_y} = \frac{X_x Y_p - X_p Y_x}{p\,X_p};$$

all three of the numerators cannot vanish simultaneously since X and Y are supposed to be independent functions.

‡ An element transformation, which is not a contact transformation, transforms precisely ∞^2 unions into unions. (See Kasner, *American Journal of Mathematics*, Vol. XXXII, p. 393). Thus, $X = x$, $Y = p$, $P = y$, which is obviously not a contact transformation, transforms the union defined by $y + p = c_1 e^x$, $y - p = c_2 e^{-x}$ for any pair of values of c_1 and c_2 into a union.

Remark 1. — Of the three functions X, Y, P in the contact transformation (117), either one of X and Y may be selected at pleasure; the other one is then determined as a solution of the linear partial differential equation (121). With X and Y selected, P is determined uniquely by (122).

The extended point transformation (§ 13) is evidently a special case of a contact transformation. For if X and Y are any functions free of p, (121) holds; while the form for the accompanying transformation of y' or p, given by (21), is exactly (122).

In what follows we shall exclude extended point transformations from consideration, unless specific mention is made to the contrary.

As an example of a contact transformation may be mentioned the transformation by reciprocal polars with respect to a conic. The transformation, in case the conic is the circle $x^2 + y^2 = 1$, takes the form

$$(A) \qquad x_1 = \frac{-p}{y - xp}, \quad y_1 = \frac{1}{y - xp}, \quad p_1 = -\frac{x}{y}.*$$

Here
$$dy_1 - p_1\, dx_1 \equiv \frac{-1}{y(y - xp)}(dy - p\,dx).$$

The transformation by reciprocal polars with respect to the parabola $x^2 = 2y$ is given by

$$(B) \qquad x_1 = p, \quad y_1 = xp - y, \quad p_1 = x.$$

Here
$$dy_1 - p_1\, dx_1 \equiv -(dy - p\,dx).$$

In the above illustrations a union whose curve is a point is transformed into one whose curve is a straight line. That *in the case of every contact transformation* (not an extended point transformation) *a union whose curve is a point†* *must be transformed into one whose*

---

* These equations may be obtained as follows : The point (x, y) of an element (x, y, p) is transformed into the polar line $xx_1 + yy_1 = 1$ whose slope is $p_1 = -\frac{x}{y}$. The line of the element,

$$Y - y = p(X - x) \text{ or } \frac{-pX}{y - xp} + \frac{Y}{y - xp} = 1,$$

is transformed into the pole

$$x_1 = \frac{-p}{y - xp}, \quad y_1 = \frac{1}{y - xp}.$$

† Excepting possible special points; e.g. the origin in Ex. 3, p. 185.

curve is an actual curve may be seen by eliminating p and p_1 from equations (117). There results from this elimination a single relation,*

$$(123) \qquad F(x, y, x_1, y_1) = 0,$$

which determines a locus for the points (x_1, y_1) corresponding to a fixed point (x, y).†

Moreover, a contact transformation is determined by a relation of the type (123), provided the three equations

$$(124) \qquad F = 0, \quad F_x + pF_y = 0, \quad F_{x_1} + p_1 F_{y_1} = 0$$

can be solved for x, y, p, and also for x_1, y_1, p_1. For, solving for x_1, y_1, p_1, there results the transformation of the three variables

$$(117) \qquad x_1 = X(x, y, p), \quad y_1 = Y(x, y, p), \quad p_1 = -\frac{F_{x_1}}{F_{y_1}}.$$

That this is a contact transformation may be seen readily. For from

$$p_1 = -\frac{F_{x_1}}{F_{y_1}} \text{ and } p = -\frac{F_x}{F_y}$$

$$dy_1 - p_1\, dx_1 = \frac{F_{x_1}\, dx_1 + F_{y_1}\, dy_1}{F_{y_1}}, \quad dy - p\, dx = \frac{F_x\, dx + F_y\, dy}{F_y}.$$

---

* If there were two independent relations,

$$F_1(x, y, x_1, y_1) = 0, \quad F_2(x, y, x_1, y_1) = 0,$$

they could be solved for x_1 and y_1 in terms of x and y, which would imply that (117) was an extended point transformation.

† We may say (fixing our attention on the curve of a union) that the effect of the contact transformation is to transform any point (a, b) into the curve $F(a, b, x_1, y_1) = 0$; while a point transformation transforms a point into a point.

Moreover, it is not difficult to show that a contact transformation, in general, transforms a union determined by a curve C into one whose curve C' is the envelope of the curves into which it transforms the various points of C, or, using the same form of expression as above, we shall say that it transforms the curve C into C'. (Thus see Lie, *Berührungstransformationen*, p. 49). If it should happen that the curve C is one of the curves $F(x, y, \alpha, \beta) = 0$, where α and β are any constants, its transform C' is the point (α, β).

Differentiating (123) gives

$$F_{x_1}\,dx_1 + F_{y_1}\,dy_1 = -(F_x\,dx + F_y\,dy).$$

Hence
$$dy_1 - p_1\,dx_1 = -\frac{F_y}{F_{y_1}}\,(dy - p\,dx),$$

which proves that (117) is a contact transformation.

The condition that (124) be solvable for x, y, p and for x_1, y_1, p_1 can be expressed very simply analytically:

In order to be able to solve for p it is necessary and sufficient that $F_y \neq 0$ when $F = 0$. Similarly, $F_{y_1} \neq 0$ when $F = 0$ is the condition that one be able to solve for p_1.

The condition that the first two equations of (124) can be solved for x_1 and y_1 is the non-vanishing of the functional determinant

$$\begin{vmatrix} F_{x_1} & F_{xx_1} + p\,F_{yx_1} \\ F_{y_1} & F_{xy_1} + p\,F_{yy_1} \end{vmatrix} \quad \text{or} \quad \begin{vmatrix} F_{x_1} & F_y F_{xx_1} - F_x F_{yx_1} \\ F_{y_1} & F_y F_{xy_1} - F_x F_{yy_1} \end{vmatrix}.$$

In the latter the factor $\dfrac{1}{F_y^2}$ is omitted since it is not zero whenever $F = 0$, because F is supposed to be generally analytic, and besides it is not infinite since $F_y \neq 0$ when $F = 0$, by hypothesis. This determinant can be put in the more symmetrical form

$$\Delta \equiv \begin{vmatrix} 0 & F_x & F_y \\ F_{x_1} & F_{xx_1} & F_{yx_1} \\ F_{y_1} & F_{xy_1} & F_{yy_1} \end{vmatrix}.$$

Since Δ contains F as a factor whenever either F_y or F_{y_1} does, the non-vanishing of Δ when $F = 0$ assures the non-vanishing of F_y and F_{y_1}. Hence *the only condition that* (124) *be solvable for* x_1, y_1, p_1 *is*

(125) $\Delta \neq 0$ *when* $F = 0$.

Because of the symmetry of Δ as to x, y and x_1, y_1, (125) is also the condition that (124) be solvable for x, y, p.

Remark 2. — It is interesting to note that $\Delta \neq 0$ is the condition that $F(x, y, x_1, y_1)$ involve x and y as two essential parameters, and also that it involve x_1 and y_1 in the same way; when such is the case $F(a, b, x_1, y_1) = 0$ defines ∞^2 curves for all choices of a and b, and $F(x, y, \alpha, \beta) = 0$ defines ∞^2 curves for all choices of α and β. For if x and y are not essential parameters in $F(x, y, x_1, y_1)$, two functions of x and y, say $\chi_1(x, y)$ and $\chi_2(x, y)$, can be found such that (see Note VII of the Appendix)

$$\chi_1 F_x + \chi_2 F_y = 0.$$

This carries with it

$$\chi_1 F_{x x_1} + \chi_2 F_{y x_1} = 0 \text{ and } \chi_1 F_{x y_1} + \chi_2 F_{y y_1} = 0.$$

$$\therefore \Delta \equiv \begin{vmatrix} 0 & F_x & F_y \\ F_{x_1} & F_{x x_1} & F_{y x_1} \\ F_{y_1} & F_{x y_1} & F_{y y_1} \end{vmatrix} = \frac{1}{\chi_1} \begin{vmatrix} 0 & \chi_1 F_x + \chi_2 F_y & F_y \\ F_{x_1} & \chi_1 F_{x x_1} + \chi_2 F_{y x_1} & F_{y x_1} \\ F_{y_1} & \chi_1 F_{x y_1} + \chi_2 F_{y y_1} & F_{y y_1} \end{vmatrix} = 0.$$

Conversely, if $\Delta = 0$

$$\frac{F_x}{F_y} = \frac{F_{x x_1}}{F_{y x_1}} = \frac{F_{x y_1}}{F_{y y_1}} = \frac{F_{x x_1} dx_1 + F_{x y_1} dy_1}{F_{y x_1} dx_1 + F_{y y_1} dy_1}.$$

$$\therefore \frac{\dfrac{\partial F_x}{\partial x_1} dx_1 + \dfrac{\partial F_x}{\partial y_1} dy_1}{F_x} = \frac{\dfrac{\partial F_y}{\partial x_1} dx_1 + \dfrac{\partial F_y}{\partial y_1} dy_1}{F_y}, \text{ and } \frac{F_x}{F_y} = \rho(x, y),$$

where ρ is a constant as far as x_1 and y_1 are concerned, but may be a function of x and y.

Hence $\Delta = 0$ carries with it a relation of the type

$$F_x - \rho(x, y) F_y = 0,$$

which is the condition that x and y are not essential parameters in $F(x, y, x_1, y_1)$.

In exactly the same way it can be shown that if $\Delta = 0$ x_1 and y_1 are not essential parameters in F.

The equations of transformation (A) and (B) in the cases of transformation by reciprocal polars given above are readily obtained by the method here given when $xx_1 + yy_1 = 1$ and $xx_1 - y - y_1 = 0$, respectively, are selected as the relation (123).

For the transformation by reciprocal polars with respect to the general conic

$$ax^2 + 2\,hxy + by^2 + 2\,gx + 2\,fy + c = 0$$

the relation (123) is the equation of the straight line

$$axx_1 + h(xy_1 + yx_1) + byy_1 + g(x + x_1) + f(y + y_1) + c = 0,$$

or

(123′) $$(ax + hy + g)x_1 + (hx + by + f)y_1 + gx + fy + c = 0.$$

Here

$$\Delta \equiv \begin{vmatrix} 0 & ax_1 + hy_1 + g & hx_1 + by_1 + f \\ ax + hy + g & a & h \\ hx + by + f & h & b \end{vmatrix}.$$

Subtracting x_1-times the second row $+\, y_1$-times the third row from the first, and taking account of (123′)

$$\Delta \equiv \begin{vmatrix} gx + fy + c & g & f \\ ax + hy + g & a & h \\ hx + by + f & h & b \end{vmatrix} = \begin{vmatrix} c & g & f \\ g & a & h \\ f & h & b \end{vmatrix} = \begin{vmatrix} a & h & g \\ h & b & f \\ g & f & c \end{vmatrix},$$

i.e. Δ equals the discriminant of the conic, and is different from zero in case the conic is an actual one and not a pair of straight lines. In this case the method given above applies. Solving

(124′) $$\begin{cases} (ax + hy + g)x_1 + (hx + by + f)y_1 + gx + fy + c = 0, \\ (a + hp)x_1 + (h + bp)y_1 + g + fp = 0, \\ ax + hy + g + (hx + by + f)p_1 = 0, \end{cases}$$

for x_1, y_1, p_1, the formulæ of transformation are

(C) $$x_1 = \frac{G(xp - y) + H - Ap}{C(xp - y) + F - Gp}, \quad y_1 = \frac{F(xp - y) + B - Hp}{C(xp - y) + F - Gp}, \quad p_1 = -\frac{ax + hy + g}{hx + by + f},$$

where A, B, C, F, G, H are the respective cofactors in the discriminant of the conic

The transformations (A) and (B) are obviously special cases of (C).

Another interesting contact transformation is obtained by selecting for (123) the equation of the circle,

(123'') $$(x - x_1)^2 + (y - y_1)^2 = r^2 \neq 0.$$

In this case $\Delta = - 8\,r^2$, and the equations of transformation are readily found to be

(D) $$x_1 = x \pm \frac{rp}{\sqrt{1 + p^2}},\quad y_1 = y \mp \frac{r}{\sqrt{1 + p^2}},\quad p_1 = p.$$

The effect of (D) is to transform any curve into a pair of parallel curves, one on each side of the original one, and at a distance r from it, as is apparent from the nature of (123''). A transformation of this type is referred to as a *dilatation*.

Find the contact transformations determined by the following relations :

Ex. 1. $(x - x_1)^2 - 2\,a(y - y_1) = 0.$

Ex. 2. $\dfrac{(x - x_1)^2}{a^2} + \dfrac{(y - y_1)^2}{b^2} = 1.$

Ex. 3. $x_1^2 + y_1^2 - (xx_1 + yy_1) = 0.$

Ex. 4. $\dfrac{x_1}{x} + \dfrac{y_1}{y} = 1.$

Ex. 5. $\dfrac{x}{x_1} + \dfrac{y}{y_1} = 1.$

50. Group of Contact Transformations. Infinitesimal Contact Transformation. — If in the one-parameter group

(126) $$x_1 = X(x, y, p, a),\quad y_1 = Y(x, y, p, a),\quad p_1 = P(x, y, p, a)$$

the condition

(118) $$dY - P\,dX \equiv \rho(x, y, p)(dy - p\,dx),$$

or its equivalent (122), holds, (126) defines a *one-parameter group of contact transformations.*

Like any one-parameter group in three variables (§ 11) the group (126) contains an infinitesimal transformation

(127) $x_1 = x + \xi(x, y, p)\,\delta a,\ y_1 = y + \eta\,(x, y, p)\,\delta a,\ p_1 = p + \pi(x, y, p)\delta a,$

whose symbol may be written

(128)
$$Bf \equiv \xi \frac{\partial f}{\partial x} + \eta \frac{\partial f}{\partial y} + \pi \frac{\partial f}{\partial p}.$$

Thus the dilatations

(D)
$$x_1 = x + \frac{ap}{\sqrt{1+p^2}}, \; y_1 = y - \frac{a}{\sqrt{1+p^2}}, \; p_1 = p$$

form a group, with the infinitesimal transformation

$$Bf \equiv \frac{p}{\sqrt{1+p^2}} \frac{\partial f}{\partial x} - \frac{1}{\sqrt{1+p^2}} \frac{\partial f}{\partial y}.$$

Similarly the transformations (Ex. 1, § 49)

$$x_1 = x - ap, \; y_1 = y - \frac{ap^2}{2}, \; p_1 = p$$

form a group, with the infinitesimal transformation

$$Bf \equiv 2 p \frac{\partial f}{\partial x} + p^2 \frac{\partial f}{\partial y}.$$

Since (127) is also a contact transformation,

(118') $dy_1 - p_1 dx_1 = dy - p \, dx + (d\eta - p \, d\xi - \pi \, dx)\delta a^* \equiv \rho(dy - p \, dx).$

where
$$\therefore \; \rho = 1 + \sigma(x, y, p)\, \delta a,$$

(129) $\sigma(x, y, p)(dy - p \, dx) \equiv d\eta - p \, d\xi - \pi \, dx = d(\eta - p\xi) + \xi \, dp - \pi \, dx.$

Writing with Lie

(130)
$$\eta - p\xi \equiv -W(x, y, p),$$

where W is known as the *characteristic function* of the infinitesimal contact transformation, the identity (129) may be replaced by

$$W_x + \pi = \sigma p, \; - W_y = \sigma, \; - W_p + \xi = 0 \, ;$$

whence, making use of (130) and eliminating σ,

(131)
$$\xi = W_p, \quad \eta = p W_p - W, \quad \pi = -W_x - p W_y.$$

---

* Here, as always in the case of infinitesimal transformations, higher powers of δa are neglected.

Moreover, for all choices of the function W, ξ, η, π are so determined by (131) that the corresponding infinitesimal transformation

$$x_1 = x + \xi \, \delta a, \; y_1 = y + \eta \, \delta a, \; p_1 = p + \pi \, \delta a$$

satisfies the condition (118') and is therefore a contact transformation; hence the

THEOREM. — *Connected with every infinitesimal contact transformation there is a characteristic function* $W \equiv -\eta + p\xi$, *in terms of which the transformation is given by means of* (131). *Conversely, starting with any function* W, *the relations* (131) *define an infinitesimal contact transformation.*

In terms of the characteristic function the infinitesimal transformation takes the form

$$(132) \qquad Bf \equiv W_p \frac{\partial f}{\partial x} + (pW_p - W)\frac{\partial f}{\partial y} - (W_x + pW_y)\frac{\partial f}{\partial p},$$

or using the Poissonian symbol (§ 49)

$$(132) \qquad\qquad Bf \equiv [Wf] - W\frac{\partial f}{\partial y}.$$

Choosing for W the form

$$W = \sqrt{1 + p^2}$$

gives the infinitesimal transformation

$$Bf \equiv \frac{p}{\sqrt{1 + p^2}} \frac{\partial f}{\partial x} - \frac{1}{\sqrt{1 + p^2}} \frac{\partial f}{\partial y},$$

which belongs to the group of dilatations (D).

The selection

$$W = \sqrt{a^2 p^2 + b^2}$$

gives the infinitesimal transformation

$$Bf \equiv \frac{a^2 p}{\sqrt{a^2 p^2 + b^2}} \frac{\partial f}{\partial x} - \frac{b^2}{\sqrt{a^2 p^2 + b^2}} \frac{\partial f}{\partial y},$$

which belongs to the group

$$x_1 = x + \frac{a^2 t p}{\sqrt{a^2 p^2 + b^2}}, \; y_1 = y - \frac{b^2 t}{\sqrt{a^2 p^2 + b^2}}, \; p_1 = p. \quad \text{(Ex. 2, § 49)}$$

When W is linear in p, the corresponding transformation is an extended point transformation.   For, if

$$W = \phi(x, y)p - \psi(x, y),$$

$$\xi = \phi(x, y), \quad \eta = \psi(x, y), \quad \pi = \psi_x + p(\psi_y - \phi_x) - p^2\phi_y.$$

$$[(24), \S 13]$$

Another fact worthy of mention in connection with the characteristic function is the effect upon it of a change of variables when the latter is effected by means of a contact transformation.   As was noted in § 11, the introduction of the new variables

$$[14'] \qquad x = F(x, y, p), \quad y = \Phi(x, y, p), \quad p = \Psi(x, y, p)$$

causes the infinitesimal transformation (128) to take the form

$$Bf \equiv Bx\,\frac{\partial f}{\partial x} + By\,\frac{\partial f}{\partial y} + Bp\,\frac{\partial f}{\partial p},$$

i.e. $$\qquad \xi = Bx, \quad \eta = By, \quad \pi = Bp.$$

By the definition of the charactertisic function (130) its form after transformation is

$$(130') \qquad \begin{cases} W = p\xi - \eta = pBx - By \\ \quad = \xi(px_x - y_x) + \eta(px_y - y_y) + \pi(px_p - y_p). \end{cases}$$

If $[14']$ is a contact transformation,

$$dy - p\,dx \equiv \rho(dy - p\,dx),$$

or $$\qquad y_x - px_x = -\rho p, \quad y_y - px_y = \rho, \quad y_p - px_p = 0;$$
whence

$$(133) \qquad W(x, y, p) = \rho(p\xi - \eta) = \rho(x, y, p)\,W(x, y, p).$$

Of course, in the right-hand member, x, y, p must be replaced by their values in terms of the new variables given by $[14']$.

The characteristic function for the group of dilatations in the case of rectangular coördinates was seen to be

$$W = \sqrt{1 + p^2}.$$

Introducing the new variables,

(B) $x = p, \quad y = xp - y, \quad p = x,$

for which $dy - p \, dx \equiv -(dy - p \, dx),$

it is easy to verify that

$$W = -\sqrt{1 + p^2} = -\sqrt{1 + x^2}.$$

On the other hand the new variables

(A) $x = \dfrac{-p}{y - xp}, \quad y = \dfrac{1}{y - xp}, \quad p = -\dfrac{x}{y},$

for which $dy - p \, dx \equiv \dfrac{1}{y(xp - y)}(dy - p \, dx)$

cause the characteristic function to assume the form

$$W = \frac{\sqrt{1 + p^2}}{y(xp - y)} = (xp - y)\sqrt{x^2 + y^2}.$$

51. Ordinary Differential Equations. — A differential equation of the first order

(134) $f(x, y, p) = 0$

may be looked upon as a relation among the three coördinates of the lineal elements of the plane, with the understanding, however, that

(135) $p = \dfrac{dy}{dx}.$

So that the differential equation defines ∞^2 lineal elements which [because of (135), which is identical with (115), § 48] are arranged in ∞^1 unions. The solutions of the differential equation are the equations of the curves of the unions.

Since all the lines through a point constitute a union, in which case the common point is the curve of the union, such unions must be taken into account when looking for the solutions of a differential equation.   Thus if the relation (134) is free of p, say

(134') $f(x, y) = 0$,

this may still be looked upon as a differential equation in which p is
arbitrary.   Such a differential equation defines, besides the union
whose curve is $f(x, y) = 0$, those unions
determined by each of the various points
of the curve.   See Fig. 13.   Each of
these points will be considered as an
integral curve of the differential equation.

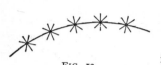

FIG. 13

Since every lineal element of the envelope of a family of ∞^1 curves
is an element of some curve of the family (compare *El. Dif. Eq.*
§§ 29, 30), the equation of the envelope must also be a solution
(*i.e.* the singular solution) of the differential equation of the family of
curves.   In the special case of a differential equation of the type
(134') the curve $f(x, y) = 0$ may be looked upon as the envelope,
and its equation is therefore the singular solution.

The Clairaut equation (*El. Dif. Eq.* § 27)

$$y - xp - f(p) = 0,$$

when transformed by

(B) $x_1 = p, \ y_1 = xp - y, \ p_1 = x,$

takes the form $y_1 + f(x_1) = 0,$

which is of the type (134').   It has for integral curves the various points of the
curve $y_1 + f(x_1) = 0$, while the equation of this curve itself is a singular solution.
Passing back to the original variables, this curve is transformed into some curve
$\phi(x, y) = 0$, and its points are transformed into the tangents of $\phi(x, y) = 0$.
Their respective equations are the singular and particular (in the aggregate,
general) solutions of the original differential equation.

The special Clairaut equation

$$y - xp - r\sqrt{1 + p^2} = 0,$$

when transformed by the dilatation

(D) $x = x_1 - \dfrac{rp_1}{\sqrt{1 + p_1^2}}, \ y = y_1 + \dfrac{r}{\sqrt{1 + p_1^2}}, \ p = p_1,$

takes the form $y_1 - x_1 p_1 = 0.$

This simple differential equation has the obvious general solution $y_1 = cx_1$, which is the equation of the family of straight lines through the origin. The envelope of this family is the origin, which determines a union that is obviously consistent with the relation defined by the differential equation. Passing back to the original variables, the origin goes into the circle $x^2 + y^2 = r^2$, which equation is therefore the singular solution of the original differential equation, while the lines through the origin go into the tangents to this circle. The equation of their family, $y = cx - r\sqrt{1 + c^2} = 0$, is the general solution.

52. First or Intermediary Integrals. — The differential equation

$$(136) \qquad\qquad \phi(x, y, p) = a,$$

for each value of the arbitrary constant a, has ∞^1 integral curves. Allowing a to take successively all possible values, (136) determines ∞^2 curves which are the integral curves of the differential equation of the second order

$$(137) \qquad\qquad \frac{d\phi}{dx} \equiv \phi_x + \phi_y p + \phi_p \frac{dp}{dx} = 0.$$

The differential equation of the first order (136) is known as a *first or intermediary integral* of (137). From the above it is seen that *a first integral of a differential equation of the second order classifies the ∞^2 integral curves of the latter into ∞^1 families of ∞^1 curves each.*

This classification is different, of course, for different first integrals, of which there is an indefinite number. For

$$(138) \qquad\qquad \psi(x, y, p) = b$$

will also be a first integral of (137), if, and only if,

$$\frac{d\psi}{dx} \equiv \psi_x + \psi_y p + \psi_p \frac{dp}{dx} = 0$$

is the same as (137), *i.e.* provided

$$\frac{\phi_x + \phi_y p}{\psi_x + \psi_y p} = \frac{\phi_p}{\psi_p},$$

or

$$(121) \qquad\qquad [\phi\psi] \equiv \begin{vmatrix} \phi_p & \phi_x + \phi_y p \\ \psi_p & \psi_x + \psi_y p \end{vmatrix} = 0.$$

Hence

THEOREM I.   *The necessary and sufficient condition that*

$$\phi(x, y, p) = a \ and \ \psi(x, y, p) = b$$

be first integrals of the same differential equation of the second order is that ϕ and ψ be in involution (§ 49).

Starting with the function $\phi(x, y, p)$, a second function $\psi(x, y, p)$ will be in involution with it provided it satisfies the linear partial differential equation

$$(139) \qquad [\phi\psi] \equiv \phi_p\frac{\partial\psi}{\partial x} + p\phi_p\frac{\partial\psi}{\partial y} - \left(\phi_x + p\phi_y\right)\frac{\partial\psi}{\partial p} = 0.$$

This linear equation in three independent variables has two independent solutions, one of which is $\phi(x, y, p)$.   All of its solutions are functions of these two.   Hence

THEOREM II.   *Knowing $\phi(x, y, p) = a$, a first integral of a differential equation of the second order, all of its first integrals may be obtained by solving the linear equation* (139). *Having found a solution of* (139), *independent of ϕ, all the first integrals are given by*

$$\Phi(\phi, \psi) = c$$

where Φ is an arbitrarily chosen function of ϕ and ψ.

Since two independent first integrals

$$\phi(x, y, p) = a \ and \ \psi(x, y, p) = b$$

of a differential equation of the second order define the same set of ∞^2 integral curves but classified in distinct manners, for a particular but arbitrary choice of a and b, say a_0 and b_0, the differential equations

$$(140) \qquad \phi(x, y, p) = a_0 \ and \ \psi(x, y, p) = b_0$$

will, in general, have an integral curve in common.   At each point of this curve both equations (140) determine the same value of p;

hence the equation of the curve

$$\omega\,(x, y, a_0, b_0) = 0$$

may be obtained by eliminating p from (140).

Still keeping a_0 fixed but allowing b to be an arbitrary constant, the result of eliminating p from $\phi = a_0$ and $\psi = b$ gives

$$\omega\,(x, y, a_0, b) = 0,$$

a solution of $\phi(x, y, p) = a_0$ containing an arbitrary constant which is, therefore, its general solution. Hence,

THEOREM III.   *If a second differential equation*

$$\psi(x, y, p) = b$$

involving an arbitrary constant can be found such that ϕ and ψ are in involution, the general solution of

$$\phi(x, y, p) = a_0$$

can be found by eliminating p from the two differential equations.

This process is frequently of service.   (See *El. Dif. Eq.* §§ 25, 26).

Eliminating p from (136) and (138) gives

$$\omega\,(x, y, a, b) = 0,$$

a solution of (137) involving two arbitrary constants.   It is therefore the general solution.   Hence,

THEOREM IV.   *If two independent first integrals of a differential equation of the second order can be found, its general solution is obtained by eliminating p from the equations of the first integrals.*

Remark. — If ϕ and ψ are in involution, it follows at once from the above that the two relations

$$\phi(x, y, p) = a, \text{ and } \psi(x, y, p) = b,$$

determine an element union (§ 48) for all choices of the constants a and b.

It should be noted, however, that

$$(113) \qquad \phi(x, y, p) = 0, \quad \psi(x, y, p) = 0$$

may determine a union without the identical vanishing of $[\phi, \psi]$; thus see Ex. 6, § 48. But in every case when the relations (113) determine a union, $[\psi, \phi]$ must equal zero, either identically or because of these relations. This follows readily from the fact that whenever (113) determine a union, the equation of the curve of the latter is an integral curve common to the two differential equations $\phi = 0$, $\psi = 0$; and conversely.

53. Differential Equation of the First Order Invariant under a Group of Contact Transformations. The general type of differential equation of the first order invariant under the group whose infinitesimal transformation is

$$(132) \qquad Bf \equiv W_p \frac{\partial f}{\partial x} + (pW_p - W) \frac{\partial f}{\partial y} - (W_x + pW_y) \frac{\partial f}{\partial p}$$

is obtained (compare § 18) by equating to zero the general solution * of the linear partial differential equation

$$(141) \qquad W_p \frac{\partial f}{\partial x} + (pW_p - W) \frac{\partial f}{\partial y} - (W_x + pW_y) \frac{\partial f}{\partial p} = 0.$$

On the other hand, the condition that the differential equation $f(x, y, p) = 0$ be invariant under the group whose infinitesimal transformation is Bf is obviously ($[12]$, § 11)

$$Bf = 0 \text{ whenever } f = 0.$$

As was noted in § 51, a differential equation of the first order

$$(142) \qquad p = \omega(x, y)$$

arranges the ∞^2 lineal elements determined by it in ∞^1 unions, the curves of which are its integral curves. If (142) is left unaltered by

---

* This solution is obviously the general expression for the *first differential invariants* of the group, the name given by Lie to invariant functions of x, y, p.

a contact transformation

$$(117)\qquad x_1 = X(x, y, p),\ \ y_1 = Y(x, y, p),\ \ p_1 = P(x, y, p),$$

the latter interchanges the integral curves of (142) among themselves, since it transforms unions into unions.

As far as the differential equation (142) is concerned, the only lineal elements operated upon by (117) are those whose coördinates are $(x, y, p = \omega(x, y))$. These elements are transformed into $(x_1, y_1, p_1 = \omega(x_1, y_1))$ by (117), since the latter leaves the differential equation unaltered. Hence the effect of the contact transformation (117) on the differential equation is the same as that of the point transformation

$$(143)\qquad x_1 = X(x, y, \omega(x, y)),\ \ y_1 = Y(x, y, \omega(x, y)).$$

Whence the

THEOREM. — *If the differential equation*

$$(142)\qquad p = \omega(x, y)$$

is invariant under the contact transformation

$$(117)\qquad x_1 = X(x, y, p),\ \ y_1 = Y(x, y, p),\ \ p_1 = P(x, y, p),$$

it is also invariant under the point transformation

$$(143)\qquad x_1 = X(x, y, \omega(x, y)),\ \ y_1 = Y(x, y, \omega(x, y)).$$

Both transformations interchange the integral curves of (142).

It follows at once that *if the differential equation*

$$p = \omega(x, y)$$

is invariant under a group of contact transformations whose infinitesimal transformation is

$$Bf \equiv \xi(x, y, p)\frac{\partial f}{\partial x} + \eta(x, y, p)\frac{\partial f}{\partial y} + \pi(x, y, p)\frac{\partial f}{\partial p},$$

it is also invariant under the group of point transformations whose infinitesimal transformation is

$$Uf \equiv \xi(x, y, \omega(x, y)) \frac{\partial f}{\partial x} + \eta(x, y, \omega(x, y)) \frac{\partial f}{\partial y}.$$

Either of the methods of §§ 12 and 20, Chapter II, may then be employed for solving the differential equation.

Remark. — Since $BW = -W_y W$, it follows that the differential equation

(144) $W(x, y, p) = 0$

is invariant under the group of contact transformations whose infinitesimal transformation has W for characteristic function.

But the invariance is of a special kind. The effect of this infinitesimal transformation is to carry the point (x, y) of an element (x, y, p) into $(x + \xi \, \delta a, \ y + \eta \, \delta a)$ where $\xi = W_p, \eta = p W_p - W$. The slope of the line joining these points is

$$\frac{\eta}{\xi} = p - \frac{W}{W_p}, = p \text{ when } W = 0.$$

Hence any element whose coördinates satisfy (144) has its point carried in the direction of the line of the element, that is, the element and the one into which it is transformed are united (§ 48). The infinitesimal transformation, therefore, leaves unaltered each of the unions (§ 51) determined by the differential equation (144), and the group has this effect on each of the integral curves of (144). Such a group is said to be *trivial* with respect to the differential equation (144), (§ 12), and is of no service in solving it.

APPENDIX

NOTE I

THE INFINITESIMAL TRANSFORMATION

In case both $\dfrac{\partial}{\partial a}\phi(x, y, a)$ and $\dfrac{\partial}{\partial a}\psi(x, y, a)$ vanish identically for the special value of $a = a_0$, or if either of them becomes infinite for that value of a, irrespective of the values of x and y that may enter, a modification of the process for finding the infinitesimal transformation employed in § 2 must be made. It should be noted that they cannot both vanish identically for all values of a, for in that case neither of the functions ϕ and ψ could involve a at all ; nor can either one of them become infinite for all values of x, y, and a, since ϕ and ψ are supposed to be generally analytic, which implies the existence of finite derivatives, except perhaps for special values of the arguments.

Let α be a value of the parameter for which $\dfrac{\partial\phi}{\partial a}$ and $\dfrac{\partial\psi}{\partial a}$ are finite and at least one of them different from zero. The transformation T_α determined by it has for inverse a definite transformation, $T_{\bar\alpha}$, of the group, corresponding to the value $\bar\alpha$ of the parameter, where $\bar\alpha$ is a function of α only. Since $T_{\bar\alpha}T_\alpha \equiv T_{a_0}$ is the identical transformation, $T_{\bar\alpha}T_{\alpha+\delta a}$ is an infinitesimal transformation. If $T_{\bar\alpha}$ is

$$x_1 = \phi(x, y, \bar\alpha), \quad y_1 = \psi(x, y, \bar\alpha),$$

the infinitesimal transformation $T_{\bar\alpha}T_{\alpha+\delta a}$ may be written, when expanded by Taylor's Theorem

$$x_2 = \phi(x_1, y_1, \alpha + \delta a) = x + \frac{\partial}{\partial \alpha} \phi(x_1, y_1, \alpha)\delta a^* + \cdots$$

$$y_2 = \psi(x_1, y_1, \alpha + \delta a) = y + \frac{\partial}{\partial \alpha} \psi(x_1, y_1, \alpha)\delta a + \cdots,$$

since $\phi(x_1, y_1, \alpha) = x$, $\psi(x_1, y_1, \alpha) = y$. Owing to the way in which α was chosen, neither of the coefficients of δa is infinite for all values of x and y, and one of them, at least, is not identically zero. Writing

$$(145) \begin{cases} \dfrac{\partial}{\partial \alpha} \phi(x_1, y_1, \alpha) = \dfrac{\partial}{\partial \alpha} \phi[\phi(x, y, \overline{\alpha}), \ \psi(x, y, \overline{\alpha}), \ \alpha] \equiv \xi(x, y, \alpha), \\[2ex] \dfrac{\partial}{\partial \alpha} \psi(x_1, y_1, \alpha) = \dfrac{\partial}{\partial \alpha} \psi[\phi(x, y, \overline{\alpha}), \ \psi(x, y, \overline{\alpha}), \ \alpha] \equiv \eta(x, y, \alpha), \end{cases}$$

it follows that *an infinitesimal transformation of the group* (1) *of the type* (2), § 2,

(2) $\delta x = \xi \delta a, \ \ \delta y = \eta \delta a$

can always be found.

The forms for ξ and η found in § 2 are exactly what the above become for the special choice $\alpha = \overline{\alpha} = a_0$.

From the above it is seen that ξ and η in (2) depend upon the choice of α. It remains to show *how* they depend upon the choice of the parameter. Let

$$\delta x = \Xi(x, y)\delta a, \ \ \delta y = H(x, y)\delta a,$$

or $$x_1 = x + \Xi(x, y)\delta a, \ \ y_1 = y + H(x, y)\delta a$$

be some known infinitesimal transformation of the group (1), where Ξ and H are not both identically zero, and neither of them is infinite, in general. The result of performing successively any transformation T_a of the group (1) and the above infinitesimal transformation is

---

* Here $\dfrac{\partial}{\partial \alpha} \phi(x_1, y_1, \alpha)$ stands for $\left[\dfrac{\partial}{\partial a} \phi(x_1, y_1, a) \right]_\alpha$.

some transformation of the group whose effect on the variables x and y differs from that of T_a by an infinitesimal amount. In other words, it is a transformation $T_{a+\Delta a}$, where Δa is an infinitesimal which is a function of a and δa only, because of the group property of (1). From the first definition of this transformation

$$x_2 = x_1 + \Xi(x_1, y_1)\delta a = \phi(x, y, a) + \Xi(\phi, \psi)\delta a,$$

$$y_2 = y_1 + \mathrm{H}(x_1, y_1)\delta a = \psi(x, y, a) + \mathrm{H}(\phi, \psi)\delta a,$$

while from the second definition

$$x_2 = \phi(x, y, a + \Delta a) = \phi(x, y, a) + \frac{\partial \phi}{\partial a}\Delta a + \cdots,$$

$$y_2 = \psi(x, y, a + \Delta a) = \psi(x, y, a) + \frac{\partial \psi}{\partial a}\Delta a + \cdots.$$

Hence

(146)

$$\begin{cases} \Xi(\phi, \psi)\delta a \equiv \dfrac{\partial \phi}{\delta a}\Delta a + \cdots, \\[2mm] \mathrm{H}(\phi, \psi)\delta a \equiv \dfrac{\partial \psi}{\partial a}\Delta a + \cdots, \end{cases}$$

for all values of x, y, a and δa, Δa being a definite function of a and δa, and an infinitesimal along with δa. By hypothesis Ξ and H do not both vanish identically; suppose, to fix the ideas, that $\Xi \not\equiv 0$. It follows that x is not left unaltered by all the transformations of the group (1) ; hence ϕ must involve a, and $\frac{\partial \phi}{\partial a} \not\equiv 0$. With a proper choice of x, y, a the coefficient of δa and that of Δa in at least the first of the two relations (146) are different from zero. By a theorem in the Theory of Functions, concerning the inversion of power series, Δa is developable in powers of δa, the development beginning with the first power. Hence

$$\Delta a = w(a)\delta a + \cdots,^*$$

---

* Since, as was noted above, Δa is a function of a and δa only, the coefficients in this development involve a only and are free of x and y.

where $w(a) \not\equiv 0$. Δa is thus of the same order of infinitesimals as δa. Putting this value in (146), dividing by δa, and passing to the limit $\delta a \doteq 0$,

$$(147) \qquad \Xi(\phi, \psi) \equiv w(a)\frac{\partial \phi}{\partial a}, \quad H(\phi, \psi) \equiv w(a)\frac{\partial \psi}{\partial a};$$

or remembering that $x = \phi(x_1, y_1, \bar{a})$, $y = \psi(x_1, y_1, \bar{a})$,

these may be written

$$\frac{\partial \phi}{\partial a} = \frac{\partial}{\partial a}\, \phi[\phi(x_1, y_1, \bar{a}), \psi(x_1, y_1, \bar{a}), a] \equiv \frac{1}{w(a)}\Xi(x_1, y_1),$$

$$\frac{\partial \psi}{\partial a} = \frac{\partial}{\partial a}\, \psi[\phi(x_1, y_1, \bar{a}), \psi(x_1, y_1, \bar{a}), a] \equiv \frac{1}{w(a)}H(x_1, y_1).$$

Using (145), and replacing x_1 and y_1 in these identities by x and y, we have

$$(148) \quad \xi(x, y, a) \equiv \frac{1}{w(a)}\Xi(x, y), \quad \eta(x, y, a) \equiv \frac{1}{w(a)}H(x, y).$$

The effect, then, of using different values of the parameter in determining an infinitesimal transformation by the method of the first part of this note is to obtain pairs of coefficients of δa in the two formulæ which are proportional, the factors of proportionality being constants. Hence, by Remark 1, § 2, *all the infinitesimal transformations so obtained are one and the same.* We have thus arrived at the

THEOREM. — *Every one-parameter group of transformations*

$$x_1 = \phi(x, y, a), \quad y_1 = \psi(x, y, a)$$

has one and only one independent infinitesimal transformation

$$\delta x = \xi(x, y)\delta a, \quad \delta y = \eta(x, y)\delta a,$$

where

$$\xi = \frac{\partial}{\partial \alpha}\phi[\phi(x, y, \bar{\alpha}), \psi(x, y, \bar{\alpha}), \alpha], \quad \eta = \frac{\partial}{\partial \alpha}\psi[\phi(x, y, \bar{\alpha}), \psi(x, y, \bar{\alpha}), \alpha],$$

and α is any value of the parameter such that at least one of $\left(\dfrac{\partial \phi}{\partial a}\right)_a$ *and* $\left(\dfrac{\partial \psi}{\partial a}\right)_a$ *is not identically zero, and neither of them is infinite for all values of x and y.*

In general a_0 is a possible value. In § 4 is shown that the transformations of the group can always be put in such form that this is true. When for a given group this value cannot be used, this is due to the way in which the parameter enters, and is not a peculiarity of the group.

Remark. — This theorem and its proof hold for *n* variables without any but obvious modifications to take account of the number of variables.

NOTE II

SOLUTION OF THE RICCATI EQUATION

$$\frac{dy'}{dx} = \frac{1}{\xi}\frac{\partial \eta}{\partial x} + \frac{1}{\xi}\left(\frac{\partial \eta}{\partial y} - \frac{\partial \xi}{\partial x}\right)y' - \frac{1}{\xi}\frac{\partial \xi}{\partial y}y'^2 \quad (§ 18).$$

In § 18 the general method for finding the differential equations invariant under a given group led to the solution of the Riccati equation

$$(39) \qquad \frac{dy'}{dx} = \frac{1}{\xi}\frac{\partial \eta}{\partial x} + \frac{1}{\xi}\left(\frac{\partial \eta}{\partial y} - \frac{\partial \xi}{\partial x}\right)y' - \frac{1}{\xi}\frac{\partial \xi}{\partial y}y'^2,$$

in which *y*, wherever it occurs, is supposed to have been replaced by its value in terms of *x* and *c* [say $y = \phi(x, c)$] obtained from $u(x, y) = c$, the solution of the differential equation

$$(11) \qquad \frac{dx}{\xi} = \frac{dy}{\eta}.$$

It is very easily seen that

$$(149) \qquad y' = \frac{\eta}{\xi} = \frac{\eta[x, \phi(x, c)]}{\xi[x, \phi(x, c)]}$$

in which y is replaced, as above, by $\phi(x,\ c)$, is a particular solution of (39). For differentiating (149)

$$\frac{dy'}{dx} = \frac{1}{\xi}\left(\frac{\partial\eta}{\partial x} + \frac{\partial\eta}{\partial y}\frac{dy}{dx}\right) - \frac{\eta}{\xi^2}\left(\frac{\partial\xi}{\partial x} + \frac{\partial\xi}{\partial y}\frac{dy}{dx}\right).$$

Remembering that $\dfrac{dy}{dx} = \dfrac{\eta}{\xi}$, this becomes

$$\frac{d\left(\frac{\eta}{\xi}\right)}{dx} = \frac{1}{\xi}\frac{\partial\eta}{\partial x} + \frac{1}{\xi}\left(\frac{\partial\eta}{\partial x} - \frac{\partial\xi}{\partial x}\right)\frac{\eta}{\xi} - \frac{1}{\xi}\frac{\partial\xi}{\partial y}\left(\frac{\eta}{\xi}\right)^2.$$

Whence follows at once that (149) satisfies (39).

It is a well-known fact that the knowledge of a particular solution of a Riccati equation enables one to find a transformation of variables which reduces the equation to a linear differential equation of the first order, whose solution requires two quadratures (see *El. Dif. Eq.* § 73, 1°). For the sake of simplicity, writing (39) in the form

$$\frac{dy'}{dx} = X_0 + X_1 y' + X_2 y'^2,$$

and its particular solution $y' = y_0'$,

the transformation $y' = \dfrac{1}{z} + y_0'$

changes the differential equation into

$$\frac{dz}{dx} + (X_1 + 2 y_0' X_2)z + X_2 = 0,$$

which is linear. If $z = \omega(x,\ k)$ is the solution of this equation,

(150) $$y' = \frac{1}{\omega(x,\ k)} + \frac{\eta[x,\ \phi(x,\ c)]}{\xi[x,\ \phi(x,\ c)]}$$

is the solution of (39). Solving (150) for k, and replacing $\phi(x,\ c)$ by y,

$$u'(x,\ y,\ y') = k$$

is the required second solution of (37), § 18.

In II, $\dfrac{dx}{-y} = \dfrac{dy}{x} = \dfrac{dy'}{1+y'^2}$. $u \equiv x^2 + y^2 = c.$ $\therefore y = \sqrt{c-x^2}.$

The Riccati equation (39) is $\dfrac{dy'}{dx} = \dfrac{1+y'^2}{-\sqrt{c-x^2}}.$

The transformation $\qquad y' = \dfrac{1}{z} + \dfrac{x}{-\sqrt{c-x^2}}$

reduces this to $\qquad \dfrac{dz}{dx} + \dfrac{2x}{c-x^2}z = \dfrac{1}{\sqrt{c-x^2}}.$

Integrating, $\qquad\qquad z = \dfrac{x\sqrt{c-x^2}}{c} + k(c-x^2)$

$$= \dfrac{xy}{x^2+y^2} + ky^2.$$

Hence $\qquad\qquad y' = \dfrac{x^2+y^2}{xy + ky^2(x^2+y^2)} - \dfrac{x}{y},$

and $\qquad\qquad k = \dfrac{y - xy'}{(x+yy')(x^2+y^2)} \equiv u'(x, y, y').$

Compare this with II, § 19.

NOTE III

ISOTHERMAL CURVES

The condition that two distinct families of curves

$$\phi(x, y) = const. \text{ and } \psi(x, y) = const.$$

divide the plane into infinitesimal squares may be obtained from the following considerations : *

Passing to the new system of coördinates

(151) $\qquad\qquad x = \phi(x, y), \quad y = \psi(x, y)$

the two families of curves have the simple equations

$$x = const. \text{ and } y = const.$$

* All this holds, practically without change, for isothermal curves on surfaces.

From $\quad dx = \dfrac{\partial \phi}{\partial x}\, dx + \dfrac{\partial \phi}{\partial y}\, dy \text{ and } dy = \dfrac{\partial \psi}{\partial x}\, dx + \dfrac{d\psi}{\partial y}\, dy,$

$$dx = \frac{\dfrac{\partial \psi}{\partial y}\, dx - \dfrac{\partial \phi}{\partial y}\, dy}{J(\phi,\,\psi)} \quad \text{and} \quad dy = \frac{\dfrac{\partial \phi}{\partial x}\, dy - \dfrac{\partial \psi}{\partial x}\, dx}{J(\phi,\,\psi)},$$

where $\qquad J(\phi,\,\psi) \equiv \dfrac{\partial \phi}{\partial x}\dfrac{\partial \psi}{\partial y} - \dfrac{\partial \phi}{\partial y}\dfrac{\partial \psi}{\partial x},$

the Jacobian of ϕ and ψ, which is not identically zero, since the two families of curves are distinct. (See *El. Dif. Eq.* Note I of the Appendix.)

The expression for the element of length of arc of any curve in the plane, in terms of the new coördinates, is

$$ds^2 = dx^2 + dy^2 = E\, dx^2 - 2\, F\, dx\, dy + G\, dy^2,$$

where the coefficients

$$E \equiv \frac{\left(\dfrac{\partial \psi}{\partial x}\right)^2 + \left(\dfrac{\partial \psi}{\partial y}\right)^2}{[J(\phi,\,\psi)]^2}, \quad F \equiv \frac{\dfrac{\partial \phi}{\partial x}\dfrac{\partial \psi}{\partial x} + \dfrac{\partial \phi}{\partial y}\dfrac{\partial \psi}{\partial y}}{[J(\phi,\,\psi)]^2}, \quad G \equiv \frac{\left(\dfrac{\partial \phi}{\partial x}\right)^2 + \left(\dfrac{\partial \phi}{\partial y}\right)^2}{[J(\phi,\,\psi)]^2},$$

are to be expressed in terms of x and y by aid of (151).

A first requirement, that the two families of curves form isothermal systems, is that they cut each other orthogonally. The condition for this is

$$-\frac{\dfrac{\partial \phi}{\partial x}}{\dfrac{\partial \phi}{\partial y}} = \frac{\dfrac{\partial \psi}{\partial y}}{\dfrac{\partial \psi}{\partial x}}, \quad \text{or } F = 0.$$

Hence a necessary condition is that the expression for the element of length of arc assume the form

$$ds^2 = E\, dx^2 + G\, dy^2.$$

For a curve of the family $x = const.$ (which will be referred to as an x-curve)

$$ds_x = \sqrt{G}\, dy,$$

while for a y-curve $\qquad ds_y = \sqrt{E}\, dx.$

If $\sqrt{E} = \sqrt{G}$ at every point in the plane, the curves divide the plane into infinitesimal squares, for choosing dx the same as dy,

$$ds_x = ds_y.$$

Moreover, if $\sqrt{E}$ and $\sqrt{G}$ contain a common factor, and each of the remaining factors is a function of the corresponding variable only, thus

$$\sqrt{E} = \lambda(x, y)\alpha(x), \quad \sqrt{G} = \lambda(x, y)\beta(y),$$

the introduction of the new variables

$$X = \int \alpha(x)dx \text{ and } Y = \int \beta(y)dy$$

gives $\qquad ds_x = \Lambda(X, Y)dX \text{ and } ds_y = \Lambda(X, Y)dY,$

where $\Lambda(X, Y)$ is what $\lambda(x, y)$ becomes when x and y are replaced by their values in terms of X and Y. The families

$$X = const. \text{ and } Y = const.$$

(which are obviously the same as $x = const.$ and $y = const.$) have the desired property. Hence the

THEOREM. — *The necessary and sufficient condition that the curves* $\phi(x, y) = const.$ *and their orthogonal trajectories* $\psi(x, y) = const.$ *divide the plane into infinitesimal squares is that the choice of variables*

$$x = \phi(x, y), \quad y = \psi(x, y)$$

reduces the expression for the element of length of arc to the form

$$ds^2 = \lambda^2(x, y)\{[\alpha(x)dx]^2 + [\beta(y)dy]^2\},$$

where, in particular, $\alpha(x)$ *and* $\beta(y)$ *may each be unity.*

Thus in the case of a family of concentric circles and their orthogonal trajectories,

$$x = x^2 + y^2, \quad y = \frac{y}{x},$$

$$ds^2 = \frac{1}{4\,x}\,dx^2 + \frac{x}{(1+y^2)^2}\,dy^2 = x\left[\left(\frac{dx}{2\,x}\right)^2 + \left(\frac{dy}{1+y^2}\right)^2\right].$$

Putting $\qquad X = \log \sqrt{x}, \quad Y = \tan^{-1}y,$

$$ds^2 = e^{2X}(dX^2 + dY^2).$$

For other examples of isothermal systems, see § 24.

NOTE IV

DIFFERENTIAL EQUATION OF THE SECOND ORDER NOT INVARIANT UNDER ANY GROUP

If the differential equation be written in the form

$$y'' - F(x, y, y') = 0$$

the condition that it be left unaltered by the group

$$Uf \equiv \xi\frac{\partial f}{\partial x} + \eta\frac{\partial f}{\partial y}$$

is [(61), § 27]

$(61')\quad -\xi\dfrac{\partial F}{\partial x} - \eta\dfrac{\partial F}{\partial y} - \eta'\dfrac{\partial F}{\partial y'} + \eta'' = 0,$ whenever $y'' = F(x, y, y').$

Here $\quad \eta' = \dfrac{\partial \eta}{\partial x} + \left(\dfrac{\partial \eta}{\partial y} - \dfrac{\partial \xi}{\partial x}\right)y' - \dfrac{\partial \xi}{\partial y}y'^2, \qquad [(24), \S\ 13],$

$$\eta'' = \frac{d\eta'}{dx} - y''\frac{d\xi}{dx}, \qquad\qquad [(58), \S\ 26],$$

$$= \frac{\partial^2 \eta}{\partial x^2} + \left(2\,\frac{\partial^2 \eta}{\partial x\,\partial y} - \frac{\partial^2 \xi}{\partial x^2}\right)y' + \left(\frac{\partial^2 \eta}{\partial y^2} - 2\,\frac{\partial^2 \xi}{\partial x\,\partial y}\right)y'^2 - \frac{\partial^2 \xi}{\partial y^2}y'^3$$

$$+ \left(\frac{\partial \eta}{\partial y} - 2\,\frac{\partial \xi}{\partial x} - 3\,\frac{\partial \xi}{\partial y}y'\right)y''.$$

Replacing y'', wherever it occurs in η'', by $F(x, y, y')$ the condition $(61')$ becomes

$$(152) \quad \begin{cases} \left(\dfrac{\partial \eta}{\partial y} - 2\dfrac{\partial \xi}{\partial x}\right)F - \xi\dfrac{\partial F}{\partial x} - \eta\dfrac{\partial F}{\partial y} - \dfrac{\partial \eta}{\partial x}\dfrac{\partial F}{\partial y'} + \dfrac{\partial^2 \eta}{\partial x^2} \\[2mm] + \left[2\dfrac{\partial^2 \eta}{\partial x\,\partial y} - \dfrac{\partial^2 \xi}{\partial x^2} - 3\dfrac{\partial \xi}{\partial y}F - \left(\dfrac{\partial \eta}{\partial y} - \dfrac{\partial \xi}{\partial x}\right)\dfrac{\partial F}{\partial y'}\right]y' \\[2mm] + \left(\dfrac{\partial^2 \eta}{\partial y^2} - 2\dfrac{\partial^2 \xi}{\partial x\,\partial y} + \dfrac{\partial \xi}{\partial y}\dfrac{\partial F}{\partial y'}\right)y'^2 - \dfrac{\partial^2 \xi}{\partial y^2}y'^3 \equiv 0 \end{cases}$$

for all values of x, y, y'.

Since (152) is an identity with respect to $x, y,$ and y', it is equivalent to a number of differential and finite equations in ξ and η, the exact number depending on the form of F. Fixing one's attention on y' alone, (152) is equivalent to at least *four* equations, and perhaps more. In general it is impossible to find functions $\xi(x, y)$ and $\eta(x, y)$ to satisfy all these conditions.

As an example, consider the differential equation

$$y'' = xy + \tan y'.$$

The identity (152) leads to

$$\left(\frac{\partial \eta}{\partial y} - 2\frac{\partial \xi}{\partial x}\right)(xy + \tan y') - \xi y - \eta x - \frac{\partial \eta}{\partial x}\sec^2 y' + \cdots$$

$$- 3\frac{\partial \xi}{\partial y}(xy + \tan y')y' - \left(\frac{\partial \eta}{\partial y} - \frac{\partial \xi}{\partial x}\right)y'\sec^2 y' + \frac{\partial \xi}{\partial y}y'^2\sec^2 y' + \cdots \equiv 0,$$

the dots standing for terms free of $\tan y'$ and $\sec y'$ and involving second derivatives of ξ and η. (See below.) This identity implies the following relations:

$$(a) \quad \frac{\partial \eta}{\partial y} - 2\frac{\partial \xi}{\partial x} = 0,$$

$$(b) \quad \xi y + \eta x = 0,$$

$$(c) \quad \frac{\partial \eta}{\partial x} = 0,$$

$$(d) \quad \frac{\partial \xi}{\partial y} = 0,$$

$$(e) \quad \frac{\partial \eta}{\partial y} - \frac{\partial \xi}{\partial x} = 0.$$

From (a) and (e) $\qquad \dfrac{\partial \eta}{\partial y} = \dfrac{\partial \xi}{\partial x} = 0.$

These together with (c) and (d) make it necessary that

$$\xi = const. \text{ and } \eta = const.$$

Hence, the omission of terms involving higher derivatives of ξ and η above.

Since (b) must hold for all values of x and y

$$\xi = \eta = 0;$$

i.e. there is no infinitesimal transformation and, therefore, no group that leaves the differential equation unaltered.

Remark. — The case of a differential equation of the first order is entirely different.   The condition that

$$y' - F(x, y) = 0$$

be invariant under $\qquad Uf \equiv \xi \dfrac{\partial f}{\partial x} + \eta \dfrac{\partial f}{\partial y}$

may be put into the form

$$(36') \quad \frac{\partial \eta}{\partial x} + \left(\frac{\partial \eta}{\partial y} - \frac{\partial \xi}{\partial x} \right) F - \frac{\partial \xi}{\partial y} F^2 - \xi \frac{\partial F}{\partial x} - \eta \frac{\partial F}{\partial y} \equiv 0.$$

Here one of the functions, say ξ, may be chosen at random, leaving a partial differential equation in η, which always has a solution ; as a matter of fact it has an indefinite number of them.   This is in entire accord with the result arrived at in § 15.

NOTE V

$$(U_1'U_2')f \equiv (U_1U_2)'f.$$

The symbol of the infinitesimal transformation of the extended group corresponding to $Uf \equiv \xi \dfrac{\partial f}{\partial x} + \eta \dfrac{\partial f}{\partial y}$ is [(24), § 13]

$$U'f \equiv \xi \frac{\partial f}{\partial x} + \eta \frac{\partial f}{\partial y} + \left(\frac{\partial \eta}{\partial x} + y' \frac{\partial \eta}{\partial y} - y' \frac{\partial \xi}{\partial x} - y'^2 \frac{\partial \xi}{\partial y} \right) \frac{\partial f}{\partial y'}.$$

Introducing the symbol

$$Bf \equiv \frac{\partial f}{\partial x} + y' \frac{\partial f}{\partial y},$$

$U'f$ may be written in the form

$$U'f \equiv \xi \frac{\partial f}{\partial x} + \eta \frac{\partial f}{\partial y} + (B\eta - y'B\xi) \frac{\partial f}{\partial y'},$$

and

$$(BU')f \equiv B\xi Bf + \rho(x, y, y') \frac{\partial f}{\partial y'},$$

where $\rho(x, y, y') \equiv B(B\eta - y'B\xi)$ is some function of x, y, y', whose actual form is of no importance in this discussion. Introducing the additional symbol

$$Cf \equiv \frac{\partial f}{\partial y'},$$

$(BU')f$ may be written in the form

$$(BU')f \equiv B\xi Bf + \rho(x, y, y') Cf.$$

Also

$$(CU')f \equiv \sigma(x, y, y') Cf,$$

where $\sigma(x, y, y') \equiv C(B\eta - y'B\xi)$ is also a function of x, y, y', whose form is of no importance here. The fact to be emphasized is that $(BU')f$ and $(CU')f$ are linear functions of Bf and Cf, the coefficients being functions of x, y, y'.

Moreover, *if* U_1f *and* U_2f *are any two groups,* $(B(U_1'U_2'))f$ *and* $(C(U_1'U_2'))f$ *are also linear in* Bf *and* Cf. For from Jacobi's identity (§ 36)

$$(B(U_1'U_2'))f + (U_1'(U_2'B))f + (U_2'(BU_1'))f \equiv 0,$$

$$(B(U_1'U_2'))f \equiv ((BU_1')U_2')f - ((BU_2')U_1')f$$

$$\equiv (B\xi_1 B + \rho_1 C, U_2')f - (B\xi_2 B + \rho_2 C, U_1')f$$

$$\equiv [U_1'(B\xi_2) - U_2'(B\xi_1)]Bf$$

$$+ [\rho_2 B\xi_1 - \rho_1 B\xi_2 + \rho_1\sigma_2 - \rho_2\sigma_1 + U_1'\rho_2 - U_2'\rho_1]Cf;$$

and in an analogous manner,

$$(C(U_1'U_2'))f \equiv (U_1'\sigma_2 - U_2'\sigma_1)Cf.$$

Since $(U_1U_2)f$ is of the same type as Uf (§ 14), it may be written

$$(U_1U_2)f \equiv \xi\frac{\partial f}{\partial x} + \eta\frac{\partial f}{\partial y},$$

and

$$(U_1U_2)'f \equiv \xi\frac{\partial f}{\partial x} + \eta\frac{\partial f}{\partial y} + (B\eta - y'B\xi)\frac{\partial f}{\partial y'}.$$

Noting that $(U_1'U_2')f$ coincides with $(U_1U_2)'f$ in the first two terms, at least, we may put

$$(U_1'U_2')f \equiv \xi\frac{\partial f}{\partial x} + \eta\frac{\partial f}{\partial y} + \omega(x, y, y')\frac{\partial f}{\partial y'}.$$

It remains to show that $\omega \equiv B\eta - y'B\xi$.

The alternant of Bf and $(U_1'U_2')f$ is

$$(B(U_1'U_2'))f \equiv B\xi\frac{\partial f}{\partial x} + (B\eta - \omega)\frac{\partial f}{\partial y} + B\omega\frac{\partial f}{\partial y'}.$$

This being linear in Bf and Cf, as was proved above,

$$B\xi\frac{\partial f}{\partial x} + (B\eta - \omega)\frac{\partial f}{\partial y} + B\omega\frac{\partial f}{\partial y'} \equiv \lambda\frac{\partial f}{\partial x} + \lambda y'\frac{\partial f}{\partial y} + \mu\frac{\partial f}{\partial y'}.$$

$$\therefore B\xi \equiv \lambda, \quad B\eta - \omega \equiv \lambda y'.$$

Whence $\qquad\qquad \omega \equiv B\eta - y'B\xi.$

This, as was noted above, establishes the identity

$$(U_1' U_2')f \equiv (U_1 U_2)'f.$$

Remark. — It can also be proved that for the m-times extended groups $U_1^{(m)}f$ and $U_2^{(m)}f$

$$(U_1^{(m)} U_2^{(m)})f \equiv (U_1 U_2)^{(m)}f.$$

NOTE VI

CONTINUOUS GROUPS INVOLVING MORE THAN ONE PARAMETER

r-parameter Group of Transformations. — The aggregate of all the transformations *

(153) $\qquad \begin{cases} x_1 = \phi(x, y, a_1, a_2, \cdots, a_r), \\ y_1 = \psi(x, y, a_1, a_2, \cdots, a_r), \end{cases}$

obtained by assigning to the parameters a_1, a_2, $\cdots$, a_r all possible values constitutes a *group,* if the transformation resulting from the successive performance of any two of them is one of the transformations of the aggregate.

As in the case of one-parameter groups (Chapter I), the groups here considered are supposed to have their transformations pair off into mutually *inverse* ones. That is, corresponding to any set of values of a_1, a_2, $\cdots$, a_r there must always be another set $\bar{a}_1$, $\bar{a}_2$, $\cdots$, $\bar{a}_r$,

---

* As before, ϕ and ψ are supposed to be generally analytic real functions of x, y, a_1, a_2, $\cdots$, a_r; and, unless specially stated, it will be understood that x and y are real and that the parameters take such values only as render x_1 and y_1 real. Groups of transformations involving two variables are considered here. For the theory of those involving n variables the student is referred to Lie's works, especially his *Transformationsgruppen,* Vol. I., and his *Continuierliche Gruppen;* also to Campbell's *Introductory Treatise on Lie's Theory.*

(functions of the former ones) such that

$$(\overline{153}) \quad \begin{cases} x = \phi(x_1, y_1, \bar{a}_1, \bar{a}_2, \cdots, \bar{a}_r), \\ y = \psi(x_1, y_1, \bar{a}_1, \bar{a}_2, \cdots, \bar{a}_r). \end{cases}$$

Another way of putting this is: If the equations (153) are solved for x and y, the latter must appear as the same functions, ϕ and ψ, respectively of x_1 and y_1 and a set of r functions of $a_1, a_2, \cdots, a_r$, as indicated by $(\overline{153})$.

Thus, consider the translations

XVII $\qquad\qquad x_1 = x + a_1, \; y_1 = y + a_2.$

If one of them be followed by a second one,

$$x_2 = x_1 + b_1, \; y_2 = y_1 + b_2,$$

the result is $\qquad\qquad x_2 = x + c_1, \; y_2 = y + c_2,$

where $\qquad\qquad c_1 = a_1 + b_1, \; c_2 = a_2 + b_2.$

Solving the equations XVII for x and y,

$$x = x_1 - a_1, \; y = y_1 - a_2.$$

Hence $\qquad\qquad \bar{a}_1 = - a_1, \; \bar{a}_2 = - a_2.$

Again, consider the *displacements*

XVIII $\quad x_1 = x \cos a_1 - y \sin a_1 + a_2, \; y_1 = x \sin a_1 + y \cos a_1 + a_3.$

A second transformation of this type

$$x_2 = x_1 \cos b_1 - y_1 \sin b_1 + b_2, \; y_2 = x_1 \sin b_1 + y_1 \cos b_1 + b_3,$$

results in

$$x_2 = x \cos c_1 - y \sin c_1 + c_2, \; y_2 = x \sin c_1 + y \cos c_1 + c_3,$$

where

$$c_1 = a_1 + b_1, \; c_2 = a_2 \cos b_1 - a_3 \sin b_1 + b_2, \; c_3 = a_2 \sin b_1 + a_3 \cos b_1 + b_3.$$

Solving the equations XVIII for x and y,

$$x = x_1 \cos(- a_1) - y_1 \sin(- a_1) - (a_2 \cos a_1 + a_3 \sin a_1),$$
$$y = x_1 \sin(- a_1) + y_1 \cos(- a_1) + (a_2 \sin a_1 - a_3 \cos a_1).$$

Hence

$$\bar{a}_1 = - a_1, \; \bar{a}_2 = - (a_2 \cos a_1 + a_3 \sin a_1), \; \bar{a}_3 = a_2 \sin a_1 - a_3 \cos a_1.$$

In the case of the *general projective* transformations

XIX $$x_1 = \frac{a_1 x + a_2 y + a_3}{a_7 x + a_8 y + a_9}, \quad y_1 = \frac{a_4 x + a_5 y + a_6}{a_7 x + a_8 y + a_9},$$

there is no difficulty in seeing that these constitute a group. For if one of the above transformations be followed by

$$x_2 = \frac{b_1 x_1 + b_2 y_1 + b_3}{b_7 x_1 + b_8 y_1 + b_9}, \quad y_2 = \frac{b_4 x_1 + b_5 y_1 + b_6}{b_7 x_1 + b_8 y_1 + b_9},$$

there results $$x_2 = \frac{c_1 x + c_2 y + c_3}{c_7 x + c_8 y + c_9}, \quad y_2 = \frac{c_4 x + c_5 y + c_6}{c_7 x + c_8 y + c_9},$$

where

$$c_1 = a_1 b_1 + a_4 b_2 + a_7 b_3,$$

$$c_2 = a_2 b_1 + a_5 b_2 + a_8 b_3,$$

$$c_3 = a_3 b_1 + a_6 b_2 + a_9 b_3,$$

$$c_4 = a_1 b_4 + a_4 b_5 + a_7 b_6,$$

$$c_5 = a_2 b_4 + a_5 b_5 + a_8 b_6,$$

$$c_6 = a_3 b_4 + a_6 b_5 + a_9 b_6,$$

$$c_7 = a_1 b_7 + a_4 b_8 + a_7 b_9,$$

$$c_8 = a_2 b_7 + a_5 b_8 + a_8 b_9,$$

$$c_9 = a_3 b_7 + a_6 b_8 + a_9 b_9.$$

Moreover, the result of solving the equations XIX for x and y is

$$x = \frac{A_1 x_1 + A_4 y_1 + A_7}{A_3 x_1 + A_6 y_1 + A_9}, \quad y = \frac{A_2 x_1 + A_5 y_1 + A_8}{A_3 x_1 + A_6 y_1 + A_9},$$

where $A_1, A_2, \cdots, A_9$ are the cofactors of the corresponding elements of the determinant

$$\begin{vmatrix} a_1 & a_2 & a_3 \\ a_4 & a_5 & a_6 \\ a_7 & a_8 & a_9 \end{vmatrix}.$$

Since the successive performance of two mutually inverse transformations results in the identical transformation, the latter must always be a member of the Lie group; hence there must always exist a set of values of the parameters, a_1^0, a_2^0, $\cdots$, a_r^0, such that

$$(153_0) \qquad \begin{cases} x_1 = \phi(x, y, a_1^0, a_2^0, \cdots, a_r^0) = x, \\ y_1 = \psi(x, y, a_1^0, a_2^0, \cdots, a_r^0) = y. \end{cases}$$

It is readily seen that for

XVII,	$a_1^0 = a_2^0 = 0$;
XVIII,	$a_1^0 = a_2^0 = a_3^0 = 0$;
XIX,	$a_1^0 = a_5^0 = a_9^0 = $ *any number (different from zero)*,
	$a_2^0 = a_3^0 = a_4^0 = a_6^0 = a_7^0 = a_8^0 = 0.$

We shall further presuppose that all of the r parameters in (153) are *essential*, that is, that the formulæ of transformation cannot be replaced by another set involving a smaller number of parameters without reducing the number of transformations represented by them.

Thus $\qquad\qquad x_1 = x + a_1 + a_3,\ \ y_1 = y + a_2$

contains no transformation that is not included in XVII. It involves only two essential parameters ; $a_1 + a_3$ is no more general than a_1.

In XIX, as is well known, there are only eight essential parameters ; since the expressions are homogeneous and of degree zero in the parameters, it is only the ratios of the latter to any one of them that count.

A group involving r essential parameters is known as an *r-parameter group*.

It is frequently possible to tell by inspection whether the parameters appearing are essential or not. An analytic criterion is given by the theorem of Note VII.

Show that the following sets of transformations constitute groups. Find the respective values of the parameters that give the inverse and those that give the identical transformations :

Ex. 1. $x_1 = a_1 x + a_2,\ \ y_1 = a_1 y + a_3.$

Ex. 2. $x_1 = a_1 x + a_2 y + a_3,\ \ y_1 = a_4 x + a_5 y + a_6.$

Ex. 3. $x_1 = x + a_1 y + a_2,\ \ y_1 = y + a_3.$

Ex. 4. $x_1 = x + a_1 y^2 + a_2,\ y_1 = a_3 y.$

Ex. 5. $x_1 = (a_1 + 1)x + (a_2 - 1)y + a_3,\ y_1 = a_1 x + a_2 y + a_3.$

Ex. 6. $x_1 = \dfrac{a_1 x}{a_2 x + a_3 y + 1},\ y_1 = \dfrac{a_1 y}{a_2 x + a_3 y + 1}.$

Infinitesimal Transformation. —The transformation

$$x_1 = \phi(x, y, a_1^0 + \delta a_1, a_2^0 + \delta a_2, \cdots, a_r^0 + \delta a_r),$$

$$y_1 = \psi(x, y, a_1^0 + \delta a_1, a_2^0 + \delta a_2, \cdots, a_r^0 + \delta a_r),$$

where $a_1^0, a_2^0, \cdots, a_r^0$ determine the identical transformation and $\delta a_1, \delta a_2, \cdots, \delta a_r$ are infinitesimals, changes x and y by infinitesimal amounts, since ϕ and ψ are supposed to be continuous functions. Developing by Taylor's Theorem,

$$x_1 = x + \sum_{i=1}^{r} \frac{\partial \phi(x, y, a^0)}{\partial a_i^0} \delta a_i + \cdots,$$

$$y_1 = y + \sum \frac{\partial \psi(x, y, a^0)}{\partial a_i^0} \delta a_i + \cdots.$$

Here $\dfrac{\partial \phi(x, y, a^0)}{\partial a_i^0}$ and $\dfrac{\partial \psi(x, y, a^0)}{\partial a_i^0}$ stand for what

$$\frac{\partial \phi(x, y, a_1, a_2, \cdots, a_r)}{\partial a_i} \text{ and } \frac{\partial \psi(x, y, a_1, a_2, \cdots, a_r)}{\partial a_i}$$

respectively become when $a_1 = a_1^0,\ a_2 = a_2^0,\ \cdots,\ a_r = a_r^0$, and the unexpressed terms are of higher degree than the first in $\delta a_1, \delta a_2, \cdots, \delta a_r$. The changes in x and y are then

$$x_1 - x = \delta x = \sum \frac{\partial \phi(x, y, a^0)}{\partial a_i^0} \delta a_i + \cdots,$$

$$y_1 - y = \delta y = \sum \frac{\partial \psi(x, y, a^0)}{\partial a_i^0} \delta a_i + \cdots.$$

We shall suppose that at least one member of the pair

$$(154) \qquad \frac{\partial \phi(x, y, a^0)}{\partial a_i^0}, \quad \frac{\partial \psi(x, y, a^0)}{\partial a_i^0},$$

for each value of i from 1 to r, does not vanish identically, and that all of them are finite. Calling them $\xi_i(x, y)$* and $\eta_i(x, y)$ respectively, the transformation may be written

$$(155) \quad \delta x = \sum_i \xi_i(x, y) \, \delta a_i + \cdots, \quad \delta y = \sum_i \eta_i(x, y) \, \delta a_i + \cdots.$$

In exactly the same way as is done for one-parameter groups in Note I, it can be shown that infinitesimal transformations of the form (155) always exist, even when the parameters enter in such a way that for the particular values $a_1^0, a_2^0, \cdots, a_r^0$ both members of some pair

$$\frac{\partial \phi(x, y, a^0)}{\partial a_i^0}, \quad \frac{\partial \psi(x, y, a^0)}{\partial a_i^0}$$

vanish identically, or if some one of them becomes infinite.†

Here $\delta a_1, \delta a_2, \cdots, \delta a_r$ are any infinitesimal increments of the first order. Taking δa as a standard infinitesimal of the first order, we may put

$$\delta a_1 = e_1 \delta a, \quad \delta a_2 = e_2 \delta a, \quad \cdots, \quad \delta a_r = e_r \delta a,$$

* Here ξ_i and η_i are written as functions of x and y only, since $a_1^0, a_2^0, \cdots, a_r^0$ appear as numerical constants.

† The general expressions for the coefficients in (155) are, in the notation of Note I,

$$(155') \quad \begin{cases} \xi_i(x, y, \alpha_1, \alpha_2, \cdots, \alpha_r) \\ \quad = \dfrac{\partial}{\partial \alpha_i} \phi[\phi(x, y, \overline{\alpha}_1, \overline{\alpha}_2, \cdots, \overline{\alpha}_r), \, \psi(x, y, \overline{\alpha}_1, \overline{\alpha}_2, \cdots, \overline{\alpha}_r), \, \alpha_1, \alpha_2, \cdots, \alpha_r], \\ \eta_i(x, y, \alpha_1, \alpha_2, \cdots, \alpha_r) \\ \quad = \dfrac{\partial}{\partial \alpha_i} \psi[\phi(x, y, \overline{\alpha}_1, \overline{\alpha}_2 \cdots \overline{\alpha}_r), \, \psi(x, y, \overline{\alpha}_1, \overline{\alpha}_2, \cdots \overline{\alpha}_r), \, \alpha_1 \alpha_2, \cdots, \alpha_r]. \end{cases}$$

Here $\alpha_1, \alpha_2, \cdots, \alpha_r$ are any set of values of the parameters for which both ξ_i and η_i are finite, and at least one of them is not identically zero. The forms (155) for ξ_i, η_i are what the general forms (155') become for the special choice $\alpha_k = \overline{\alpha}_k = a_k^0$ $(k = 1, 2, \cdots, r)$.

where $e_1, e_2, \cdots, e_r$ are any finite constants. The general type of an infinitesimal transformation may then be written

(156)
$$\begin{cases} \delta x = (e_1\xi_1 + e_2\xi_2 + \cdots + e_r\xi_r)\delta a + \cdots, \\ \delta y = (e_1\eta_1 + e_2\eta_2 + \cdots + e_r\eta_r)\delta a + \cdots. \end{cases}$$

For the sake of brevity we shall write

(157)
$$\delta x = \xi\,\delta a + \cdots, \quad \delta y = \eta\,\delta a + \cdots,$$

where $\xi \equiv \sum e_i\xi_i$ and $\eta \equiv \sum e_i\eta_i$. Introducing the symbol

$$Uf \equiv \xi\frac{\partial f}{\partial x} + \eta\frac{\partial f}{\partial y} = \sum e_i\left(\xi_i\frac{\partial f}{\partial x} + \eta_i\frac{\partial f}{\partial y}\right),$$

and similarly

$$U_i f \equiv \xi_i\frac{\partial f}{\partial x} + \eta_i\frac{\partial f}{\partial y},$$

we have

(158)
$$Uf \equiv e_1 U_1 f + e_2 U_2 f + \cdots + e_r U_r f.$$

It can be proved * that when the r parameters of the group are essential $U_1 f, U_2 f, \cdots U_r f,$ (in which $\xi_i, \eta_i,$ are given by (155') for any properly selected set of values of the parameters, in particular they may have the special forms (155)), are *linearly independent;* that is, that it is impossible to find a set of constants $c_1, c_2, \cdots, c_r$ such that

$$c_1 U_1 f + c_2 U_2 f + \cdots + c_r U_r f \equiv 0,$$

which is equivalent to saying that for no set of constants $c_1, c_2, \cdots, c_r$ can both the relations

$$c_1\xi_1 + c_2\xi_2 + \cdots + c_r\xi_r \equiv 0,$$
$$c_1\eta_1 + c_2\eta_2 + \cdots + c_r\eta_r \equiv 0$$

---

* Thus, for example, see Lie, *Continuierliche Gruppen,* Chapter 6, or his *Transformationsgruppen,* Chapter 4. Also Campbell, *loc. cit.,* § 42.

The object of this Note is to present as compactly as possible, consistent with a clear understanding of the chain of reasoning, the relations between r-parameter groups and their infinitesimal transformations. Consequently when long and tedious, the proofs of certain facts are omitted here. These may, however, be obtained from the references given.

hold simultaneously.   Moreover, it can also be proved that if

$$\delta x = \Xi\, \delta a + \cdots, \quad \delta y = \mathrm{H}\, \delta a + \cdots,$$

is any infinitesimal transformation of the group, Ξ is a linear function of $\xi_1, \xi_2, \cdots, \xi_r$ with constant coefficients, and H is the same function of $\eta_1, \eta_2, \cdots, \eta_r$, thus,

$$\Xi = l_1\xi_1 + l_2\xi_2 + \cdots + l_r\xi_r,$$
$$\mathrm{H} = l_1\eta_1 + l_2\eta_2 + \cdots + l_r\eta_r,$$

where the set

$$U_i f \equiv \xi_i \frac{\partial f}{\partial x} + \eta_i \frac{\partial f}{\partial y} \quad (i = 1, 2, \cdots, r)$$

is any linearly independent one.

The coefficients of δa in (156) can therefore never both vanish identically.   Hence at least one of the terms of first order must appear.   Infinitesimals of higher order than the first may consequently be neglected, and the *infinitesimal transformation* may be written in the form

$$(159) \quad \delta x = (e_1\xi_1 + e_2\xi_2 + \cdots + e_r\xi_r)\, \delta a, \; \delta y = (e_1\eta_1 + e_2\eta_2 + \cdots + e_r\eta_r)\delta a.$$

The change in any function $f(x, y)$ produced by (159) is then

$$\delta f \equiv Uf\, \delta a,$$

where

$$(158) \quad Uf \equiv e_1 U_1 f + e_2 U_2 f + \cdots + e_r U_r f,$$

as in § 3, is the *symbol of the transformation* (159) and will be used to represent it.

The above may now be expressed as follows :

THEOREM I. — *Every continuous Lie group involving r essential parameters contains r linearly independent infinitesimal transformations $U_1 f$, $U_2 f$, $\cdots$, $U_r f$, in terms of which every infinitesimal transformation of the group can be expressed linearly with constant coefficients, thus*

$$(158) \quad Uf \equiv e_1 U_1 f + e_2 U_2 f + \cdots + e_r U_r f.$$

Moreover, every transformation of the type (158), *for all choices of the constants $e_1, e_2, \cdots e_r$, belongs to the group.*

Remark 1. — It follows that in any set of infinitesimal transformations of the group, only r at most can be linearly independent.
Moreover, starting with any r linearly independent transformations
$U_1 f,\ U_2 f,\ \cdots,\ U_r f$, every set

$$V_k f \equiv e_{1k} U_1 f + e_{2k} U_2 f + \cdots + e_{rk} U_r f$$

$$(k = 1,\ 2,\ \cdots,\ r)$$

will be linearly independent provided

$$\Delta \equiv \begin{vmatrix} e_{11}, & e_{21}, & \cdots, & e_{r1} \\ e_{12}, & e_{22}, & \cdots, & e_{r2} \\ \cdot & \cdot & \cdot & \cdot \\ e_{1r}, & e_{2r}, & \cdots, & e_{rr} \end{vmatrix} \neq 0.$$

Any set of r linearly independent infinitesimal transformations,
$V_1 f,\ V_2 f,\ \cdots,\ V_r f$, may be taken as the r transformations (referred to
in Theorem I) in terms of which all the infinitesimal transformations
can be expressed linearly with constant coefficients ; for, since $\Delta \neq 0$,
each of $U_1 f,\ U_2 f,\ \cdots,\ U_r f$ is a linear function of $V_1 f,\ V_2 f,\ \cdots,\ V_r f$
with constant coefficients.

In the case of XVII $\delta x = \delta a_1 = e_1 \delta a,\ \ \delta y = \delta a_2 = e_2 \delta a.$

$$\therefore\ U f \equiv e_1 \frac{\partial f}{\partial x} + e_2 \frac{\partial f}{\partial y}.$$

A set of linearly independent transformations is

$$U_1 f \equiv \frac{\partial f}{\partial x},\ \ U_2 f \equiv \frac{\partial f}{\partial y}.$$

In the case of XVIII,

$$\delta x = - y\, \delta a_1 + \delta a_2 = (- e_1 y + e_2)\, \delta a,\ \ \delta y = x \delta a_1 + \delta a_3 = (e_1 x + e_3)\, \delta a.$$

$$\therefore\ U f \equiv e_1 \left(- y \frac{\partial f}{\partial x} + x \frac{\partial f}{\partial y} \right) + e_2 \frac{\partial f}{\partial x} + e_3 \frac{\partial f}{\partial y}.$$

A set of linearly independent transformations is

$$U_1 f \equiv y \frac{\partial f}{\partial x} - x \frac{\partial f}{\partial y},\ \ U_2 f \equiv \frac{\partial f}{\partial x},\ \ U_3 f \equiv \frac{\partial f}{\partial y}.$$

In the case of XIX there are only eight essential parameters.   Putting $a_9 = 1$,

$$x_1 = x + \delta x = \frac{(1 + \delta a_1)x + y\,\delta a_2 + \delta a_3}{x\,\delta a_7 + y\,\delta a_8 + 1}.$$

But $$\frac{1}{x\,\delta a_7 + y\delta a_8 + 1} = 1 - x\,\delta a_7 - y\,\delta a_8 + \cdots,$$

where the dots stand for terms of higher degree than the first.

$$\therefore\ x_1 = x + \delta x = x + x\delta a_1 + y\,\delta a_2 + \delta a_3 - x^2\,\delta a_7 - xy\delta a_8 + \cdots.$$

Whence, $\delta x = (e_1 x + e_2 y + e_3 - e_7 x^2 - e_8 xy)\,\delta a.$

Similarly, $\delta y = (e_4 x + e_5 y + e_6 - e_7 xy - e_8 y^2)\,\delta a.$

$$\therefore\ Uf \equiv e_1 x \frac{\partial f}{\partial x} + e_2 y \frac{\partial f}{\partial x} + e_3 \frac{\partial f}{\partial x} + e_4 x \frac{\partial f}{\partial y} + e_5 y \frac{\partial f}{\partial y} + e_6 \frac{\partial f}{\partial y} - e_7 \left(x^2 \frac{\partial f}{\partial x} + xy \frac{\partial f}{\partial y} \right)$$

$$- e_8 \left(xy \frac{\partial f}{\partial x} + y^2 \frac{\partial f}{\partial y} \right).$$

A set of linearly independent transformations is

$$U_1 f \equiv \frac{\partial f}{\partial x},\ \ U_2 f \equiv \frac{\partial f}{\partial y},\ \ U_3 f \equiv x \frac{\partial f}{\partial x},\ \ U_4 f \equiv y \frac{\partial f}{\partial x},\ \ U_5 f \equiv x \frac{\partial f}{\partial y},\ \ U_6 f \equiv y \frac{\partial f}{\partial y},$$

$$U_7 f \equiv x^2 \frac{\partial f}{\partial x} + xy \frac{\partial f}{\partial y},\ \ U_8 f \equiv xy \frac{\partial f}{\partial x} + y^2 \frac{\partial f}{\partial y}.$$

Ex. 7.   Find the infinitesimal transformations of the groups in Ex. 1, 2, 3, 4, 5, 6 above.

Group Generated by Infinitesimal Transformations. — Starting with the infinitesimal transformation

$$(158)\ Uf \equiv e_1 U_1 f + e_2 U_2 f + \cdots + e_r U_r f$$

$$\equiv (e_1 \xi_1 + e_2 \xi_2 + \cdots + e_r \xi_r) \frac{\partial f}{\partial x} + (e_1 \eta_1 + e_2 \eta_2 + \cdots + e_r \eta_r) \frac{\partial f}{\partial y},$$

in which the constants $e_1,\ e_2,\ \cdots,\ e_r$ are fixed, the finite transformations of the group generated by it may be obtained either by finding those solutions of

$$(160)\ \ \frac{dx_1}{\Sigma e_i \xi_i (x_1,\ y_1)} = \frac{dy_1}{\Sigma e_i \eta_i (x_1,\ y_1)} = dt,$$

for which $x_1 = x$ and $y_1 = y$ when $t = 0$ (§ 4), or in the form (§ 5),

$$
(161) \quad
\begin{cases}
x_1 = x + t \, \Sigma e_i U_i x + \dfrac{t^2}{2!} \, \Sigma \Sigma e_i e_k U_i U_k x + \cdots, \\[2mm]
y_1 = y + t \, \Sigma e_i U_i y + \dfrac{t^2}{2!} \, \Sigma \Sigma e_i e_k U_i U_k y + \cdots.
\end{cases}
$$

In both cases t is the parameter, and $t = 0$ gives the identical transformation.

If $e_1, e_2, \cdots, e_r$ are arbitrary constants and $U_1 f, U_2 f, \cdots, U_r f$ are linearly independent, the infinitesimal transformation contains $r - 1$ parameters (viz. the ratios of any $r - 1$ of the e's to the remaining one), and the general expression (161) for the finite transformations generated by it contains r parameters. That these parameters are essential follows from the linear independence of $U_1 f, U_2 f, \cdots, U_r f$. A proof of this fact may be found in Lie's *Continuierliche Gruppen*, pp. 186–190. Hence *there are ∞^r transformations in the set* (161).

If $U_1 f, U_2 f, \cdots, U_r f$ are r linearly independent infinitesimal transformations of an r-parameter group, every transformation of the set (158) belongs to the group (Theorem I). All the transformations of the one-parameter group generated by any transformation (158) belong to the r-parameter group (Lie, *Continuierliche Gruppen*, p. 183). The ∞^r transformations (161) therefore belong to the group. Moreover, every transformation of the r-parameter group (at least all such for which the values of the parameters are sufficiently small so that when developed by Taylor's Theorem in powers of the parameters, as (161) are, the series are convergent) is included in (161) (Lie, *Transformationsgruppen*, Vol. I, Ch. 4, § 18). Hence

THEOREM II. *If $U_1 f, U_2 f, \cdots, U_r f$ are r linearly independent transformations of an r-parameter group, the latter* is precisely the aggre-*

---

* At least all its transformations corresponding to values of the parameters which differ by limited amounts perhaps (see above) from those which give the identical transformation.

gate of all the one-parameter groups generated by the ∞^{r-1} infinitesimal transformations

$$U_1 f \equiv e_1 U_1 f + e_2 U_2 f + \cdots + e_r U_r f.$$

Remark 2. Since t and the e's appear in (161) in the combinations $te_1,\ te_2,\ \cdots,\ te_r$, there will be no loss in suppressing the t and writing the finite transformations of the group in the form

(161′)
$$\begin{cases} x_1 = x + \Sigma\, e_i U_i x + \dfrac{1}{2\,!}\,\Sigma\,\Sigma\, e_i e_k U_i U_k x + \cdots, \\[2mm] y_1 = y + \Sigma\, e_i U_i y + \dfrac{1}{2\,!}\,\Sigma\,\Sigma\, e_i e_k U_i U_k y + \cdots, \end{cases}$$

where the e's are now r distinct parameters. The identical transformation is given by $e_1 = e_2 = \cdots = e_r = 0$, and the inverse transformation by $\bar{e}_i = -\,e_i$ $(i = 1, 2, \cdots, r)$.

In the case of XVII the general type of infinitesimal transformation is

$$Uf \equiv e_1 \frac{\partial f}{\partial x} + e_2 \frac{\partial f}{\partial y}.$$

The finite transformations (161′) are seen at once to be

$$x_1 = x + e_1,\ y_1 = y + e_2.$$

In the case of XVIII

$$Uf \equiv e_1 \left(-y \frac{\partial f}{\partial x} + x \frac{\partial f}{\partial y} \right) + e_2 \frac{\partial f}{\partial x} + e_3 \frac{\partial f}{\partial y}.$$

$$\therefore x_1 = x - e_1 y + e_2 - \frac{1}{2\,!} e_1{}^2 x + \frac{1}{3\,!} e_1{}^3 y + \frac{1}{4\,!} e_1{}^4 x - \cdots$$

$$= x \cos e_1 - y \sin e_1 + e_2.$$

Similarly
$$y_1 = x \sin e_1 + y \cos e_1 + e_3.$$

Remark 3. The expressions for x_1 and y_1 in (161′) may at times become extremely complicated, as for example in the case of the group XIX. Also the actual problem of integrating equations (160) with the e's arbitrary constants is usually a difficult one. To overcome this practical difficulty Lie suggested the following method, which was also given independently by Maurer (*Math. Ann.*, Vol. 39):

Having found

$$(162) \qquad x_1 = \phi_i(x, y, a_i), \quad y_1 = \psi_i(x, y, a_i),$$

$$(i = 1, 2, \cdots, r),$$

the finite transformations of the one-parameter groups generated by each of the r linearly independent infinitesimal transformations $U_1 f, U_2 f, \cdots, U_r f$ of an r-parameter group, the result of performing successively one transformation (with arbitrarily selected parameter) out of each of the r groups (162) is a transformation belonging to the r-parameter group and involving the r parameters $a_1, a_2, \cdots, a_r$. That these are essential follows also from the linear independence of $U_1 f, U_2 f, \cdots, U_r f$. (See Lie, *Continuierliche Gruppen*, p. 194.)

In the case of XVII

$$U_1 f \equiv \frac{\partial f}{\partial x} : \quad x_1 = x + a_1, \; y_1 = y,$$

$$U_2 f \equiv \frac{\partial f}{\partial y} : \quad x_2 = x_1, \qquad y_2 = y_1 + a_2.$$

The successive performance of these gives

$$x_2 = x + a_1, \; y_2 = y + a_2.$$

In XVIII

$$U_1 f \equiv -y \frac{\partial f}{\partial x} + x \frac{\partial f}{\partial y} : x_1 = x \cos a_1 - y \sin a_1, \; y_1 = x \sin a_1 + y \cos a_1,$$

$$U_2 f \equiv \frac{\partial f}{\partial x} : \qquad x_2 = x_1 + a_2, \qquad\qquad y_2 = y_1,$$

$$U_3 f \equiv \frac{\partial f}{\partial y} : \qquad x_3 = x_2, \qquad\qquad y_3 = y_2 + a_3.$$

The successive performance of these gives

$$x_3 = x \cos a_1 - y \sin a_1 + a_2, \; y_3 = x \sin a_1 + y \cos a_1 + a_3.$$

In XIX

$$U_1 f \equiv \frac{\partial f}{\partial x} : \qquad x_1 = x + a_1, \quad y_1 = y,$$

$$U_2 f \equiv \frac{\partial f}{\partial y} : \qquad x_2 = x_1, \qquad y_2 = y_1 + a_2,$$

$$U_3 f \equiv x \frac{\partial f}{\partial x} : \qquad x_3 = a_3 x_2, \qquad y_3 = y_2,$$

$$U_4 f \equiv y \frac{\partial f}{\partial x} : \qquad x_4 = x_3 + a_4 y_3, \quad y_4 = y_3,$$

$$U_5 f \equiv x \frac{\partial f}{\partial y} : \qquad x_5 = x_4, \qquad y_5 = a_5 x_4 + y_4,$$

$$U_6 f \equiv y \frac{\partial f}{\partial y} : \qquad x_6 = x_5, \qquad y_6 = a_6 y_5,$$

$$U_7 f \equiv x^2 \frac{\partial f}{\partial x} + xy \frac{\partial f}{\partial y} : \ x_7 = \frac{x_6}{1 - a_7 x_6}, \ y_7 = \frac{y_6}{1 - a_7 x_6},$$

$$U_8 f \equiv xy \frac{\partial f}{\partial x} + y^2 \frac{\partial f}{\partial y} : \ x_8 = \frac{x_7}{1 - a_8 y_7}, \ y_8 = \frac{y_7}{1 - a_8 y_7}.$$

The successive performance of these gives

$$x_8 = \frac{a_3 x + a_4 y + a_1 a_3 + a_2 a_4}{\alpha_7 x + \alpha_8 y + \alpha_9},$$

$$y_8 = \frac{a_3 a_5 a_6 x + (a_6 + a_4 a_5 a_6) y + a_2 a_6 + a_1 a_3 a_5 a_6 + a_2 a_4 a_5 a_6}{\alpha_7 x + \alpha_8 y + \alpha_9}$$

where
$$\alpha_7 = -(a_3 a_7 + a_3 a_5 a_6 a_8), \quad \alpha_8 = -(a_4 a_7 + a_6 a_8 + a_4 a_5 a_6 a_8),$$

$$\alpha_9 = 1 - (a_1 a_3 a_7 + a_2 a_4 a_7 + a_2 a_6 a_8 + a_1 a_3 a_5 a_6 a_8 + a_2 a_4 a_5 a_6 a_8).$$

Find the finite transformations generated by the following :

Ex. 8. $Uf \equiv (e_1 x + e_2) \dfrac{\partial f}{\partial x} + (e_1 y + e_3) \dfrac{\partial f}{\partial y}.$

Ex. 9. $Uf \equiv (e_1 + e_2 x + e_3 y) \dfrac{\partial f}{\partial x} + (e_4 + e_5 x + e_6 y) \dfrac{\partial f}{\partial y}.$

Ex. 10. $Uf \equiv (e_1 y + e_2) \dfrac{\partial f}{\partial x} + e_3 \dfrac{\partial f}{\partial y}.$

Ex. 11. $Uf \equiv (e_1 y^2 + e_2) \dfrac{\partial f}{\partial x} + e_3 y \dfrac{\partial f}{\partial y}.$

Ex. 12. $Uf \equiv (e_1 + e_2 x + e_3 y) \dfrac{\partial f}{\partial x} + (e_1 + e_2 x + e_3 y) \dfrac{\partial f}{\partial y}.$

Ex. 13. $Uf \equiv (e_1 x + e_2 x^2 + e_3 xy) \dfrac{\partial f}{\partial x} + (e_1 y + e_2 xy + e_3 y^2) \dfrac{\partial f}{\partial y}.$

Lie's Principal Theorem. — It was shown above (Theorem II) that if U_1f, U_2f, $\cdots$, U_rf are r linearly independent infinitesimal transformations of an r-parameter group, the aggregate of the ∞^r transformations of the ∞^{r-1} one-parameter groups, each generated by an infinitesimal transformation of the set

$$(158) \qquad Uf \equiv e_1U_1f + e_2U_2f + \cdots + e_rU_rf,$$

forms an r-parameter group. On the other hand, starting with *any* r linearly independent infinitesimal transformations U_1f, U_2f, $\cdots$, U_rf (without knowing whether they form a complete set for some group), there is no reason to suppose that the ∞^r transformations generated by the various transformations (158) form a group.

Thus, starting with $\qquad U_1f \equiv \dfrac{\partial f}{\partial x}, \quad U_2f \equiv x\dfrac{\partial f}{\partial y},$

the transformations generated by

$$Uf \equiv e_1 \frac{\partial f}{\partial x} + e_2x\frac{\partial f}{\partial y}$$

are $\qquad x_1 = x + a_1, \; y_1 = a_2x + y + \dfrac{a_1a_2}{2}.$

While these transformations involve two essential parameters, it is very easily seen that they do not form a group.

A definite answer as to when the ∞^r transformations generated by the various transformations of the set (158) form a group is given by LIE'S PRINCIPAL THEOREM : * *The necessary and sufficient conditions that the ∞^r transformations generated by the ∞^{r-1} infinitesimal transformations*

$$e_1U_1f + e_2U_2f + \cdots + e_rU_rf,$$

---

* Lie calls this theorem " Der Hauptsatz der Gruppentheorie," and gives a proof of it for groups involving two variables in his *Continuierliche Gruppen*, Ch. 12. In his treatment of the general theory of continuous groups, this theorem is the second of his "three fundamental theorems." See his *Continuierliche Gruppen*, Ch. 15, or his *Transformationsgruppen*, Vol. I, Ch. 9 ; also Campbell, *loc. cit.*, Ch. IV.

A detailed proof of this theorem would be beyond the scope of this Note. A statement of it with illustrative examples will suffice.

Lie first deduced this theorem in 1874.

Q

where $U_1 f$, $U_2 f$, $\cdots$, $U_r f$ *are linearly independent and* e_1, e_2, $\cdots$, e_r *are any constants, constitute a Lie r-parameter group are that*

$$(163) \qquad (U_i U_k) f \equiv c_{ik1} U_1 f + c_{ik2} U_2 f + \cdots + c_{ikr} U_r f,$$
$$(i, k = 1, 2, \cdots, r),$$

where the c's are constants.

Remark 4. — This theorem is equivalent to the following two :

1°. *The infinitesimal transformations of an r-parameter group form an r-parameter group of infinitesimal transformations.*   (§ 43.)

2°. *The transformations of the groups generated by the transformations of an r-parameter group of infinitesimal transformations form an r-parameter group.*

In the case of XVIII,

$$U_1 f \equiv y \frac{\partial f}{\partial x} - x \frac{\partial f}{\partial y}, \quad U_2 f \equiv \frac{\partial f}{\partial x}, \quad U_3 f \equiv \frac{\partial f}{\partial y}.$$

Here $(U_1 U_2) f \equiv U_3 f$, $(U_1 U_3) f \equiv - U_2 f$, $(U_2 U_3) f \equiv 0$.

In XIX

$$(U_1 U_2) f \equiv 0, \quad (U_1 U_3) f \equiv U_1 f, \quad (U_1 U_4) f \equiv 0, \quad (U_1 U_5) f \equiv U_2 f,$$
$$(U_1 U_7) f \equiv 2 U_3 f + U_6 f, \quad (U_1 U_8) f \equiv U_4 f, \quad (U_3 U_7) f \equiv U_7 f, \quad (U_3 U_8) f \equiv 0,$$

and so on.

Ex. 14.   Show that the infinitesimal transformations in Ex. 8 to 13 satisfy the conditions (163).

NOTE VII

CONDITION FOR ESSENTIAL PARAMETERS

The r parameters in

$$(153) \qquad x_1 = \phi(x, y, a_1, a_2, \cdots, a_r), \quad y_1 = \psi(x, y, a_1, a_2, \cdots, a_r)$$

are *not* essential if (153) can be replaced by

$$(164) \qquad x_1 = \Phi(x, y, a_1, a_2, \cdots, a_{r-m}), \quad y_1 = \Psi(x, y, a_1, a_2, \cdots, a_{r-m})$$
$$(1 \leq m < r).$$

In this case the identities

(165) $$\phi \equiv \Phi, \quad \psi \equiv \Psi$$

for all values of x and y, determine $\alpha_1, \alpha_2, \cdots, \alpha_{r-m}$ as functions of $a_1, a_2, \cdots, a_r$; for by saying that (164) replaces (153) is meant that as soon as the a's are given a set of the α's is determined (not necessarily uniquely) which will give rise to the same transformation.

A homogeneous linear partial differential equation of the first order in r variables

(166) $$Af \equiv \chi_1(a_1, a_2, \cdots, a_r)\frac{\partial f}{\partial a_1} + \cdots + \chi_r(a_1, a_2, \cdots, a_r)\frac{\partial f}{\partial a_r} = 0$$

is determined uniquely by $r - 1$ independent solutions.* An equation of this type can therefore be constructed which shall have for solutions

$$\alpha_1, \alpha_2, \cdots, \alpha_{r-m}, \beta_{r-m+1}, \cdots, \beta_{r-1},$$

where $\beta_{r-m+1}, \cdots, \beta_{r-1}$, any convenient functions of the a's independent of the α's, are added to the latter to make up the number $r - 1$ in case $m > 1$. This equation will have for solution also any functions of the α's, in particular Φ and Ψ, x and y appearing as parameters; or owing to the identities (165), by which the α's are defined, ϕ and ψ will also be solutions.

Conversely, if ϕ and ψ satisfy an equation of the type (166), they are functions of some or all of its $r - 1$ solutions;

$$\gamma_1(a_1, a_2, \cdots, a_r), \quad \gamma_2(a_1, a_2, \cdots, a_r), \quad \cdots, \quad \gamma_{r-1}(a_1, a_2, \cdots, a_r);$$

i.e. the a's enter ϕ and ψ in such a way that for all values of x and y

$$\phi(x, y, a_1, a_2, \cdots, a_r) \equiv \Phi(x, y, \gamma_1, \gamma_2, \cdots, \gamma_{r-1}),$$
$$\psi(x, y, a_1, a_2, \cdots, a_r) \equiv \Psi(x, y, \gamma_1, \gamma_2, \cdots, \gamma_{r-1}).$$

* A proof of this for the case of $r = 3$ is given in the first footnote of § 34. The proof for r any number is exactly the same.

Hence the

THEOREM. — *The necessary and sufficient condition that the r para-meters in* (153) *be essential is the impossibility of finding r functions of them* $\chi_1, \chi_2, \cdots, \chi_r$ *such that the resulting linear equation* (166) *shall have* ϕ *and* ψ *for solutions.*

Remark. — There is nothing in the above to show whether the $r - 1$ parameters $\gamma_1, \gamma_2, \cdots, \gamma_{r-1}$ are essential or not. The same test must be applied to them also, unless, as is frequently the case, the exact state of affairs is obvious on inspection.

To illustrate, consider the transformation

$$x_1 = xa^{\log b} + b^{\log a} + c \equiv \phi(x, y, a, b, c),$$
$$y_1 = ya^{\log b} \qquad\qquad \equiv \psi(x, y, a, b, c).$$

If a, b, c are not essential it must be possible to find three functions of them, $\chi_1(a, b, c), \chi_2(a, b, c), \chi_3(a, b, c)$, such that the equation

(166) $$Af \equiv \chi_1 \frac{\partial f}{\partial a} + \chi_2 \frac{\partial f}{\partial b} + \chi_3 \frac{\partial f}{\partial c} = 0$$

is satisfied identically (for all values of x and y) by ϕ and ψ; that is

$$A\phi \equiv \frac{\log b}{a}(xa^{\log b} + b^{\log a})\chi_1 + \frac{\log a}{b}(xa^{\log b} + b^{\log a})\chi_2 + \chi_3 \equiv 0,$$
$$A\psi \equiv ya^{\log b}\left(\frac{\log b}{a}\chi_1 + \frac{\log a}{b}\chi_2\right) \equiv 0$$

for all values of x and y. These two identities are equivalent to

$$a^{\log b}\left(\frac{\log b}{a}\chi_1 + \frac{\log a}{b}\chi_2\right) = 0,$$

$$b^{\log a}\left(\frac{\log b}{a}\chi_1 + \frac{\log a}{b}\chi_2\right) + \chi_3 = 0,$$

$$a^{\log b}\left(\frac{\log b}{a}\chi_1 + \frac{\log a}{b}\chi_2\right) = 0.$$

By inspection, a set of forms for χ_1, χ_2, χ_3 are found to be

$$\chi_1 = a \log a, \quad \chi_2 = - b \log b, \quad \chi_3 = 0.$$

Hence the three parameters are *not* essential.

To express the formulæ of transformation in terms of a smaller number, one proceeds to solve the equation

(166') $$a \log a \frac{\partial f}{\partial a} - b \log b \frac{\partial f}{\partial b} = 0.$$

Passing to the corresponding system of ordinary differential equations

$$\frac{da}{a \log a} = \frac{db}{- b \log b} = \frac{dc}{0},$$

it is obvious that $\qquad \log a \log b$ and c

are a set of solutions of (166'). Putting

$$\log a \log b = \alpha, \text{ whence } a^{\log b} = b^{\log a} = e^\alpha,$$

the formulæ of transformation take the form

$$x_1 = (x + 1)e^\alpha + c, \quad y_1 = y e^\alpha,$$

or, more simply still, $\qquad x_1 = a_1 x + a_2, \quad y_1 = a_1 y.$

TABLE I

IN this table is given a list of the more readily recognizable forms*
of differential equations of the first order which are known to be invariant under certain groups. The same type of equation is sometimes given in various forms, and special cases are also noted when
this seems desirable.

In the second column appear the groups under which the equations
are invariant. The numbers are those employed in § 19. For the
sake of simplicity p and q are used instead of $\dfrac{\partial f}{\partial x}$ and $\dfrac{\partial f}{\partial y}$ respectively.

The corresponding integrating factors of § 12 are given in the
third column.

In the fourth column appear the canonical variables.†

When variables which are separable in the transformed equation
(§ 20) can be obtained easily, they are given in the fifth column;
the form of the group resulting from the introduction of these variables is given in the last column.

---

* Other forms will be found in § 19.

† There is a certain degree of freedom in the choice of canonical variables, since
they are particular solutions of the differential equations (16′), § 10, or of the corresponding ones in case the group is to be reduced to the form $\dfrac{\partial f}{\partial x}$. Moreover, the right-hand
member, 1, in one of these equations may be replaced by any convenient constant (see
Remark 1, § 2) ; use of this fact is made when it will simplify the form of the resulting
variable.

Differential Equation	Group	Int. Factor	Canonical Variables	Other Variables	
$y' = F(x)$, or $f(x, y') = 0$	I; $q \equiv \dfrac{\partial f}{\partial y}$				
$y' = F(y)$, or $f(y, y') = 0$	I'; $p \equiv \dfrac{\partial f}{\partial x}$	$\dfrac{1}{F(y)}$			
$y' = yF(x)$, or $f\left(x, \dfrac{y'}{y}\right) = 0$, homogeneous in y and y'	III; yq	$\dfrac{1}{y}$	$x = x,\ y = \log y$		
$xy' = F(y)$	III'; xp	$\dfrac{1}{xF}$	$x = \log x,\ y = y$		
$y' = F(ax + by)$	XII; $bp - aq$	$\dfrac{1}{a + bF}$	$x = x,\ y = ax + by$		
$y' = \phi(x)\,\psi(y)$	VIII; $\psi(y)q$ VIII'; $\dfrac{1}{\phi(x)}p$	$\dfrac{1}{\psi(y)}$	$x = x,\ y = \int \dfrac{dy}{\psi}$ $x = \int \phi\, dx,\ y = y$		
$y' = F\left(\dfrac{y}{x}\right)$, or $M\,dx + N\,dy = 0$, M and N homogeneous of same degree	IV; $xp + yq$	$\dfrac{1}{Mx + Ny}$	$x = \log x,\ y = \dfrac{y}{x}$	$x = x,\ y = \dfrac{y}{x}$ or polar coörds. $\rho = \sqrt{x^2 + y^2}$, $\theta = \tan^{-1}\dfrac{y}{x}$	III'
$xy' = yF(xy)$, or $yf_1(xy)\,dx + xf_2(xy)\,dy = 0$	V; $xp - yq$	$\dfrac{1}{xy(F + 1)}$ $\dfrac{1}{xy(f_1 - f_2)}$	$x = \log x,\ y = xy$	$x = x,\ y = xy$	III'

TABLE I 233

DIFFERENTIAL EQUATION	GROUP	INT. FACTOR	CANONICAL VARIABLES	OTHER VARIABLES	
$xy' = yF\left(\dfrac{y}{x^n}\right)$, or $f(x, y, y') = 0$, homogeneous when x, y, y' are given the weights 1, n, $n-1$ respectively, or $xy' = yF(x^a y^\beta)$	VI; $xp + nyq$; $\beta xp - ayq$	$\dfrac{1}{xy(F-n)}$; $\dfrac{1}{xy(\beta F + a)}$	$x = \log x, y = \dfrac{y}{x^n}$; $x = \log x, y = x^a y^\beta$	$x = x, y = \dfrac{y}{x^n}$; $x = x, y = x^a y^\beta$	III'
$xy' - y = \phi(x)F\left(\dfrac{y}{x}\right)$, or in particular $xy' - y = x^k F\left(\dfrac{y}{x}\right) \equiv$ homogeneous function of degree k	$\dfrac{x}{\phi}(xp + yq)$; $x^{1-k}(xp+yq)$; X, 2°;	$\dfrac{1}{x^2 F}$	$x = \int \dfrac{\phi}{x^2}\, dx, y = \dfrac{y}{x}$; $x = x^{k-1}[k \neq 1] = \log x\,[k=1]$ $y = \dfrac{y}{x}$	$x = x, y = \dfrac{y}{x}$	VIII'
$xy' - y = \psi(y)F\left(\dfrac{x}{y}\right)y'$	X', 2°; $\dfrac{y}{\psi}(xp+yq)$	$\dfrac{1}{y^2 F}$	$x = \dfrac{y}{x}, y = \int \dfrac{\psi}{y^2}\, dy$	$x = \dfrac{y}{x}, y = y$	VIII
$xy' + y = \phi(x)F(xy)$, or in particular $xy' + y = y^k F(xy) = \dfrac{\Phi(xy)}{x^k}$	X, 3°; $\dfrac{1}{x\phi}(xp - yq)$; $x^{k-1}(xp - yq)$	$\dfrac{1}{F}$ $\dfrac{1}{\Phi}$	$x = \int \phi\, dx, y = xy$; $x = x^{1-k}[k \neq 1] = \log x\,[k=1]$ $y = xy$	$x = x, y = xy$	VIII'
$xy' + y = \psi(y)F(xy)y'$, or in particular $xy' + y = x^k F(xy)y' = \dfrac{\Phi(xy)}{y^k}y'$	X', 3°; $\dfrac{1}{y\psi}(xp - yq)$; $y^{k-1}(xp - yq)$	$\dfrac{1}{F}$ $\dfrac{1}{\Phi}$	$x = xy, y = \int \psi\, dy$; $x = xy,$ $y = y^{1-k}[k \neq 1] = \log y\,[k=1]$	$x = xy, y = y$	VIII

Differential Equation	Group	Int. Factor	Canonical Variables	Other Variables	
$xy' - ny = x^k F\left(\dfrac{y}{x^n}\right)$, or $axy' - by = x^k F\left(\dfrac{y^a}{x^b}\right)$ where $\dfrac{b}{a} = n$	X, 1°; $x^{n-k}(xp + nyq)$	$\dfrac{1}{x^{n+1}F}$	$x = x^{k-n}\,[k \neq n]$ $= \log x\,[k=n]$ $y = \dfrac{y}{x^n}$	$x = x,\ y = \dfrac{y}{x^n}$	VIII'
Riccati equation $xy' - ay + by^2 = cx^n$ when $n = 2a$, a particular case of the above	X, 1°; $x^{-a}(xp + ayq)$	$\dfrac{1}{x^{a+1}\left[c - b\left(\dfrac{y}{x^a}\right)^2\right]}$	$x = x^{-a},\ y = \dfrac{y}{x^a}$	$x = x,\ y = \dfrac{y}{x^a}$	VIII'
$xy' - ny = x^s y^s F\left(\dfrac{y}{x^n}\right)$	X', 1°; $y^{-s}(xp + nyq)$	$\dfrac{1}{xyF}$	$x = \dfrac{y}{x^n},\ y = y^s$	$x = \dfrac{y}{x^n},\ y = y$	VIII
The linear equation $y' + P(x)y = Q(x)$, or in particular $xy' - ry = F(x)$	VII; $e^{-\int Pdx} q$ $x^r q$	$e^{\int Pdx}$ $\dfrac{1}{x^{r+1}}$	$x = x,\ y = e^{\int Pdx} y$ $x = x,\ y = \dfrac{y}{x^r}$		
The Bernoulli equation $y' + P(x)y = Q(x)y^s$	IX; $e^{\int(s-1)Pdx} y^s q$	$\dfrac{e^{\int(1-s)Pdx}}{y^s}$	$x = x,$ $y = e^{\int(1-s)Pdx} y^{1-s}$		
The linear equation (y independent variable) $\dfrac{1}{y'} + P(y)x = Q(y)$, or in particular $y - sxy' = y'F(y)$	VIII'; $e^{-\int Pdy} p$ $y^s p$	$e^{\int Pdy}$ $\dfrac{1}{y^{s+1}}$	$x = xe^{\int Pdy},\ y=y$ $x = \dfrac{x}{y^s},\ y=y$		

TABLE I 235

Differential Equation	Group	Int. Factor	Canonical Variables	Other Variables	
$f\left(x^2+y^2,\ \dfrac{y-xy'}{x+yy'}\right)=0$, or $[xF(x^2+y^2)-y]\,dx$ $+[yF(x^2+y^2)+x]\,dy=0$, or $x+yy'=\sqrt{1+y'^2}\,F(x^2+y^2)$, or $y-xy'=\sqrt{1+y'^2}\,F(x^2+y^2)$	$\text{II};\ -yp+xq$	$\dfrac{1}{x^2+y^2}$	$x=\sqrt{x^2+y^2}\equiv\rho$ $y=\tan^{-1}\dfrac{y}{x}\equiv\theta$ *i.e.* polar coörds. Here $x=\rho\cos\theta$ $y=\rho\sin\theta$		
$x\pm yy'=\phi(x)F(x^2\pm y^2)$	$\text{XIV};\ \dfrac{1}{\phi}\left(p\mp\dfrac{x}{y}q\right)$	$\dfrac{1}{F}$	$x=\int\phi\,dx,$ $y=x^2\pm y^2$	$x=x,\ y=x^2\pm y^2$	VIII'
$x\pm yy'=\psi(y)F(x^2\pm y^2)y'$	$\text{XIV};\ \dfrac{1}{\psi}\left(\dfrac{y}{x}p\mp q\right)$	$\dfrac{1}{F}$	$x=x^2\pm y^2,$ $y=\int\psi\,dy$	$x=x^2\pm y^2,\ y=y$	VIII
$\dfrac{y^{s-1}y'}{x^{r-1}}=F\left(\dfrac{x^r}{r}\pm\dfrac{y^s}{s}\right),\ r,s\neq0,$ or in particular for $s=r$ $\left(\dfrac{y}{x}\right)^{r-1}y'=F(x^r\pm y^r)$	$\text{XV};$ $x^{1-r}p\mp y^{1-s}q$ $x^{1-r}p\mp y^{1-r}q$	$\dfrac{x^{r-1}}{F\pm1}$	$x=x^r,$ $y=\dfrac{x^r}{r}\pm\dfrac{y^s}{s}$ $x=x^r,\ y=x^r\pm y^r$	$x=x,\ y=\dfrac{x^r}{r}\pm\dfrac{y^s}{s}$ $x=x,\ y=x^r\pm y^r$	VIII'

TABLE II

General types of differential equations of higher order than the first, invariant under given groups, are usually complicated and not easy to recognize. In this table are given a few which a little experience will enable one to recognize.* Such characterizations as are simple are added.

Differential Equation	Group	Characterization
$f(x, y', y'', \cdots, y^{(r)}) = 0$	I; q	y is absent
$f(y, y', y'', \cdots, y^{(r)}) = 0$	I'; p	x is absent
$f(ax+by, y', y'', \cdots, y^{(r)}) = 0$	XII; $bp - aq$	x and y enter in the combination $ax + by$ only
$f\left(x, \dfrac{y'}{y}, \dfrac{y''}{y}, \cdots, \dfrac{y^{(r)}}{y}\right) = 0$	III; yq	Homogeneous in $y, y', \cdots, y^{(r)}$
$f\left(\dfrac{y}{x^n}, \dfrac{y'}{x^{n-1}}, \cdots, \dfrac{y^{(r)}}{x^{n-r}}\right) = 0$	VI; $xp + nyq$	Homogeneous when weights of $x, y, y', \cdots, y^{(r)}$ are $1, n, n-1, \cdots, n-r$ respectively
$f\left(\dfrac{y}{x}, y', xy'', \cdots, x^{r-1}y^{(r)}\right) = 0$	IV; $xp + yq$	Special case of above, for $n=1$
$f(y, xy', x^2y'', \cdots, x^r y^{(r)}) = 0$	III'; xp	Another special case, for $n=0$
$f(x, \phi y' - \phi' y, \phi y'' - \phi'' y, \cdots, \phi y^{(r)} - \phi^{(r)} y) = 0$	VII; $\phi(x)q$	A linear function of the various elements, except x, gives rise to a linear differential equation
$f[x, xy' - ky, x^2y'' - k(k-1)y, \cdots, x^r y^{(r)} - k(k-1)\cdots(k-r+1)y] = 0$	VII; $x^k q$	A special case, for $\phi(x) = x^k$

* Other forms will be found in § 28.

TABLE II   237

Differential Equation	Group	Characterization
$f(x,\ xy'-y,\ y'',\ y''',\ \cdots,$ $y^{(r)})=0$	VII; xq	A more special case, for $\phi(x)=x$
$f\left(y,\ \dfrac{y}{y'}-sx,\ \dfrac{y''y}{y'^s}+\dfrac{s-1}{y'}\right)=0$	VII'; $y^s p$	
$f\left(y,\ \dfrac{y}{y'}-x,\ \dfrac{y''}{y'^r}\right)=0$	VII'; yp	
$f(x,\ yy',\ yy''+y'^2)=0$	VIII; $\dfrac{1}{y}q$	
$f\left(\dfrac{y}{x},\ xy'-y,\ x^3y''\right)=0$	X; x^2p+xyq	
$f(xy,\ xy'+y,\ xy''+2y')=0$	X; $p-\dfrac{y}{x}q$	
$f\left(x^2+y^2,\ \dfrac{y-xy'}{x+yy'},\ \dfrac{y''^2}{(1+y'^2)^3}\right)$ $=0,\text{ or}$ $f\left(x^2+y^2,\ \dfrac{x+yy'}{\sqrt{1+y'^2}},\ \dfrac{y''^2}{(1+y'^2)^3}\right)$ $=0,\text{ or}$ $f\left(x^2+y^2,\ \dfrac{y-xy'}{\sqrt{1+y'^2}},\ \dfrac{y''^2}{(1+y'^2)^3}\right)$ $=0$	II; $-yp+xq$	Each of the elements appearing in the differential equation has a geometrical significance, which assures invariance under the group of rotations

ANSWERS

Section 1

1. $\bar{a} = \dfrac{1}{a}$; $a_0 = 1$; the equilateral hyperbolas $x_1 y_1 = xy = const.$

2. $\bar{a} = \dfrac{1}{a}$; $a_0 = 1$; the parabolas $\dfrac{y_1^2}{x_1} = \dfrac{y^2}{x} = const.$

3. $\bar{a} = \dfrac{1}{a}$; $a_0 = 1$; the semicubical parabolas $\dfrac{y_1^2}{x_1^3} = \dfrac{y^2}{x^3} = const.$

4. $\bar{a} = -a$; $a_0 = 0$; the ellipses $x_1^2 + 2y_1^2 = x^2 + 2y^2 = const.$

5. $\bar{a} = -a$; $a_0 = 0$; the equilateral hyperbolas $x_1^2 - y_1^2 = x^2 - y^2 = const.$

6. $\bar{a} = -a$; $a_0 = 0$; the straight lines $\dfrac{y_1}{x_1} = \dfrac{y}{x} = const.$

7. $\bar{a} = \dfrac{1}{a}$; $a_0 = 1$; the straight lines $y_1 = y = const.$

8. $\bar{a} = -a$; $a_0 = 0$; the spirals $\log \sqrt{x_1^2 + y_1^2} - \tan^{-1} \dfrac{y_1}{x_1}$

$$= \log \sqrt{x^2 + y^2} - \tan^{-1} \dfrac{y}{x} = const.$$

Section 2

1. $\xi = x,\ \eta = -y.$

2. $\xi = 2x,\ \eta = y.$

3. $\xi = 2x,\ \eta = 3y.$

4. $\xi = \dfrac{1}{x},\ \eta = -\dfrac{1}{2y}.$

5. $\xi = y,\ \eta = x.$

6. $\xi = x^2,\ \eta = xy.$

7. $\xi = x + y,\ \eta = 0.$

8. $\xi = x - y,\ \eta = x + y.$

Section 4

1. $x_1 = e^t x,\ y_1 = e^{-t} y.$ 2. $x_1 = e^{2t} x,\ y_1 = e^t y.$ 3. $x_1 = e^{2t} x,\ y_1 = e^{3t} y.$

4. $x_1^2 = x^2 + 2t,\ y_1^2 = y^2 - t.$ $\therefore x_1 = +\sqrt{x^2 + 2t},\ y_1 = +\sqrt{y^2 - t}.$

5. $x_1 + y_1 = e^t(x + y),\ x_1 - y_1 = e^{-t}(x - y).$

$\therefore 2x_1 = x(e^t + e^{-t}) + y(e^t - e^{-t}),\ 2y_1 = x(e^t - e^{-t}) + y(e^t + e^{-t}),$

or $\qquad x_1 = x \cosh t + y \sinh t,\ y_1 = x \sinh t + y \cosh t.$

6. $\dfrac{y_1}{x_1} = \dfrac{y}{x},\ \dfrac{1}{x_1} = \dfrac{1}{x} - t.$ $\therefore x_1 = \dfrac{x}{1 - xt},\ y_1 = \dfrac{y}{1 - xt}$

7. $y_1 = y,\ x_1 + y_1 = e^t(x + y).$ $\therefore x_1 = e^t x + (e^t - 1)y,\ y_1 = y.$

8. $x_1^2 + y_1^2 = e^{2t}(x^2 + y^2),\ \tan^{-1} \dfrac{y_1}{x_1} = \tan^{-1} \dfrac{y}{x} + t.$ $\therefore x_1 = e^t(x \cos t - y \sin t),$ $y_1 = e^t(x \sin t + y \cos t).$

239

Section 5

1. $x_1 = e^t x,\ y_1 = e^{-t} y.$ **2.** $x_1 = e^{2t} x,\ y_1 = e^t y.$ **3.** $x_1 = e^{2t} x,\ y_1 = e^{3t} y.$

4. $x_1 = x + \dfrac{1}{x} t - \dfrac{1}{x^3} \dfrac{t^2}{2!} + \dfrac{3}{x^5} \dfrac{t^3}{3!} - \dfrac{3 \cdot 5}{x^7} \dfrac{t^4}{4!} + \cdots = + \sqrt{x^2 + 2t}.$

$y_1 = y - \dfrac{1}{2y} t - \dfrac{1}{4y^3} \dfrac{t^2}{2!} - \dfrac{3}{8y^5} \dfrac{t^3}{3!} - \dfrac{3 \cdot 5}{16y^7} \dfrac{t^4}{4!} - \cdots = + \sqrt{y^2 - t}.$

5. $x_1 = x\left(1 + \dfrac{t^2}{2!} + \dfrac{t^4}{4!} + \cdots\right) + y\left(t + \dfrac{t^3}{3!} + \dfrac{t^5}{5!} + \cdots\right) = x \cosh t + y \sinh t.$

$y_1 = x\left(t + \dfrac{t^3}{3!} + \dfrac{t^5}{5!} + \cdots\right) + y\left(1 + \dfrac{t^2}{2!} + \dfrac{t^4}{4!} + \cdots\right) = x \sinh t + y \cosh t.$

6. $x_1 = x(1 + xt + x^2 t^2 + \cdots) = \dfrac{x}{1 - tx},\ y_1 = y(1 + xt + x^2 t^2 + \cdots) = \dfrac{y}{1 - tx}.$

7. $x_1 = e^t x + (e^t - 1)y,\ y_1 = y.$

8. While the coefficients in the developments can be obtained readily, it is not easy to recognize the functions represented by the infinite series.

Section 6

1. $xy.$ **2.** $\dfrac{y^2}{x}.$ **3.** $\dfrac{y^2}{x^3}.$ **4.** $x^2 + 2y^2.$ **5.** $x^2 - y^2.$ **6.** $\dfrac{y}{x}.$ **7.** $y.$

8. $\log \sqrt{x^2 + y^2} - \tan^{-1} \dfrac{y}{x}.$

Section 7

1. $xy = c$, p. c.,* $x = y = 0$, i. p.   **6.** $y = cx$, p. c., $x = 0$, l. i. p.

2. $y^2 = cx$, p. c., $x = y = 0$, i. p.   **7.** $y = c$, p. c., $x + y = 0$, l. i. p.

3. $y^2 = cx^3$, p. c., $x = y = 0$, i. p.   **8.** $\log \sqrt{x^2 + y^2} - \tan^{-1} \dfrac{y}{x} = c$, p. c.,

4. $x^2 + 2y^2 = c$, p. c. $x = y = 0$, i. p.

5. $x^2 - y^2 = c$, p. c., $x = y = 0$, i. p.

Section 10 †

1. $x = xy,\ y = \log x.$

2. $x = \dfrac{y^2}{x},\ y = \log y.$

3. $x = \dfrac{y^2}{x^3},\ y = \log x.$

4. $x = x^2 + 2y^2,\ y = y^2.$

* The abbreviations here used are: p. c. for path-curve, i. p. for invariant point, l. i. p for locus of invariant points.

† The answers given for the exercises of this section are not unique, since they are particular solutions of the differential equations (16′). Besides, the right-hand member of the second of these equations may be replaced by any convenient constant (see Remark 1, § 2); use of this fact has been made in the case of Ex. 3, 4, 6.

5. $x = x^2 - y^2$, $y = \log(x + y)$.

6. $x = \dfrac{y}{x}$, $y = \dfrac{1}{x}$.

7. $x = y$, $y = \log(x + y)$.

8. $x = \log\sqrt{x^2 + y^2} - \tan^{-1}\dfrac{y}{x}$,

$y = \tan^{-1}\dfrac{y}{x}$.

Section 11

1. $Uf \equiv z\dfrac{\partial f}{\partial z}$; $x = a$, $y = b$, p. c.;* $z = 0$, l. i. p.; $x = x$, $y = y$, $z = \log z$, c. v.

2. $Uf \equiv x\dfrac{\partial f}{\partial x} + y\dfrac{\partial f}{\partial y}$; $y - ax$, $z = b$, p. c.; $x = y = 0$, l. i. p.; $x = \tan^{-1}\dfrac{y}{x}$,

$y = \log\sqrt{x^2 + y}$, $z = z$, c. v. $\therefore x = e^y \cos x$, $y = e^y \sin x$, $z = z$.

3. $Uf \equiv x\dfrac{\partial f}{\partial x} + y\dfrac{\partial f}{\partial y} + z\dfrac{\partial f}{\partial z}$; $z - ax = 0$, $z - by = 0$, p. c.; $x = y = z = 0$, i. p.;

$x = \tan^{-1}\dfrac{u_1 u_2}{\sqrt{u_1^2 + u_2^2}} = \tan^{-1}\dfrac{z}{\sqrt{x^2 + y^2}}$, $y = \tan^{-1}\dfrac{y}{x}$, $z = \log\sqrt{x^2 + y^2 + z^2}$, c. v.

$\therefore x = e^z \cos x \cos y$, $y = e^z \cos x \sin y$, $z = e^z \sin x$.

The introduction of polar coördinates reduces the group to the form of the group appearing in Ex. 1.

4. $Uf \equiv x\dfrac{\partial f}{\partial x} + y\dfrac{\partial f}{\partial y} + xy\dfrac{\partial f}{\partial z}$; $y - ax = 0$, $xy - 2z = b$, p. c.; $x = y = 0$, l. i. p.

$x = \tan^{-1}\dfrac{y}{x}$, $y = xy - 2z$, $z = \log\sqrt{x^2 + y^2}$, c. v.

5. $Uf \equiv (x - y)\dfrac{\partial f}{\partial x} + (x + y)\dfrac{\partial f}{\partial y} + z\dfrac{\partial f}{\partial z}$; $\tan^{-1}\dfrac{y}{x} - \log\sqrt{x^2 + y^2} = a$, $x^2 + y^2$

$- bz^2 = 0$, p. c.; $x = y = z = 0$, i. p.; $x = u_1$, $y = u_2$, $z = \log z$, c. v.

Section 12

2. $x^2 + y^2 - cy = 0$.

3. $\tan^{-1}\dfrac{y}{x} = \sqrt{x^2 + y^2} + c$, spirals $[\rho = \theta + c]$.

4. $\tan^{-1}\dfrac{y}{x} = k\log\sqrt{x^2 + y^2} + c$, logarithmic spirals $\left[\rho = ce^{\frac{\theta}{k}}\right]$.

5. $x^2 + y^2 - cx = 0$.

Section 21

3. $xy = c^2x + c$, g. s.,† $4x^2y + 1 = 0$, s. s., $y = 0$, p. s. for $c = 0$; § 25, 5.‡

* The abbreviations used in the answers of § 7 are also employed here, with the additional one c. v. for canonical variables.

† The abbreviations used here are g. s. for general solution, s. s. for singular solution, p. s. for particular solution.

‡ While the methods of §§ 12 and 20, especially the latter, may frequently be employed in finding the general solution, serious practical difficulties may arise. The references here given are to the places in *El. Dif. Eq.*, where these differential equations appear

4. $a^2y^2 + 2cx + c^2 = 0$, g. s., $x^2 - a^2y^2 = 0$, s. s., $y = 0$, p. s. for $c = 0$, § 27, 8.

5. $y = c(x - c)^2$, g. s., $y(27y - 4x^3) = 0$, s. s., also $y = 0$, p. s. for $c = 0$; § 26, 4.

6. $y^2 = 2cx + c^3$, g. s., $(32x^3 + 27y^4) = 0$, s. s., $y = 0$, p.s. for $c = 0$; § 27, 7.

7. $x + cxy + c^2 = 0$, g. s., $xy^2 - 4 = 0$, s. s.; § 28, 3.

Section 24

1. The equilateral hyperbolas $x^2 - y^2 = c$.

2. $y^a = cx^b$. $\therefore y = cx$, when $b = a$; $xy = c$, when $b = -a$.

3. The circles $x^2 + y^2 + 1 = cx$.

Section 26

1. $U^{(n)}f \equiv \dfrac{\partial f}{\partial x}$.

2. $U^{(n)}f \equiv x\dfrac{\partial f}{\partial x} - y'\dfrac{\partial f}{\partial y'} - 2y''\dfrac{\partial f}{\partial y''} - \cdots - ny^{(n)}\dfrac{\partial f}{\partial y^{(n)}}$.

3. $U^{(n)}f \equiv x\dfrac{\partial f}{\partial x} - y\dfrac{\partial f}{\partial y} - 2y'\dfrac{\partial f}{\partial y'} - \cdots - (n+1)y^{(n)}\dfrac{\partial f}{\partial y^{(n)}}$.

4. $U^{(n)}f \equiv ax\dfrac{\partial f}{\partial x} + by\dfrac{\partial f}{\partial y} + (b-a)y'\dfrac{\partial f}{\partial y'} + (b-2a)y''\dfrac{\partial f}{\partial y''} + \cdots$
$$+ (b-na)y^{(n)}\dfrac{\partial f}{\partial y^{(n)}}.$$

5. $U^{(n)}f \equiv \phi\dfrac{\partial f}{\partial x} - \phi'y'\dfrac{\partial f}{\partial y'} - (\phi''y' + 2\phi'y'')\dfrac{\partial f}{\partial y''} - (\phi'''y' + 3\phi''y''$
$$+ 3\phi'y''')\dfrac{\partial f}{\partial y'''} - \cdots - \left[\phi^{(n)}y' + \binom{n}{1}\phi^{(n-1)}y'' + \binom{n}{2}\phi^{(n-2)}y''' + \cdots\right.$$
$$\left. + \binom{n}{n-1}\phi'y^{(n)}\right]\dfrac{\partial f}{\partial y^{(n)}}.$$

6. $U^{(n)}f \equiv \phi\dfrac{\partial f}{\partial y} - \phi'\dfrac{\partial f}{\partial y'} - \phi''\dfrac{\partial f}{\partial y''} - \cdots - \phi^{(n)}\dfrac{\partial f}{\partial y^{(n)}}$.

7. $U^{(n)}f \equiv x^2\dfrac{\partial f}{\partial x} + rxy\dfrac{\partial f}{\partial y} + [ry + (r-2)xy']\dfrac{\partial f}{\partial y'} + [2(r-1)y'$
$$+ (r-4)xy'']\dfrac{\partial f}{\partial y''} + \cdots + [n(r-n+1)y^{(n-1)} + (r-2n)xy^{(n)}]\dfrac{\partial f}{\partial y^{(n)}}.$$

as exercises. Practicable methods may be found there. But when the methods of the text can be carried out, they should be employed, to obtain practice in them.

However, the method of § 21 for finding the singular solution leaves nothing to be desired. (Compare *El. Dif. Eq.* Chapter V.)

Section 28

3. $y = c_1 x e^{\frac{c_2}{x}}$. 4. $y = x \log\left(\dfrac{c_1}{x} + c_2\right)$. 5. $y = x(c_1 \log x + c_2)$.

Section 29

$$c_1(x^2 - y^2) - 2xy = c_2.$$

Section 32

3. $x^2 + y^2$. 4. $\dfrac{xy}{z}$. 5. $\dfrac{cy - bz}{cx - az}$. 6. $x^2 + y^2 + z^2 - 2yz - 2zx - 2xy$.

7. $\dfrac{(x+y)(1+z)}{(x-y)(1-z)}$.

Section 34

The group 1 leaves a and d unaltered.
The group 2 leaves a unaltered.
The group 3 leaves c unaltered.
The group 4 leaves a, b and c unaltered.

Section 35

2. $u \equiv \dfrac{x^2 + y^2}{z^2}$, $v \equiv x - y - z$.

3. $u \equiv y - x$, $v \equiv (x + y)(x + y + 4z)$, or $xy + yz + zx$.

4. $u \equiv \dfrac{y + x + yz + xz}{y - x - yz + xz}$, $v \equiv y - x - yz + xz$, or $u \equiv y + xz$, $v \equiv x + yz$.

Section 38

3. Method **A**, $3°$ applies. 4. Method **B**, $4°$, (a) applies.

5. Method **B**, $1°$ applies. $u \equiv x - y$, $v \equiv y - z$.

6. Method **B**, $3°$ applies. $u \equiv \dfrac{y + xz}{x + yz}$, $v \equiv (x^2 - y^2)(1 - z^2)$.

Section 39

3. $y = \log \sec (x + a) + b$. 4. $y^2 = ax^2 + bx$.

Section 40

5. $y = \log \sec (x + a) + b$. 6. $\dfrac{x}{y} = c_1 e^{\frac{c_2}{x}}$. 8. $e^y = ax^2 + bx$.

Section 44

1. α.   **2.** δ.   **3.** β.   **4.** β.   **5.** γ.   **6.** γ.

Section 45 *

1. $x = \tan^{-1} \dfrac{y}{x}$, $y = \tan^{-1} \dfrac{y}{x} + \log \sqrt{x^2 + y^2}$.

2. Since $(U_1 U_2)f \equiv U_1 f - U_2 f$, consider $V_1 f \equiv U_1 f - U_2 f \equiv y\,\dfrac{\partial f}{\partial x}$ and $V_2 f \equiv U_2 f \equiv x\,\dfrac{\partial f}{\partial x}$. For these $x = y$, $y = \dfrac{x}{y}$.

3. $x = \dfrac{x-y}{x+y}$, $y = \dfrac{1}{x+y}$.   **4.** $x = \sqrt{x^2 + y^2}$, $y = \tan^{-1} \dfrac{y}{x}$.

5. $x = \dfrac{y}{x}$, $y = x + y$.

6. Since $(U_1 U_2)f \equiv U_2 f$, consider $V_1 f \equiv U_2 f$, $V_2 f \equiv -U_1 f$. For these $x = \dfrac{y}{x(x+y)}$, $y = \dfrac{1}{x}$.

Section 49

1. $x_1 = x - ap$, $y_1 = y - \frac{1}{2} ap^2$, $p_1 = p$.

2. $x_1 = x \pm \dfrac{a^2 p}{\sqrt{a^2 p^2 + b^2}}$, $y_1 = y \mp \dfrac{b^2}{\sqrt{a^2 p^2 + b^2}}$, $p_1 \equiv p$.

3. $x_1 = \dfrac{p(xp - y)}{p^2 + 1}$, $y_1 = \dfrac{y - xp}{p^2 + 1}$, $p_1 = \dfrac{x + 2yp - xp^2}{y - 2xp - yp^2}$.

4. $x_1 = -\dfrac{x^2 p}{y - xp}$, $y_1 = \dfrac{y^2}{y - xp}$, $p_1 = -\dfrac{y}{x}$.

5. $x_1 = \dfrac{px - y}{p}$, $y_1 = y - xp$, $p_1 = -\dfrac{xp^2}{y}$.

NOTE VI

1. $\bar{a}_1 = \dfrac{1}{a_1}$, $\bar{a}_2 = -\dfrac{a_2}{a_1}$, $\bar{a}_3 = -\dfrac{a_3}{a_1}$; $a_1{}^0 = 1$, $a_2{}^0 = a_3{}^0 = 0$.

2. $\bar{a}_1 = \dfrac{a_5}{\Delta}$, $\bar{a}_2 = \dfrac{-a_2}{\Delta}$, $\bar{a}_3 = \dfrac{a_2 a_6 - a_3 a_5}{\Delta}$, $\bar{a}_4 = \dfrac{-a_4}{\Delta}$, $\bar{a}_5 = \dfrac{a_1}{\Delta}$, $\bar{a}_6 = \dfrac{a_3 a_4 - a_1 a_6}{\Delta}$, $\Delta = a_1 a_5 - a_2 a_4$; $a_1{}^0 = a_5{}^0 = 1$, $a_2{}^0 = a_3{}^0 = a_4{}^0 = a_6{}^0 = 0$.

3. $\bar{a}_1 = -a_1$, $\bar{a}_2 = -a_2 + a_1 a_3$, $\bar{a}_3 = -a_3$; $a_1{}^0 = a_2{}^0 = a_3{}^0 = 0$.

* Since multiplying its symbol by a constant does not affect the infinitesimal transformation of a group (Remark 1, § 2), the answers in this section are not unique. Use is made of this fact in Ex. 1, 3, 4, 6.

4. $\bar{a}_1 = -\dfrac{a_1}{a_3{}^2}$, $\bar{a}_2 = -a_2$, $\bar{a}_3 = \dfrac{1}{a_3}$; $a_1{}^0 = a_2{}^0 = 0$, $a_3{}^0 = 1$.

5. $\bar{a}_1 = \dfrac{-a_1}{a_1 + a_2}$, $\bar{a}_2 = \dfrac{1 + a_1}{a_1 + a_2}$, $\bar{a}_3 = \dfrac{-a_3}{a_1 + a_2}$; $a_1{}^0 = a_3{}^0 = 0$, $a_2{}^0 = 1$.

6. $\bar{a}_1 = \dfrac{1}{a_1}$, $\bar{a}_2 = -\dfrac{a_2}{a_1}$, $\bar{a}_3 = -\dfrac{a_3}{a_1}$; $a_1{}^0 = 1$, $a_2{}^0 = a_3{}^0 = 0$.

7. $U_1 f \equiv (e_1 x + e_2)\dfrac{\partial f}{\partial x} + (e_1 y + e_3)\dfrac{\partial f}{\partial y}$.

$U_2 f \equiv (e_1 x + e_2 y + e_3)\dfrac{\partial f}{\partial x} + (e_4 x + e_5 y + e_6)\dfrac{\partial f}{\partial y}$.

$U_3 f \equiv (e_1 y + e_2)\dfrac{\partial f}{\partial x} + e_3 \dfrac{\partial f}{\partial y}$.

$U_4 f \equiv (e_1 y^2 + e_2)\dfrac{\partial f}{\partial x} + e_3 y \dfrac{\partial f}{\partial y}$.

$U_5 f \equiv (e_1 x + e_2 y + e_3)\left(\dfrac{\partial f}{\partial x} + \dfrac{\partial f}{\partial y}\right)$.

$U_6 f \equiv (e_1 + e_2 x + e_3 y)\left(x \dfrac{\partial f}{\partial x} + y \dfrac{\partial f}{\partial y}\right)$.

The groups generated by the infinitesimal transformations of Ex. 8 to 13 are precisely the respective groups of Ex. 1 to 6.

ERRATA.

Page 7 line 16 Replace $k\xi(x,\eta)\delta a$ by $k\xi(x,y)\delta a$.

"   12 "   5 from bottom
Replace $\therefore v(x,y)\equiv$ by $v(x_1,y_1)\equiv$.

"   14 "   16 Replace $\equiv\xi_1\dfrac{\partial f_1}{\partial t}+\eta_1\dfrac{\partial f_1}{\partial t}$ by $\equiv\xi_1\dfrac{\partial f_1}{\partial x_1}+\eta_1\dfrac{\partial f_1}{\partial y_1}$

"   25 "   17   " $=\dfrac{\partial x}{\partial a}=$ by $=\dfrac{\delta x}{\delta a}=$

"   29 "   5 from bottom
Replace $\equiv\dfrac{\partial x}{\partial a}=$ by $\equiv\dfrac{\delta x}{\delta a}=$

"   "   "   4 from bottom
Replace $\equiv\dfrac{\partial y}{\partial a}=$ by $\equiv\dfrac{\delta y}{\delta a}=$

"   "   "   3 from bottom
Replace $\xi\equiv\dfrac{\partial z}{\partial a}=$ by $\zeta\equiv\dfrac{\delta z}{\delta a}$

"   32 "   6 from bottom
Replace where $u_1u_2,\cdots$ by where $u_1,u_2,\cdots$

"   53 "   8 Replace $\xi\equiv-x,$ by $\xi\equiv-y,$

"   56 "   15   " $\equiv\phi(x)\dfrac{\partial f}{\partial x}$ by $\equiv\phi(x)\dfrac{\partial f}{\partial y}$

"   61 "   3   " $ry-sxy'$ by $ry+sxy'$

"   71 "   4   " (42) by $(42')$

"   102 "   4   "   I.   by III.

"   106 "   4   "   and Af by and A_2f

"   127 "   13 Replace $\alpha,$ by $\alpha_1,$

"   132 "   11 The "2" of $2xy\dfrac{\partial f}{\partial y}$ seems badly broken.

"   149 "   7 from bottom
Replace $(2<k<r)$ by $(2\lesssim k<r)$

"   150 formula (105)
Replace $(U_1,c_2U_2f+c_3U_3f+\cdots+c_rU_rf)\equiv$
by $(U_1,c_2U_2+c_3U_3+\cdots+c_rU_r)f\equiv$

"   151 line 1 Replace a_{ijk} by a_{1jk}

"   177 "   6 from bottom
Replace $-\cos t$ by $-\cot t$

"   188 "   14 Replace charactertisic by characteristic.

"   241 "   7 Replace $y-ax$ by $y=ax$.

INDEX

The numbers refer to pages.

The following abbreviations are used : dif. eq. $\equiv$ differential equation ; gr. $\equiv$ group ; infl. $\equiv$ infinitesimal ; i. u. $\equiv$ invariant under ; ord. $\equiv$ order ; tr. $\equiv$ transformation.

Affine tr., 3, 54
Alternant, 44
 of symbols of extended trs., 209
Asymptotic lines, 80

Bernoulli equation, 58

Canonical form, 26, 34, 64, 155
Canonical variables, 26, 34, 64, 156
Change of variables, 23, 33, 188
Characteristic function of infl. contact tr., 186
Classification of two-parameter grs., 152
Commutator, 45
Complete system, 104, 106, 110
 equivalent, 106
 Jacobian, 107, 110
Contact tr., 178, 181 ; infl., 185
Curvature, lines of, 81
Curve of union of elements, 175, 189

Differential equation of 1. ord., 189
 i. u. gr., 40, 44, 45, 46, 48, 50, 52, 194, 231
Dif. eq. of 2. ord. i. u. gr., 86, 90, 134, 137, 148, 165, 236
 not i. u. any gr., 206
Dif. eq. of n. order i. u. gr., 99, 101, 236
Differential invariant, 51, 88, 194
Dilatations, 185, 186
Displacements, 212
Distinct grs., 122, 123, 125
Distinct infl. trs., 7

Elements, lineal, 175
 union of, 175, 194
Equivalent complete systems, 106
Essential parameters, 214
 condition for, 226

Extended gr., 42, 84
Extended point tr., 41, 83, 180

First differential invariant, 51, 194
First integral, 191

General expression for gr. leaving dif. eq. of 1. ord. unaltered, 49
Group, 1, 28, 211
 distinct, 122, 123, 125
 extended, 42, 84
 generated by infl. tr., 10, 12, 14, 30, 220
 involving one parameter, 1, 28
 involving r parameters, 211
 of contact trs., 185
 of infl. trs., 146
 property, 2
 trivial, 39, 119, 196

Homogeneous dif. eq. (Boole), 93

Identical tr., 4
Independent linear partial dif. eqs., 104
Infinitesimal contact tr., 185
 characteristic function of, 186
 symbol of, 186
Infinitesimal tr., 6, 29, 197, 215, 218
 distinct, 7
 gr. generated by, 10, 12, 14, 30, 220
 linearly independent, 143, 217
 r-parameter gr. of, 146
 symbol of, 8, 42, 84, 85, 218
Integrating factor, 37, 47, 69, 76
 common to two dif. eqs., 72
 two, for the same dif. eq., 48
Intermediary integral, 191
Invariant, 16, 31
 curve, 17, 18, 31, 32

247